CANADIAN BUILDING LAW

FIFTH EDITION

COMPILED AND EDITED BY

EVAN B. STREGGER, PQS(F), ASCT, C. ARB., GSC

Published by:
Canadian Institute of Quantity Surveyors
P.O. Box 124, Station R
Toronto, ON   M4G 3Z3
Telephone: (905) 471-0882
Fax: (905) 471-7545
e-mail info@ciqs.org
web site www.ciqs.org

Front cover photograph of the Supreme Court of Canada, Ottawa, ON courtesy of Evan B. Stregger

Canadian Building Law
ISBN # 1-896606-34-2, 5th edition, 2001
ISBN # 1-896606-24-5, 4th edition, 1998
(ISBN # 1-896606-20-2, 3rd edition, 1997)
2nd edition, 1979
1st edition, 1977

BRIEF TABLE OF CONTENTS

Table of Contents

7 TENDERING AND CONTRACT EXECUTION

by Clive E.J. Evans, FRICS, PQS(F), C.Arb

8 THE GENERAL CONDITIONS OF A CONSTRUCTION CONTRACT

by Clive E.J. Evans, FRICS, PQS(F), C.Arb.

9   CONSTRUCTION SPECIFICATIONS GENERALLY

by Claude Lawrenson, RSW, RHI

10   ARBITRATION

by Kenneth M. Macdonald, PQS, FRICS, C.Arb

14 CONSTRUCTION SAFETY

by Evan B. Stregger, PQS(F), AScT, C.Arb., GSC

15 THE BUSINESS OF SUBCONTRACTING

by Evan B. Stregger, PQS(F), AScT, C.Arb., GSC

PREFACE

ORIGINS

This book first originated in October 1974 with the publication of a series of lectures delivered by Mr. George W. Slee to construction technician students at Algonquin College of Applied Arts and Technology in Ottawa. The lectures were published in the official journal of the Canadian Institute of Quantity Surveyors, known at that time as C.I.P.H.E.R., currently known as The Construction Economist.

The lectures were first published in book form in 1977 and George Slee noted that, while the contents of that volume had no legal significance, it was intended that they create some appreciation of the various legal and quasi-legal aspects of construction contracts, as well as the administration of them.

AUTHENTICITY

While the title "Canadian Building Law" might suggest that this book is based on legal fact, it must be realized that it is designed primarily to assist students in preparing for examinations set by the Canadian Institute of Quantity Surveyors. As such, it provides an invaluable and unique reference, not only to these students, but also to all in the construction industry whose responsibilities demand knowledge and understanding of the legal aspects of construction. While Canadian Building Law provides advice on legal matters pertaining to construction, it does not profess to provide irrefutable legal advice since those who are responsible for its production do not have professional legal background. While this book should provide a useful reference, we strongly recommend that any matter requiring legal advice be referred to a member of the law profession.

CCDC 2

Much of the content deals with the various articles contained in standard forms of construction contracts, particularly in respect of the articles of agreement, definitions and general conditions. Since, at the time of writing, the Canadian Construction Documents Committee form of contract entitled "Stipulated Price Contract" (and more generally known as CCDC 2 - 1994) is one of the most widely accepted and used forms of construction contracts. Readers are encouraged to make regular reference to CCDC 2 - 1994 as they progress with the various chapters of the book.

FEEDBACK

As we deal in an evolving and ever changing industry, this fourth edition of Canadian Building Law will not be the last. The publisher and editor encourage all who use it to provide us with constructive comment and advice where corrections or improvements might be incorporated in future editions. As the editor of this document, I trust that it will be as well received and found to be as useful as previous editions.

ACKNOWLEDGEMENTS

This edition of Canadian Building Law has been a combined effort of many and the contributing authors are identified in the Table of Contents with the chapter they have authored or revised. To them I say thank-you. I also wish to acknowledge Lois Metcalfe who assisted all of us in our endeavours.

Evan B. Stregger, PQS(F), AScT, C.Arb., GSC
Editor

1

THE ORIGIN AND NATURE OF THE LAW
IN RESPECT OF CONTRACTS

by Harland C. Lindsay, FRICS, CHE, PQS(F), FICArb, FAIC, MAACE

"The law, which is perfection of reason"

Sir Edward Coke (1552-1634)

1.1   INTRODUCTION

The Laws of Canada have grown and have developed by amendment, as Canada has grown and developed as a Nation. The expansion of our social, political and business relations created new requirements, with the passing of time, for the protection of the rights of the individual. As a result, the Laws of Canada have become inter-woven as a blanket covering all of us, and controlling practically every activity of every individual.

As the Law has a vast number of usages in so many areas, many of which are of a complex nature, it is extremely difficult to define the word "Law" precisely. In very broad and general terms, the word **LAW** in our context of use of the word could mean those rules, procedures, practices, concepts, customs, traditions, etc., which, when adopted, enacted or established according to accepted procedures, are considered to be fixed unless they are repealed or amended. Thus, it would appear that the **LAW** is a body of enacted customary rules recognized by the community as binding with respect to individual rights, responsibilities and liabilities.

1.2   ORIGIN AND DEVELOPMENT OF LAW

Beginning with the emergence from the mists of antiquity and continuing to our present era, the **LAW**, like modern man, has been the result of progressive evolution. The rights and privileges of the family and the tribe in early primitive society were established by custom and whatever was customary and considered to be right eventually became law. As man's evolution progressed, so did his realization that his individual interests were often in conflict with those of others. He realized that his neighbours had rights which were either equal to his own or in conflict with them and, in order to keep the peace, it was necessary to regulate the rights of all so as to interfere as little as possible with the private rights of individuals. Therefore, to protect and enjoy individual property and rights it became necessary to make laws to regulate individual conduct. The laws became known through the lands of their origin as Codes of Law.

It is believed that the first systematic body of law, the Code of Hammurabi of Babylon, was established about the year 2000 BC The Laws of Moses, the Ten Commandments, is believed to have been about the year 300 BC, and the great Justinian Code of Rome was published about the year 533 AD. Parts of these ancient codes of law are to be found in the laws of today, for out of them evolved a great many systems and classifications of law such as:

a)   Moral Law
       1.   Define Law
       2.   Ecclesiastical Law

b)   Natural, or Scientific Law
       1.   Law of Physical Sciences
       2.   Law of Natural Sciences
       3.   Law of Social Sciences

c)   Laws of Arts and Literature

d)   International Law

       1)   Private International Law
       2)   Law of Nations or Public International Law

e)   Governmental Law (Enacted Law or Law by Usage)

       1.   Constitutional Law
       2.   Statute Law
       3.   Common Law
       4.   The Law of Equity

Of these systems and classifications, this book will concentrate on Governmental Law as it applies to the building industry.

Governmental Law consists of rules which are enforceable in our Courts of Law, and which regulate both our civil rights and conduct as individuals. Of the four classifications of Governmental Law, the most fundamental law is Constitutional Law, which takes precedence over the other three classifications of law. Although Common Law is older than Statute Law and the Law of Equity, Statute Law takes precedence. Constitutional Law and Statute Law are the enactments of legislative bodies who are vested with powers to originate law and enforce the laws they enact.

1.3   CONSTITUTION & CONSTITUTIONAL LAW

According to the Encyclopaedia Britannica -- "*The term constitution means, in its wider sense, the whole scheme whereby a country is governed; and this includes much else besides law*".

In its narrower sense "constitution" means the leading legal rules, usually collected into one set of documents which come to be venerated as "The Constitution".

In form, a written constitution derives its authority from the people or from some constituent authority. It is this derivation that gives Constitutional Law a superior binding force because it is either the will of the majority of the people, or the enactment of a superior lawmaking authority such as a constituent assembly elected by the majority of the people. For this reason, once a constitution has been established and generally accepted, it receives the support of a whole series of forces in favour of what is existing and opposing change. Today, in Canada, we are in the midst of great controversy concerning amendments to what we consider our constitution. This controversy has no place in this volume, other than to illustrate the difficulties which occur when changes in accepted law are advocated.

By virtue of the British North American Act, an enactment of the British Government, the various governments of Canada had jurisdiction over a variety of matters as set out in the Act. By virtue of the provisions of the B.N.A., the provinces in turn could delegate certain legislative power to municipalities such as cities, towns, counties, and to school board, for the purpose of extending the democratic process of self-government. Therefore, in Canada, the origin of Constitutional Law, and Statute Law for that matter, is in the provisions of the British North American Act, which, over the years, came to be considered as the Canadian Constitution. On April 17, 1982, the Constitution was amended and repatriated to Canada under Prime Minister Pierre Elliot Trudeau.

1.4   STATUTE LAW

All enactments of the governments of Canada and the provinces, councils of municipalities, and school corporations to whom legislative powers have been granted by virtue of the Constitution are properly Statute Law. We look to these legislative bodies for both the origin of and amendment to our Statute Law, by means of Acts, to meet the various changes brought about by the normal progress of our country. Our Courts of Law can, and do, to a certain extent, amend existing principles of procedure as new circumstances arise, requiring changes to what is existing. However existing Law as to provision, can only be amended by new law which must be enacted by the legislature having jurisdiction. The legislatures pass the Acts of Law which the Courts of Law interpret.

The main body of Canadian Law, regardless of origin, is to be found in the Common Law. Perhaps about only one-fourth of Canadian Law is Statute Law, the jurisdiction of which is as follows:

a)   Laws passed by the Canadian Parliament, in force throughout Canada, whether the enforcement of them be by Canadian Government authority or other legal authority

b)   Acts passed by provincial legislatures which are enforceable only within the province in which they are enacted.

c)   By-laws enacted by municipal and county councils which are only valid within the legal boundaries of the legislative authority enacting such By-laws.

d)   Resolutions passed by school boards which have been approved by the authority having jurisdiction.

Arising out of Statute Law is an administrative process governing the administrative agencies of governments. This process is frequently referred to as Administrative Law, which provides for the delegation of authority to make reasonable rules and findings conforming to the regulations or standards prescribed by the Statute Law creating the administrative agency. The law which established the St. Lawrence Seaway Authority is, in effect not only Statute Law, but Administrative Law as well. An Act to provide for a Provincial Building Code can be classified by the foregoing premise as Administrative Law, as the application of the Code is provided in the Statute Law.

1.5   COMMON LAW

1.5.1   Origins

Common Law, which comprises the bulk of our Law in Canada, means Law that is common to the whole of the country, as distinct from Law peculiar to certain classes of people such as the Law Merchant of the Middle Ages. The Common Law, as practised in all of the Provinces of Canada, with the exception of the Province of Quebec, has its origin in the English Common Law.

The Common Law of England dates back to early Saxon times. William the Conqueror, 1066, while introducing some of the European Code Laws, by and large permitted the continued use of Anglo-Saxon Law, some of which was similar to Statute Law being compiled in "doom books", while most law was based on long usage. Edward I, (1239-1307), recognizing that no code of laws could possibly be sufficiently comprehensive to cover all situations, established Courts of Law to ensure that justice would be obtained in courts even though no Statute Law was applicable. It was in these courts that Common Law became firmly established.

The Province of Quebec in 1866 formally adopted the old French Law, which had been founded upon Roman Law and had become known as Civil Law. This adoption of Civil Law, which was not only based upon old French Law, includes portions of the Code

Napoleon of France. Nevertheless, the Civil Law of Quebec is not too dissimilar to the English Common Law. It is, however, sufficiently different on the whole to forbid the assumption it agrees with the Common Law entirely. In some matters the Common Law and the Civil Law of Quebec differ widely. It should be noted that the Civil Law of Quebec is French origin and was assured to the citizens of the Province of Quebec under the provisions of the Quebec Act of 1774.

Common Law is predicated upon the decisions of the Judges of the Courts and, for this reason, it is commonly called Case Law. The foundation of Common Law is, therefore, the compilation of decisions by precedent, or long established customs which, over the centuries have become established as well-defined legal principles. These principles are applied to every case which comes before a Court of Law where Statute Law is not involved. From this practice, the Common Law has also become known as the Law of the Courts. The decisions of the Lower Courts, following precedents in giving judgement, are binding, unless these decisions are reversed by a higher court. In Common Law, the circumstances of one case are rarely identical to those of another, even though there may be a similarity between the two cases. This fact makes it most difficult to apply precedented principles and to avoid inflicting hardship.

Nevertheless, it has been held that it is better to apply precedented principles so that the Law may become widely <u>known</u> than to apply varying principles that would cause the Law to be <u>unknown</u>.

The principles of the Law of Contract are almost entirely the creation of the Courts of Common Law, legislation having had little to do with their development. In fact, the Law of Contracts differs from other branches of Law in that it does not establish rights and duties which the Law will enforce. Rather, it consists of a number of limiting principles which the parties to a contract create for themselves, which are enforceable in the Courts.

1.5.2   Rights and Wrongs

Included in the Common Law are substantive laws defining rights and wrongs. Rights include legal rights which the Courts of Law will recognize and defend. Where there are wrongs which the Courts of Law will recognize, the Courts will offer redress.

Blackstone, in his Commentaries on the Laws of England (first published in 1756) subdivided rights into the rights of persons and rights of things. The rights of persons he related to the persons of men as distinguished from their property, including the right of every man to enjoy personal security, personal liberty and personal property. Included among these rights are the liabilities and rights arising from mutual relations as between master and servant, principal and agent, guardian and ward, husband and wife, parent and child.

Also included among the rights of things are those laws which are concerned with the acquisition of property and the ownership of real and personal property, including both the rights and liabilities accompanying them.

Wrongs are classified as either public wrongs or private wrongs. Public wrongs are those committed against the community and are known as crimes or misdemeanours. Private wrongs are those which are not dangerous to the community in general, but which inflict loss on the individual and are known as Torts.

Public wrongs are penalized by fines and imprisonment or both. Private wrongs are usually easily remedied by redress, including restitution for losses suffered.

Remedy for wrongs is the basis of Remedial Law which controls the organization of the courts and establishes the method for enforcing claims in these courts. From the application of Remedial Law, there developed in Canada, as in England, the two great systems of courts; the Courts of Common Law and the Courts of Equity, although they are now known by other names such as the County Court.

Originally the Law of Equity consisted of rules based on good conscience which were created, and enforced, by what was known formerly as the Court of Chancery. These rules, intended to aid, supplement and correct the Common Law, were predicated upon the principle that fairness was the most elemental of all fundamentals of Law. Today these rules of equity are incorporated in all law and, therefore, affect all contracts.

The Term "equity" has two meanings, one professional and the other personal. To a lawyer, equity may mean that part of the Law of England which was derived not from customary usage or by legislation, but from decisions of the old Court of Chancery. An individual may think of equity as being the ideal justice, not regulated by Law and which may even be contrary to the Law.

Both of these assumptions are apparently correct. The basic premise of equity appears to be that when a plaintiff (complainant) asks the Court to grant legal remedy for a wrong committed, he or she is demanding legal right under the Law. If facts can be proved which establish his or her right to remedy, the Court must give the remedy. However, it should be noted that upon entering a Court of Equity, the plaintiff must enter with "clean hands"; he or she must be free of wrong.

Civil wrongs arising from a breach of duty imposed by Law, or infringement of a legal right given by Law, are called TORTS, which may be classified as follows:

a)   Personal wrongs, such as slander, libel and fraud.

b)   Trespass, such as the violation of one's property, patents or copyrights

c)   <u>Nuisance</u>, the act of causing injury or annoyance to a person or property, although the act may be committed elsewhere than on one's person or property.

d)   <u>Negligence</u>, which is the failure to observe the necessary care and vigilance to protect the interests and rights of another person.

e)   <u>Violation of water rights</u>, and the <u>right of support</u> such as the foundations of adjacent buildings which must not be disturbed, etc.

Although a contract may state what a person must do and what he or she has agreed to do, the Law of Equity and the Rules of Torts may prohibit him or her from doing certain things which would violate the natural rights of others. These natural rights may be defined by either Common Law or Statute Law, or they may not be specifically defined. In the latter case, the Court will decide whether a wrong has been committed.

The following are the most common ways of settling Torts:

a)   By a Civil Suit for damages.

b)   By arbitration and agreement.

c)   By the death of either party to a contract, unless a Statute Law provides that the Tort shall survive the death of either party.

d)   By bankruptcy (except in cases of fraud and wilful or malicious wrongs).

e)   By a Statute of Limitation, the time limit restricting when any action may be initiated and which discharges the Tort automatically if no action is taken to recover within the stated time of limitation, following the occurrence of the injury. It is from this principle that the phrase, "Do not sleep upon your rights" originated.

This Chapter is a basic overview of the subject matter. Further details are best left to someone more qualified. It will, however, provide a basic legal background for further discussions related to the subjects which are to follow.

TYPICAL QUESTIONS

1. Define the word "Law"
2. What are the five (5) basic systems of Law?
3. Define "Constitution".
4. What is "Constitutional Law"?
5. What is "Statute Law"?
6. What is meant by "Administrative Law"?
7. Define "Common Law".
8. What is meant by "Substantive Law"?
9. Define (a) Rights (b) Wrongs.
10. Define the "Law of Equity".
11. What are "Torts"?
12. What are the remedies for Torts?

REFERENCES

Anger's Digest of Canadian Law
Encyclopaedia Britannica, 1960 Edition
Fundamentals of Canadian Law, F.A.R. Chapman
History of Sources of the Common Law - C.H.

2

OF RIGHTS AND RESPONSIBILITIES
by Harland C. Lindsay, FRICS, CHE, PQS(F), FICArb, FAIC, MAACE

2.1   INTRODUCTION

The principal parties involved in a Construction Contract are:

1.   The **OWNER**, an individual, firm or corporation who commissions a construction work and pays for its cost.

2.   The **ARCHITECT** or **ENGINEER** who, on behalf of and representing the OWNER, furnishes the professional and technical skill required for the planning of the Work, the preparation of the drawings and specifications for its construction, administration of the contract and review of construction work.

3.   The **CONTRACTOR** who, together with those sub-trades whom he elects to employ, provides the materials, labour, equipment and skills for the physical accomplishment of the project, taking financial risks an **OWNER** will not usually take.

The purpose of this Chapter is to consider both the duties and liabilities of the Architect or Engineer not only to the Owner, but to the Contractor also,.whether believed or not, Architects and Engineers do have obligations to Contractors building projects they have designed.

The words **PROFESSION** and **PROFESSIONAL** appear in many text books, technical journals and other publications whenever Architects and Engineers and their work come under discussion. For this reason these words are now defined briefly:

The Encyclopaedia Britannica Dictionary defines a Profession as:

"*An occupation that properly involves a liberal education, or its equivalent, and mental, rather than manual labour; any calling or occupation involving special attainments or disciplines.*"

A Professional is one belonging to, or connected with a profession. A Professional is a practitioner who is paid for services he renders, based upon his knowledge, judgement and skill. He does not derive his livelihood from the sale or barter of goods or products. Architects and Engineers are separate groups of professionals, who have qualified by education and experience, and have developed the required abilities to practise their respective disciplines.

The late W.G. Raymore, FRAIC, stated - "*one does not become a professional by joining an organization, even one dedicated to the high aim of serving society effectively, nor does specialization confer the status*", to which could be added - **one must qualify for professional recognition.**

2.2   THE PROFESSIONALS

As the Architect or Engineer is a principal party involved in a Construction Contract, it is necessary to provide amplified definitions as follows:

2.2.1   Architect

The functions of an Architect are manifold and of a highly technical nature. Not only must he be an expert in the planning of buildings, he must also be acquainted with the various kinds of structures and the accommodation capabilities of each. He must know how to arrange all parts of the structures he plans in the most economical manner. He must have adequate knowledge of the materials and methods of architectural construction. The complexity of building has increased during the past 60 years. So has the origin and growth of such specialized engineering professions as Heating, Ventilating, Air-Conditioning, Refrigeration, Electrical, etc. whose work is usually integrated and coordinated by the Architect responsible for the design of the whole of a Work. He must, therefore, know how to finance building, know the Law, and how to prepare adequate documents for the contracting of the work.

2.2.2   Engineer

Laidlaw, Young and Dick, in their textbook "Engineering Law" state, "The term 'engineer' is not capable of precise definition". For present discussion it is intended to restrict the meaning to persons "versed in or who following as a calling or profession any branch of engineering".

To this brief definition could be added the following definition adopted by the Engineers Council for Professional Development (UK) in 1949:

"An Engineer is characterized by his ability to apply creatively scientific principles to design or develop structures, machines, apparatus, or manufacturing process, or works utilizing them singly or in combination; or construct or operate the same with full cognizance of their design; or to forecast their behaviour under specific operating conditions; all as respects to an intended function, economics and safety to life and property".

2.3   ENGINEERING AND ARCHITECTURAL LAW

We have seen that "Law" is a binding custom or practice of a community, and those portions of it relating to the practice of Architecture of Engineering, governing the professional conduct and - discipline of Architects and Engineers is called Architectural and Engineering Law. Such "Law" is Statutory Law and is to be found in the Architects Act or Professional Engineers Act of the various Provinces.

2.4   NATURE AND SOURCE OF DUTIES

It is not sufficient for an Architect or Engineer to perform only the duties imposed by his fellow citizens. The low demands that he also confirm other requirements imposed on him in connection with the exercise of his profession. The original of duties of an architect or engineering stem from:

a)   <u>Common Law</u>: i.e., from established custom;

b)   <u>Statutes</u>: enacted by the Parliament of Canada, or by legislation of the various Provinces, legislative Orders-in-Council; by-laws, rules and regulations passed by municipal and other bodies; and by express agreement with another person or person, i.e. by contract.

While the duties of the Architect and Engineer arise out of the relationship of Architect and Engineer to the public, to the employer, to the Contractor and to members of his profession, it may be found in the Statutes that:

a)   The design of structures should be carried out to the satisfaction **of the authority having jurisdiction**.

b)   The construction of any building or part thereof shall be carried out under the direction of the person responsible for its design.

c)   The construction of any building may be supervised by a person other than required in b.) above where the person is qualified and professionally competent in the specific field of construction being carried out, or where **the authority having jurisdiction specifically authorizes**.

The foregoing expressly imply particular duties, those of **being qualified to design a Work and supervise the construction of it**. Duties of Architects and Engineers to the Public, Owners and to Contractors will be later dealt with separately.

2.5   FOUNDATION OF LIABILITY

The word "jurisdiction" has at least three particular interpretation:

1.   The right to exercise legal authority granted by virtue of statute law, or regulation of such law for its administration.

2.   The extent of power; e.g. the jurisdiction of a court of law or a government. In law, the right of a court to pass upon a given case; also, the scope of authority of the court.

3.   The district or area over which any legal authority extends.

In a Building Code, "the person having jurisdiction" would probably mean the Building Inspector, the extend of whose legal authority is established by the articles of a By-law.

The two essential things to remember concerning the Foundation of Liability are:

1.   When jurisdiction has been properly established and carried out, the certain acts made unlawful, it does not matter what the source of laws may be.

2.   To create a liability there must be a failure to perform a prescribed duty recognized as a legal requirement.

2.6   DUTIES AND LIABILITIES TO THE PUBLIC

The law requires all those who practise architecture or engineering professionally to possess sufficient ability to protect the Public as to health and safety. Therefore, in all phases of their designs they are liable for all consequences arising from them as they affect the Public.

The foregoing legal requirement requires Architects and Engineers to perform their work with "a reasonable degree of skill".

What is skill? Skill may be defined as the familiar knowledge of any science or art, **as shown by dexterity of execution, in its application to practical purposes**. In the case of Architects or Engineers, <u>skill</u> means technical ability, while <u>care</u> is a positive display of regard, interest or concern with respect to some person, thing or event. To exercise reasonable care and skill, Architects and Engineers must display their concern for the Public with respect to their work, and possess the required qualifications expected of them as to knowledge and experience. Mere knowledge is not sufficient, nor is experience alone but together and properly applied, a skill is demonstrated. In Law, exceptional skill is not expected, **but average skill is demanded** of Architects and Engineers. It is, therefore, the duty of Architects and Engineers to:

a)   Possess the reasonable degree of skill, learning and experience ordinarily possessed by those in a professional position.

b)   Obey the Law with respect to the practice of their profession.

c)   Employ reasonable and average care, diligence, skill, knowledge and judgment.

PUBLIC, in the present context, means anything which pertains to or affects the community as a whole, as distinguished from that which is private or personal. Practically all Law is Public, or it has been enacted, and is enforced, for the benefit of the community.

LIABILITY is the state of being responsible for damage, burden, accidental or incidental result, or occurrence affecting the rights of the Public or the Individual, for which acts a person is liable to penalty. Liability is, therefore, the state of being legally responsible for all acts.

An Architect or Engineer, in the eyes of the Law, is in much the same positions as individuals such as you and I. We are admonished to "keep the peace"; should we breach it, we are legally responsible for what may ensure as to penalties. A violation of Public Rights causes the wrongdoer to be liable for a persecution of a criminal nature, whereas, a violation of Private Rights is a Tort, causing an action in Civil Law for redress. The Statutes and their regulations impose duties upon the Architect and Engineer. Since Architects and Engineers do not enjoy special exemption from the Law, they are found to perform those duties as prescribed, failure to do so being the liability to such penalty as prescribed by the Law. Therefore, Architects or Engineers who violate a Public Right are liable to penalty, which may be a fine, or imprisonment or both. **Contractors are also subject to penalties arising out of violations of Public Rights which they may have committed.**

2.7   INFRINGEMENT OF PRIVATE RIGHTS

Private Rights come within the confines of Private or Civil Law, a branch of the Common Law, which is sub-divided into:

a)   The Law of Obligations

b)   The Law of Property.

It has been said that every one of use is a bundle of rights and duties. Each of us has certain duties, or obligations, to other people, and correspondingly each of us has certain rights affecting other persons. Many of these obligations have been imposed upon us by either Statute Law, or Common Law. Apart from committing crimes each of us is obliged to restrain from trespassing on land, goods, persons or reputations of persons. Violation of these obligations is to commit a Tort, providing the means for the injured party to sue for redress.

An Architect or Engineer must personally assume responsibility for any breach of the law on his part which infringes any right in law of another person.

2.8   DUTIES AND LIABILITIES

2.8.1   To the Employer

The personal qualifications and character of an Architect or Engineer are usually the most import consideration of an employer, who retains him (usually the Owner). It is generally accepted that the Architect or Engineer will undertake in person the authority conferred upon him by his employer. The employer expects and is entitled to, the personal services of the Architect or Engineer in all matters requiring the exercise of professional skill and care. It has been held that such matters cannot be delegated, nor can he substitute the services of another person in matters in which his employer is entitled to the Architect's or Engineer's personal judgement, care and skill.

While the Architect or Engineer cannot implicitly trust his assistants, he may make sure of their labour and skill provided he retains control of his work and, while he assumes responsibility for their acts, he must exercise his own skill and care to ensure the rights of his employer are protected fully.

The professional services of the Architect or Engineer usually consist of taking instructions from the Owner, selecting engineering consultants and instructing them; preparing the necessary design plans and estimates of costs; preparing the working drawings and specifications; preparation of the tender and contract documents and advising upon the tender proposals; specifications necessary for the proper carrying out of the work; reviewing shop or setting drawings and manufacturer's brochures for specified products and equipment; issuing certificates for progress payments for work done; and the general review of the work under construction.

It must be assumed that:

a)   **the Owner, upon engaging an Architect or Engineer, must assume he is employing a person with both qualifications and character**

b)   **The Architect or Engineer, upon being employed in his professional capacity, does not warrant that his designs will be the most suitable, the most economical or the most durable.**

2.8.2   To the Owner

Architects or Engineers in preparing Preliminary Plans will do so usually from the viewpoints of shelter and use functions, more generally termed the functions of use and occupancy. These functions must be based upon the needs of the Owner. Regardless of the Owner's needs, the Architect or Engineer must, in the preparation of preliminary plans, take into account how they might affect the general public unavoidably. **In this advisory capacity and design capacity Architects and Engineers are servants of the Owner**. It is at this stage that the Owner should furnish his Architect or Engineer with:

a)   Full information, legal and topographical, concerning the Site of the Work. This includes a complete and accurate survey of the Site of the Work, giving lines, grades, lines of streets, pavements and adjoining properties, and the site contours.

b)   Description of the rights, restrictions, easements, boundaries of the site of the Work.

c)   Full information of buried utilities such as sewers, water supply, gas, electric power, telephone, underground steam supply, etc.

d)   Reports of all preliminary soil testing such as bore holes and best pits for soil bearing capacity.

The cost of which must be borne by the Owner.

Although there is only implied warranty by the Architect or Engineer concerning the suitability of the drawings and specifications they prepare, there is the liability by law that **they are responsible for the safety of their designs**. If the designs are inadequate, uneconomical or nondurable, Architects and Engineers are liable only if these defects are the result of their failure to use reasonable knowledge, skill and diligence: **in short, have been negligent. They must, at their peril, protect health and safety and, therefore, are responsible for the consequent of these aspects of their designs**.

To properly perform their functions, Architects and Engineers should have accurate knowledge of Statutes, By-laws, etc., governing both the design and construction of their work. This does not imply they should give legal advice, nor profess they are authorities in legal matters.

In the preparation of the working drawings and specifications, Architects and Engineers are performing a design function as servants of an Owner.

Whenever the Architect or Engineer prepares Tender Documents, which will be discussed more fully in a later chapter, he does so as a servant of the Owner. However, when either the Architect or Engineer advertises for Tenders on behalf of the Owner, carries on preliminary negotiations prior to the award of a Construction Contract on behalf of the Owner and, following the award of Contract, reviews the Contractor's Work, he does so as legal Agent of the Owner. In the context of our discussions, according to Law, an Agent is a person with express or implied authority to act for another, who is known as the Principal. Therefore, an Architect or Engineer who has express or implied authority to act on behalf of his principal (the Owner) may conclude an agreement with a third party (the Contractor). As Agents, neither the Architect nor the Engineer have rights of duties, even though there may be a separate contract of agency between them and the Owner. However, by virtue of the provisions of the Law of Agency, their acts are binding upon the Owner.

2.9   SELECTING CONSULTANTS

Before anything can be built it must be planned. Modern construction requires drawings and specifications which can only be produced by highly skilled Architects, Engineers, Specifications Writers and Draughtsmen. The Owner's Architect or Engineer has responsibility, not only in the matter of selecting the most competent consultants, but in co-ordinating the work of such specialists. There are many examples of projects where, from lack of co-ordination and collaboration, the structural architectural, mechanical and electrical design specialists of the project appeared to be not on speaking terms with each other.

2.10   DUTIES AND LIABILITIES TO THE CONTRACTOR

Neither the Architect nor Engineer is liable to the Owner, for the negligence of the Contractor. However, the Architect or Engineer should protect himself from unapproved work or methods of the Contractor. It is held that the Architect or Engineer, although not a legal authority, should have knowledge of the Law with respect to construction and the Contractor's performance. They should have sufficient knowledge of the Law to know when the actions of a contractor are likely to become illegal, or when failure to act may be illegal also. It is their responsibility to see that neither actions, nor failures to act, by the Contractor occur, or prevent the Owner and the Contractor becoming involved in penalties.

It is the responsibility of the Architect or Engineer, to both the Owner and the Contractor, to make working drawings and specifications as complete, clear and thorough as possible. These documents will exhibit the extend of "due diligence and reasonable skill" that has been exercised in their preparation. The quality of these documents will influence the exactness of budgetary estimating, and effectiveness in bidding. The working drawings and specifications, therefore, must be consistent, and jointly provide all the necessary information a Contractor requires to build a Work. More will be said in this regard in a later Chapter.

One of the basic, and legally required obligations of an Architect or Engineer to his employer is to make certain the actual construction of a project complies with the design drawings and specifications. Also, it has been long recognized that an Architect or Engineer should administer the construction of the project he has designed. It is also generally accepted that the safety, suitability and economy of any structure depends upon the design skill and judgement of the Architect or Engineer, and upon the success with which the intent of the drawings and specifications has been implemented. This is a responsibility to the Owner. But what of the responsibility to the Contractor? To a considerable extent, the Construction's execution of the work is influenced by the ability of the Architect or Engineer, and his impartiality in his administration of a contract.

The drawings and specifications used by the Contractor have been warranted by the Architect or Engineer who issued them. This is a warranty by implication only. The Contractor can quite properly take the position that he is not responsible for the adequacy of the drawings and specifications, and that he cannot be held liable for defects in the work when he has complied with the inferable intent of these documents. It is this inferable intent that so often becomes controversial. It is the prerogative of the Architect or Engineer to authoritatively interpret what he had drawn or written. However, judgement must be exercised when interpreting ambiguities for the Contractor. It is an axiom of Contract Law that in constructing a contract, if the language is capable of more than one interpretation, then all doubts must be resolved against the person using the language or writing.

When dispute arises on the project involving an interpretation of the specifications, many Architects and Engineers believe it is their prerogative to resolve any ambiguity and that the Contractor must proceed according to their interpretation. It is natural that Architects and Engineers in representing the Owner, may, without being aware of the fact, resolve questions of ambiguity in favour of the Owner and, indirectly, in favour of their own work rather than in favour of the Contractor where there might be an "Extra" involved. Frequently a Contractor will accept such interpretation with loud complaint but, rather than make an issue of the matter, will comply with the Architect's or Engineer's instruction to his disadvantage. Such a practice is unfair.

2.11   EXTRAS

"Extras" usually arise from two sources:

a)   Defective drawings and specifications or,
b)   Changes in Owner's requirements.

Defective drawings and specifications frequently result in the issue of costly addenda after contract award, at the expense of the Owner. Mr. Fred Sackett, a retired General Contractor, in his article appearing in the March 1962 issue of Progressive Architecture, said in this regard:

"Ambiguities in the contract documents are not considered defects by the Contractor, for they are potential change orders from which a major portion of job profits may come. A reasonable number of addenda he accepts with aplomb; but too many he views with alarm, since they indicate discovered oversights, and he wonders how many remain undiscovered."

These remarks are as applicable today, as they were in 1962.

Any changes to original contract requirements, whether they are additions to or deletions from the original scope of work, should only be authorized in writing, and over the signature of the Owner. In negotiations in this regard, the Architect or Engineer must be scrupulously fair. Under no circumstances should Contractor be pressured into gratuitously performing work to rectify Consultants, errors or omissions in the Contract Documents. Only physicians and surgeons are permitted to bury their mistakes.

It has been held:

> *"The number of changes is not in and of itself. A single change which is beyond the scope of a contract may be serious enough to constitute an actionable breach of that contract".*
> (Saddler vs. US, 287, F. 2d 411)

It has also been held:

> *"Any changes must be directed to furthering the original design and must not be destructive of that design or disproportionate in size or amount".*
> (278 NY 154)

In the interpretation of the contract documents, and determining the effects a change may have upon the Owner or the Contractor, the Architect or Engineer must perform the quasi-judicial function of an arbiter, and must make a decision accordingly.

2.12   LEGAL DEFINITION OF EXTRAS

The most common contract used in the industry, CCDC2 1994, defines a Change Order as a written amendment to the Contract prepared by the Consultant and signed by the Owner and the Contractor stating their agreement upon a change in the Work; the method of adjustment or the amount of the adjustment in the Contract price, if any, and the extent of the adjustment in the contract time. General Condition 6.1.2 reads "The Contractor shall not perform a change in the work without a Change Order." In a perfect world under perfect conditions a change order should address all changes to the work before the work is done. However, construction is by it's very nature not a perfect science. With pressures of schedule and other demands, it is not unusual that a contractor will proceed with changes to the work without a signed Change Order. In the majority of cases this does not pose a problem. Nonetheless, there are exceptions and these exceptions usually lead to a dispute between the Owner and the Contractor. Some of these disputes are resolved with the assistance of the Consultant, but others are left to be resolved through arbitration or litigation.

Knowing how a Court may analyze the alleged Changes to the work is important and for this I refer to a test used by Justice Egbert of the Supreme Court of Alberta in *Chittick v. Taylor* which set out rules for determining what are "extras" within the meaning of a building contract.

Justice Egbert set out the following four rules:

> *"Rule 1.   An item specifically provided for in the contract is not an "extra."*
>
> *Rule 2.   When the plaintiff supplied material of a better quality than the minimum quality necessary for the fulfilment of the contract, without any instructions, express or implied, from the defendant to do so, he is not entitled to charge the extra cost as an "extra."*
>
> *Rule 3.   When the plaintiff did work or supplied materials not called for by the contract (plans or specifications) without instructions, express or implied, from the defendant, or the consent of the defendant, he is not entitled to charge this additional work or materials as an "extra."*
>
> *Rule 4.   When the plaintiff did work or supplied material not called for by the contract on the instructions, express or implied, of the defendant, he is entitled to charge for additional work or materials as an "extra."*
>
> *What amounted to instructions from the defendant is dependent on the circumstances relating to each item. If the defendant, without giving definite instructions, knew the plaintiff was doing extra work or supplying extra materials and stood by and approved of what was being done and encouraged the plaintiff to do it, that, in my opinion, amounts to an implied instruction to the plaintiff and the defendant is liable."*

The first three rules place the onus on the Contractor and relive the Owner of liability, but Rule 4 corrects this by introducing the idea of "implied instructions."

Justice Downs of the Supreme Court of British Columbia more recently applied these same rules in her decision in *Alex Gair & Sons Ltd. v. Lepiriski.* The lawsuit centered on the issue of changes and extras. Justice Downs applied these rules to the scores of items in dispute. The value of these disputed items ranged from less than $100 to many thousands of dollars. In doing so, the court relied upon the quantities and measurements supplied by a Quantity Surveyor.

Owners and Contractors may benefit by applying the above rules to the claims prior to beginning an action either in arbitration or in court. At a minimum, application of these rules to the claimed changes could lead to elimination, either through abandonment or agreement, of at least some alleged claims, or to resolution of the entire dispute.

2.13 REVIEW OF CONSTRUCTION

The review of the Contractor's work is by far the most important single function of the Architect or Engineer once work has commenced. Because of the importance of this function of the Architect or Engineer, a separate Chapter is devoted to this subject.

2.14 SUMMATION

It has been shown that, to practice professionally, Architects and Engineers must:

a) Be professionally competent.

b) Perform their work with diligence and skill.

c) Have principles of integrity.

d) Hold themselves liable for the health and safety of the public.

It has been shown that they have not only duties and responsibilities to their employer, the Owner, but the Contractor also.

TYPICAL QUESTIONS

1. Define "Architect", "Engineer".
2. What are some of the implied obligations of an Architect or Engineer when employer by an Owner?
3. What responsibilities does an Architect or Engineer assume when he designs structures?
4. What is meant by "Extras"? What is the responsibility of the Architect or Engineer concerning them?
5. If an Architect of Engineer is given complete authority by contract with an Owner to accept or reject work, are there any conditions which might limit his authority?
6. When is an Architect or Engineer (a) a Servant (b) and Agent?
7. What duties does an Architect or Engineer have as an Agent?
8. What is meant by "Liability", "Public Liability"?
9. What are "infringements of Private Rights"? What Law provides redress?
10. What is the usual result when a Court of Law considers ambiguity in the Contract Documents?
11. What would cause a breach of contract with respect to changes in the original contract requirements?

REFERENCES

Anson's Principles of the English Law of Contract, Chapt. XVIII
Contracts, Specifications and Engineering Relations, Mead, Mead and Akerman
Encyclopedia Britannica
Engineering Contracts and Specifications - Robert W. Abbett
Fundamentals of Canadian Law - F.A.R. Chapman, Chapter 15

3

THE LAW OF CONTRACT - PART 1
by Claude Lawrenson, RSW, RHI and Evan Stregger, PQS(F), AScT, C.Arb., GSC

"We may provisionally define the law of Contract as that branch of the law which determine the circumstances in which a promise shall be legally binding on the person making it."

Anson's Principles of the English Law of Contract, 22nd ed.

3.1   INTRODUCTION

It has been long held that the preparation by an Architect or Engineer of Contract Documents, (Specifications, General and other Conditions of a Construction Contract, Drawings and other technical details) does not in itself constitute the practice of Law. On the other hand, the preparation of the actual construction contract between an Owner and a Contractor does involve the retention of a legal service which should be rendered by a lawyer.

Meridith Fleming, Q.C., writing in the March 1968 issue of Mechanical Contracting & Engineering remarked: -

"There is a feeling on the part of those engaged in the various fields of the construction industry, and even on the part of many lawyers, that the law relating to construction contracts is a mystery beyond the ken of all but the high priests of the fraternity."

Without some knowledge of the Law of Contract, however, Construction Contracts can be difficult to interpret and execute, let alone understand. Therefore, it is considered advisable to review the Law of Contract, before discussing the various forms of contracts which we may encounter in the construction industry.

3.2   WHAT IS A CONTRACT?

"A contract consists in an actionable promise or promises. Every such promise involves two parties, a promisor and a promisee, and an expression of common intention and of expectation as to the act or forbearance promised. When a contract consists, as it often does, of mutual promises, each party is of course both a promisor and a promisee, and this fact should not be lost sight of in any discussion of this subject....

We may start, therefore, with the principle that the law requires the parties to make their own contract; it will not make a contract for them out of terms which are indefinite or illusory."

Anson's Principles of the English Law of Contract, 22 ed.

As mentioned previously there is in Common Law a particular portion of it known as Private or Civil Law. Private Law is usually divided into two classifications: -

1.   The Law of Property, and,

2.   The Law of Obligations

It is by the Law of Obligations we become obliged to pay sums of money to others, or to supply them with goods or services, <u>because we voluntarily undertook to do these for personal reasons</u>. The Law of Obligations, which governs these voluntary obligations is also called the Law of Contract.

Not all contracts are lengthy formal documents, overflowing in legal phraseology. Nor are contracts usually entered into with great solemnity. Practically all business transactions are contracts in one form or another.

It has been long held a person cannot be under a contractual obligation unless they voluntarily agree to do so. Therefore, all contracts are agreements of various kinds. However, not all agreements are contracts. Only those agreements conform to rigorous requirements that are contracts.

3.3   A CONTRACT DEFINED

Before defining a Contract, we should consider the legal status of the following words which will be used frequently in this context.

<u>Valid</u>: sound, just, effective in law, therefore, a Contract is valid when it is in full force and its terms and conditions are enforceable by court action.

<u>Void</u>: empty, clear or free. A void Contract is one which has no legal effect, which is to say has no status at law, and is, therefore, unenforceable by court action, as if it had never been made.

<u>Voidable</u>: capable of being made void, therefore, a voidable Contract is one in which one of the parties to it is able to enforce it or reject it at his option. Also, a voidable Contract is one which may bind one party, and may or may not bind the other party at his option. Contracts with infants (minors) are usually voidable at the option of the infant.

<u>Enforceable</u>: to compel obedience to, as to laws. An enforceable Contract, then, is one in which the parties to it have the intention to go, or be taken, to law for a breach of the Contract.

Unenforceable: is the opposite to enforceable. An Unenforceable Contract is one that cannot be enforced in a Court of Law, even though it may be valid contract in all other respects. An unenforceable contract is usually one which contains a technical defect barring it from court action. Such a contract is one entered into with either the Federal or Provincial Governments who cannot be sued except by their consent, by fiat. This principle is based on the old legal axiom - "The Crown can do no wrong."

Consideration: as related to Contracts is a promise or performance of an act or forbearance as the price of a promise given another; the benefit conferred or the detriment suffered in return for a promise. It is an essential element in contracts under seal, which will be discussed later.

In Anger's Digest of Canadian Law a Contract is defined as "a deliberate engagement between competent parties upon a legal consideration to do or abstain from doing some act."

F.A.R. Chapman, in his book - "Fundamentals of Canadian Law" - defines a contract as: -

"A legally enforceable contract is a deliberate agreement between two or more competent parties (not necessarily in writing) which is supported by mutual consideration to do some legal act voluntarily."

Although the wording of each of these definitions may be slightly different, they are similar in meaning. From these definitions it will be noted that in order to have a valid contract, and it is this with which we are most concerned, it is necessary that: -

1. There is a deliberate act to enter into.

2. There is an agreement with one or more other parties or persons.

3. The parties to an agreement are competent to do so.

4. The agreement preferably in writing although it is not absolutely essential.

5. There is mutual consideration, i.e., as in a Tender Proposal for a Contract.

6. The agreement is entered into voluntarily.

7. The agreement has legal status.

In our discourse the world "deliberate" will be taken to mean acting with deliberation, without haste, and only after serious consideration of an action to take. While the word "agreement," in the legal sense, is to be of one mind, regardless of whether there are two or more persons involved. Therefore, a "deliberate agreement" could be interpreted to mean - the intention of two or more persons, who have mutual intentions, or are of the same mind, agreeing to do, or refrain from doing an act. It has also been held in Law that when an agreement is deliberate it means that the parties to the agreement have the mutual intention that a breach of their agreement is followed by legal consequences, such as going to or being taken to the Law.

3.4   WHAT IS AN AGREEMENT?

A Contract is a deliberate agreement between two or more parties, or persons. It may be apparent that when two parties have mutually agreed upon an action involving them both they have reached an agreement. However, it is frequently difficult to determine when an agreement has been reached. Frequently, the negotiations leading up to the signing of a contract are prolonged affairs and are quite involved. There may be considerable time spent in letter writing, telephone conversations, offers and counter offers, suggestions and counter-suggestions, etc. The question then, is to determine when an agreement has been reached. It has been long held in Law that an agreement is reached when the offer of one party has been accepted by the other.

If the Courts find that what the Offeror, has said or written (or has enacted in a manner which) amounts to a bona fide offer to do a definite thing, and the Offeree, has in some manner indicated that he has unconditionally accepted the offer, they will rule that an agreement has been reached, and a contract entered into at the moment of acceptance. An agreement is founded upon the manner by which an offer is made and accepted.

3.5   OFFER

The invitation from one party to another to make an offer was not previously considered in itself to be an offer nor an acceptance of an offer. However the Courts in Ron Engineering & Construction (Eastern) Ltd. v. Ontario and Water Resources Commission, [1981] 1 S.C.R. 111 (S.C.C.)] *(Ron Engineering)* introduced the concept of two separate contracts, contract A and contract B.

In *Ron Engineering* the Supreme Court of Canada created the paradigm known as "Contract A" and "Contract B". Contract A is the tender process including the rules of the game, and Contract B is the prize - the job.

In *Ron Engineering*, Ron the low bidder made an invisible error in its tender - it omitted work in preparing its price. There was nothing in the tender to alert the owner to this error. The contractor discovered its mistake after all bids were open. The owner refused the contractor's request to withdraw. Then, Ron refused to sign the contract and the work was awarded to another contractor. Ron then sued for return of its $100,000 deposit that the owner had refused to return. In its decision, the Supreme Court said that there was a preliminary, initial and "unilateral contract" which the court called "Contract A" and the main contract, which the court called "Contract B."

Contract A (which creates no obligation on any party until a bid is made) provides that the person issuing the tender can select one of the tenderers and enter Contract B with the tenderer so selected. Upon the person doing so, the tenderers, other than the one so selected, would be discharged from any obligation under Contract A. The tenderer selected, however, would then be required to enter into contract B with the person issuing the tender (the process has been compared to a leaseholder exercising an option to purchase). Contract B, however, does not come into force until executed by both parties. Here, under the terms of Contract A, the deposit was not refundable. The court said that the person that issues a call for tender creates an "offer to contract" which, once a bid is submitted both in conformity with, and in response to, the invitation to tender, is binding and is irrevocable if the tender conditions say that the bids are irrevocable.

Ruling for the owner,

In Ron, Mr. Justice Estey made the following statement in his reasons:

"There is no disagreement between the parties here about the form and procedure in which the tender was submitted by the respondent and that it complied with the terms and conditions of the call for tenders. Consequently, Contract A came into being. The principal term of Contract A is the irrevocability of the bid, and the corollary term is the obligation of both parties to enter upon the contract (Contract B) upon acceptance of the tender. Other terms include the qualified obligations of the owner to accept the lowest tender, and the degree of this obligation is controlled by the terms and conditions established in the call for tenderers."

Contract B is the construction contract and contract A is a separate contract arising out of the invitation to tender – which is the offer – and the submission of the tender in response thereto – which is the acceptance. If the invitation specifies terms and conditions such as not to revoke the tender for a specified period, such conditions will form part of Contract A and can be enforced in the same way as any other contractual obligations. However as far as contract B was concerned, the tender remained as only an offer which may or may not be accepted by the owner. Contract A was not perceived to be an agreement to enter into contract B. While the Owner still has wide latitude in accepting or rejecting tenders the rules for acceptance of a submitted bid or tender was defined in a case known as *M.J.B. Enterprises Ltd.* (MJB) *v. Defence Construction (1951) Ltd.* (Defence),

Defence had accepted the lowest tender (submitted on an altered, or non-compliant, tender form). MJB was the second lowest tenderer, and its tender had been submitted on an unaltered tender or compliant form. MJB, alleging that Defence had an obligation to award the work (Contract B) to a contractor which had submitted a compliant tender, claimed in the action for loss of profit arising out of its not being awarded the contract. On April 22, 1999, the Supreme Court of Canada found that Defence did not have the right to accept the lowest tender where that tender did not comply with the tender documents and awarded MJB damages in the amount of the profits it would have realized had it been awarded Contract B.

In considering the decision, the Court found that the Instructions to Tenderers and the Tender Form were crucial for determining the conditions of Contract A (precedent setting *Ron Engineering* case). On reviewing these documents the Court found that the contractor: (1) was to submit a compliant bid; and (2) could not negotiate over the terms of the Tender Documents. The Court said that the Tender Documents govern the terms, if any, of Contract A and they include no explicit term imposing an obligation to award Contract B to the lowest valid or compliant tender. The obligation was for Defence to accept only a compliant tender, although Defence *need not accept* the lowest compliant tender. In the above case, Defence accepted the lowest bid which was a non-compliant tender. In doing so, the court found that Defence breached its obligation to MJB, and to the other tenderers.

In a similar case, *W.I.B. Construction Ltd.* (WIB) *v. School District No. 23* (the District) Justice Lamperson of the Supreme Court of British Columbia reviewed the law of tendering and the construction industry custom in British Columbia. He found that the industry custom and practice were the basis for the decision to award Contract B on two criteria: (1) that the bid must meet all requirements of the bid documents; and (2) that the bidder must be qualified to do the work. He also held that it was an implied term of the bidding contract (Contract A) that the Owner must consider all the tenderers in good faith and apply the criteria established in the call for tenders fairly and impartially. It had been previously agreed that WIB had complied with the requirements of the call for tenders.

This particular tender call contained the requirement that the tenderers provide the name and résumé of the site superintendent. The architectural firm on the project had previously worked with the site superintendent named by WIB. Based on that experience, it believed that the person named by WIB could not properly supervise the project. It was on this basis that the Architect recommended that WIB's bid not be accepted, and the District awarded the contract to the second lowest bidder. The Court found that the District, since it acted fairly and objectively, was entitled to place considerable importance on the identity and qualifications of the site superintendent in making its decision. The Court dismissed WIB's action against the School District and also WIB's action against the Architect in tort.

What emerges from both of the above cases is that the party calling for tenders has the right to determine the terms of Contract A, including the right to privilege. However after setting the terms of Contract A, it must abide by the terms set when awarding Contract B. Those submitting tenders must also be aware that failing to comply with the terms of the tender could in most cases void their tenders, and that even if they submit the lowest valid tender, they may not be awarded the work.

3.6   MAKING AN OFFER

In Law, an offer is the act of tendering a definite promise with the expressed willingness to implement it if the other party accepts the offer; an acceptance of an offer results in a contract, provide other elements of a contract, such as consideration, intention to be legally bound, etc., are present. Regardless of how an offer is made, such as:

a)   An express verbal offer

b)   An offer in writing

c)   Or to be implied from the conduct of the offeror,

it must be made with serious intent. To accept an offer, the offeree must have reasonable grounds for believing that the offer was seriously intended by the offeror. The offeror, therefore, must clearly and distinctly indicate his willingness to carry out the promise of the offer upon its acceptance by the offeree.

The mere intent to make an offer is not, in itself, an offer, for there is an absence of an expressed willingness to be bound to the promise offered.

There is a time limit for the acceptance of an offer once it has been made. A verbal offer, however, which does not include a provision as to time for acceptance becomes invalid, or lapses, immediately the conversing parties separate. A written offer which does not stipulate a time limit as to validity of the offer is good until it is accepted, provided the acceptance is within a reasonable time of the offer.

Frequently, an offer will (and should) contain a definite time limiting the acceptance of the offer. Failure to the offeree to accept the offer within the stipulated time results in an automatic revocation of the offer. The most usually stipulated times for acceptance of offers are 30 days or 60 days. The Canadian Standard Form of Construction Tender, which sets out the offer of a bidder to furnish all materials, plant and labour necessary for the completion of the work upon which the offer is based, states:

"In the event of our tender (the offer) not being accepted within ....days of the time stated for the closing of receipt of tenders, the bid bond/certified uncashed cheque will be returned to us forthwith unless a satisfactory arrangement is made with us covering its retention for a further stated period."

This qualification of an offer provides for revocation of the offer owing to the lapse of time. It is a rule of Law that a promise to keep an offer open which does not included legal consideration must be made under seal to make it binding.

3.7   OFFER LAPSES

There are some fairly definite conditions creating the automatic lapse of an offer: -

1.   The particular time limits that may have been stated by the offeror.

2.   The acceptance of the offer is not within a "reasonable time" if no time limit has been particularly specified.

3.   The question of what is considered to be a reasonable time for the acceptance of an offer before it lapses often arises. There is no specific time limit in the Law in circumstances of this nature. The Courts will rule upon each case separately and according to the circumstances of the offer and the elapsed time which has occurred. It is reasonable to assume an offer cannot be kept open for six months. An offer made in June and not accepted until November may not be considered valid by the Courts, who would most likely rule that the offer had lapsed.

4.   The death of either the offeror or offeree.

Normally the offeree cannot accept an offer after he has been informed of the death of the offeror. Also, an acceptance communicated to the personal representative to the deceased offeror cannot be held as binding.

It is generally accepted that, if the offeree accepts an offer in ignorance of the offeror's death, it is invalid, as the offer has been terminated automatically, the knowledge of the offeror's death being irrelevant.

5.   By the destruction or impairment of the thing which is the subject-matter of a proposed contract, (where the contract requires for its performance, the existence of a particular thing which has been either lost, destroyed or impaired before the acceptance of the offer being made).

3.8   THE REVOCATION OF AN OFFER

As sometimes happens, a bidder will make a mistake in his tender and seeks to withdraw or amend the tender. If the tender is irrevocable an owner is under no obligation to allow the bidder to do either and is entitled to accept the tender and to compel the contractor to carry out the contract on the terms tendered. If however the bid has not been accepted, and there is no enforceable agreement which makes the tender irrevocable the contractor is entitled to withdraw his bid or submit a corrected bid.

3.9   PRIVILEGE

The bidding or tender process has been defined by the principle of Contract A/Contract B that arose out of *Ron Engineering*. This principle is that the owner offers to contract under specific conditions and those that submit tenders or bids that are compliant with the offer enter into Contract A. Contract A fixes the terms for evaluation of the bid and the offer to contract and may become the basis for Contract B, the work.

Approximately three years ago the case known as *MJB* placed an onus on the Owner to honor the offer to contract by accepting only compliant tenders.

In a recent case the bid documents included as part of the long and elaborate privilege clause said in part:

> *"Criteria which may be used by the OWNER in evaluating tenders and awarding the Contract are in the OWNER's sole and absolute discretion and, without limiting the generality of the foregoing, may include one or more of: price; total cost to OWNER; the amount of B.C. content; the amount of Canadian content; reputation; claims history of Tenderer; qualifications and experience of the Tenderer and its personnel; quality of services and personnel proposed by the Tenderer; ability of the Tenderer to ensure continuous availability of qualified and experienced personnel; the Construction Schedule and Plan; the proposed Labour and Equipment; and the proposed Supervisory Staff.*
>
> *Should the OWNER not receive any tender satisfactory to the OWNER in its sole and absolute discretion, the OWNER reserves the right to re-tender the Project, or negotiate a contract for the whole or any part of the Project with any one or more persons whatsoever, including one or more of the Tenderers."*

The above clause gave the Owner virtually unlimited right to reject or accept any bid "in its sole and absolute discretion".

3.10   ACCEPTANCE OF AN OFFER

In order for a valid offer to become accepted, it must be communicated. An offer is made when, and not until, it is communicated or made known to the offeree.

There are a number of legally accepted means of making an offer known to the offeree:

1.   The offeror, in conversation with the offeree, may make a <u>verbal offer at that time</u>. Although verbal offers lapse immediately upon the separation of the parties to the conversation, (provided there has been no acceptance by the offeree before their separation), an exception would be when a time limit for acceptance had been established during the conversation.

2.   A written offer delivered to the offeree by the offeror personally or by a messenger as his agent.

3.   A written offer sent by mail.

4.   An offer sent by telegraph, telex or facsimile.

It is generally understood that the method used to communicate an offer invites an acceptance by the same means, (unless it has been otherwise definitely expressed in the offer). In the matter of use of any telegraphed means of communicating an offer, it would be wise to confirm the offer by Registered Mail to safeguard the offer.

The acceptance of an offer must be absolutely unconditional, i.e., without any qualification whatsoever by the offeree. If an offer is not accepted as made, then the so-called "acceptance" is in reality a counter offer.

Once an offer is accepted, <u>a contract has been entered into at that time</u>. The formal signing of a Contract Agreement is the formal confirmation of the offer and the acceptance of it.

A common practice in the industry is the issuing by an owner of a Letter of Intent to a Contractor which states that it is <u>the intention</u> of the Owner to award a construction contract. Many contractors unwittingly accept a Letter of Intent as acceptance of their tender. **IT IS NOT**.

A Letter of Intent is merely an "agreement to agree" and is not recognized in Law as a binding commitment. Any Contractor who starts work on a project on the strength of a Letter of Intent is taking an unnecessary risk since the Owner is not bound to pay for any work executed.

A Letter of Award, accepting the tender submitted <u>is binding</u> and is therefore desirable.

On occasions where a Letter of Intent is necessitated, it should authorize the Contractor to proceed with a specific portion of the Work and state the amount of money payable by the Owner for such partial work. Since this is, in effect, a counter offer by the Owner, acceptance by the Contractor is required to make it binding. It essentially creates a "mini" contract.

If the acceptance of an offer is in the manner and time intended, the acceptance cannot be revoked. It should be noted that it has been ruled that a telegram revoking an acceptance already mailed is not effectual in law.

Frequently it is necessary to know the precise moment at which an acceptance converts to Contract A into Contract B. Apart from the possibility of a mailed acceptance being lost, or a telephoned, faxed or telegraphed acceptance being garbled upon receipt, there are other reasons why the moment of acceptance is important.

1.   Should the offeror die or become bankrupt, the validity of an agreement will depend upon whether the acceptance of the offer was before the event.

2.   Should the offeree learn of the revocation of an offer, the validity of the agreement will depend upon the exact amount at which the offer was accepted.

3.   The acceptance of an offer, by mail, is affected the moment the letter of acceptance is dropped into the mail box. This is because the offeror, (is either actually stipulating, or implying an acceptance by mail), appointed the mail as his representative or agent.

       It is not unusual for mail to go astray, particularly unregistered mail. In a case such as this, where the letter of acceptance has not been delivered, it has been held in Law, 1879, 4 Exchequer Division 216, "the offeror must bear the risk of the letter of acceptance being lost or delayed."

4.   The handing of a telegram of acceptance to the telegraph messenger is considered the precise moment of acceptance since the messenger is the offeror's implied agent.

       However, when the offeror leaves it to the offeree to accept an offer in any reasonable manner, the moment of acceptance may vary, according to whether the offeree used the offeror's implied agency, or his own. If the offeree accepts in exactly the same manner by which the offer was sent, he is communicating through the offeror's agent. If, however, the offeree chooses some other means of communicating an acceptance, he is employing his own agency and must assume the responsibility of the proper functioning of his agency.

       If two persons verbally discuss a transaction, and the offeror suggests to the offeree that the latter takes his time to consider the offer, it has been held that an acceptance by mail is valid, being an acceptance through the offeror's implied agent.

       In the case of Halifax Graving Dock Co. v. R. (1921) 62 SCR 338 it was ruled:

       "If an acceptance of an offer is given subject to a provision as to the execution of a contract, then the stipulation as to the contract is a term of assent and there is no agreement independent of that stipulation." This ruling implies a valid offer, not a counter offer as it would at first appear. What is meant is that the offeree accepts the offer made on the condition that the offeror will enter into a contract *(Contract A)*. Until both the offeror and offeree jointly sign a formal contract there is no agreement *(Contract B)*.

3.11   TENDER ERRORS

The bidding process is due to time constraints and other problems can lead to errors in the bids or offer submitted.   There are essentially two types of errors. Those that are hidden or not obvious and those that are obvious on the face of the bid.

In Ron Engineering & Construction (Eastern) Ltd. v. Ontario and Water Resources Commission, Ron the low bidder made an invisible error in its tender - it omitted work in preparing its price. There was nothing in the tender to alert the owner to this error. The contractor discovered its mistake after all bids were open. The owner refused the contractor's request to withdraw. Then, Ron refused to sign the contract and the work was awarded to another contractor. Ron then sued for return of its $100,000 deposit that the owner had refused to return. In its decision, the Supreme Court said that there was a preliminary, initial and "unilateral contract" which the court called "Contract A" and the main contract, which the court called "Contract B."

In a recent case, Canvar Construction (1991) Inc. v. Ottawa City Non-Profit Housing Corp, Canvar submitted a tender which included a Bid Bond in the amount $149,500 that was 5% of the *intended* tender price of $2,989,000. However the stated tender price, had been entered at $2,289,000. Canvar was immediately aware of the error and advised the City requesting that their tender price be adjusted to reflect the intended tender price. The City refused and awarded the contract, which Canvar in turn refused. The city then awarded the contract to the next bidder at an increased cost of $841,000 and commenced an action against Canvar. At trial the judge, based on the Ron Engineering ruling awarded the City damages of $841,000. On appeal it was found that the error in Canvar's tender was evident and one that did not require an explanation outside the tender documents, the error could have been determined from a perusal of the documents and the quantum of the tender and bid bond and that the error would have been obvious to a reasonable person. The Ontario Court of Appeal held that the error committed by Canvar was an "error on the face of the tender" and therefore outside the scope of Ron Engineering and that Canvar was within its legal right to refuse to execute the contract.

3.12   OTHER OFFERS

What happens when instead of responding to the Owner's offer a new offer is proposed by the bidder?

The bidding or tender process has been defined by the principle of Contract A/Contract B that arose out of *Ron Engineering*. This principle is that the owner offers to contract under specific conditions and those that submit tenders or bids that are compliant with the offer enter into Contract A. Contract A fixes the terms for evaluation of the bid and the offer to contract and may become the basis for Contract B, the work. Approximately three years ago the case known as *MJB* placed an onus on the Owner to honor the offer to contract by accepting only compliant tenders.

In the case quoted under 3.10 Privilege above the Owner reserved their rights as follows:

> *"Should the OWNER not receive any tender satisfactory to the OWNER in its sole and absolute discretion, the OWNER reserves the right to re-tender the Project, or negotiate a contract for the whole or any part of the Project with any one or more persons whatsoever, including one or more of the Tenderers."*

What are the standards when no compliant bids are received and the Owner elects to negotiate with one or more of the bidders?

In this case the Owner entered into negotiations with two of the bidders in an effort to conclude a contract. Ultimately only one Contractor was successful and the unsuccessful Contractor sued the Owner for breach of contract (Contract A per *Ron Engineering*).

The Owner applied to the Supreme Court of British Columbia for judgement dismissing the Contractor's action. The Contractor argued that because the "privilege clause" gave the Owner a discretion to accept non-compliant bids, any serious bid was "capable of acceptance" by the defendant, and therefore sufficiently compliant to give rise to a Contract A. The Supreme Court of British Columbia decided that if the bid does not strictly comply with the requirements of the bid documents published by the Owner there is no Contract A and that the bid submitted was, at best, a counter offer to the Owner's offer. As Contract A did not exist there was no contractually implied duty of fairness.

The Contractor also argued that the Owner was in breach of a "freestanding duty of fairness" independent of Contract A, and this point was allowed to proceed to trial.

At trial the appeal court in its judgement said:

> *"Whether such an independent duty of fairness exists is a pure question of law. The learned trial judge said he knew of no "free-standing enforceable duty of fairness simpliciter". Counsel did not refer us to any authority where such a duty has been held to exist. Such a duty is quite inconsistent with an adversarial, competitive tendering process. To find such a duty would cause great uncertainty in this area of the law.*

In my respectful view, the learned trial judge erred in law in holding that this claim might possibly succeed. As no such duty exists in law, the claim based on its alleged breach was bound to fail."

When the Contractor decided to be non-compliant they removed themselves from the Contract A/Contract B process and the fairness entrenched in that process and left themselves exposed to the no-holds-barred business negotiation process.

In summary the invitation to tender is an offer and the submission of a "compliant" bid is acceptance of that offer. Submission of a "non-compliant" bid is at best a counter offer by the Contractor and Contract A does not exist. Negotiation is a process where the parties attempt to agree on a contract, but until agreement is reached, there exist no contractual obligations or free standing duty of fairness.

3.13 WITHOUT PREJUDICE

In Law, where a statement is made by a party to a controversy for the express purpose of settling the controversy, and is offered WITHOUT PREJUDICE it is made in order to present, or to settle, legal action. Should the statement or offer so made not be accepted by the other party, the statement or offer cannot be used as evidence against the first party, unless his express permission is given.

In other words, if a party attempts to settle a dispute to avoid litigation, either in the Courts or by Arbitration, but does not want to prejudice his own legal position in the event that his attempt to settle fails, he may use the phrase WITHOUT PREJUDICE in the wording of his offer to settle.

WITHOUT PREJUDICE means "without prejudice to a party's legal right " therefore an offeror may verbally state or preferably, write, "Without Prejudice, I make the following proposition, etc." Such an offer cannot be used against the offeror and the offer is not binding until accepted by the offeree.

The only time the WITHOUT PREJUDICE offer can be used without consent is in legal or arbitration proceedings where costs are being argued and the settlement offer was grater than the judgement of the court or award of the arbitrator. The premise being that the offer was more than fair and if it had been accepted the party making the offer would not have incurred the additional cost of trial or arbitration.

TYPICAL QUESTIONS

1. What is the nature of the Law which governs Contracts? Explain fully.
2. Define a "Contract".
3. Define (a) Valid (b) Void (c) Voidable (d) Enforceable (e) Unenforceable and (f) Consideration.
4. What is an Agreement and how is an Agreement reached?
5. Define "Offer."
6. Define "Acceptance".
7. What is meant by the "lapse of an offer"?
8. How may an acceptance be effected?
9. Can an offer be revoked, and if so how?
10.. What is meant by "Without Prejudice"?

REFERENCES

Anson's Principles of English Law of Contract
G.C. Cheshire & C.H. Fifoot - The Law of Contract
Fundamentals of Canadian Law - F.A.R. Chapman

4

THE LAW OF CONTRACT - PART II

by Claude Lawrenson, RSW, RHI and Evan B. Stregger, PQS(F), AScT, C.Arb., GSC

"One cannot doubt that, as an ordinary rule of law, an acceptance of an offer made ought to be notified to the person who makes the offer, In Order that the two minds may come together. Unless this is done, the two minds may be, apart, and there is not that consensus, which is necessary according to the, rules of English Law- 1, say nothing- about the laws of other countries - to make a contract."

Bowen, L.J., (2893) 19.3. 256, at p. 269.

4.1   INTRODUCTION

In chapter 3 we examined, to some length, the primary principle of a contract, the deliberate agreement. Without an agreement there can be no contract. To be legally enforceable the agreement must conform to rigid precedented rules governing the offer and the, acceptance of the offer, and, <u>immediately upon the acceptance of an offer a contract comes into being.</u> This Chapter examines the other elements which comprise a legal contract, one that is enforceable.

4.2   COMPETENCY OF PARTIES TO A CONTRACT

The competency of the contracting parties, or their contractual capacity, is fundamental to the validity of contracts. The offeror must be <u>competent</u> to make an offer and the offeree must have the capacity to accept it, so that there may be a valid offer and valid acceptance for an agreement culminating in an enforceable contract. The phrase - "Competency of Parties to a Contract" - is synonymous with the phrase "Capacity of the Parties" - and with a phrase also frequently used - "Legal Capacity of Parties." Except for certain classes of individuals, whose interests are protected by Law, anyone may be competent as a party to a contract. Those parties who are incompetent are those who have been made, incapable legally, either wholly or partly, of binding themselves to contracts, or of enforcing contracts made with them. Such incapacity has been well established by either the precedents of Common Law, or the provisions of Statutory Law.

"Certain persons are, by Law, incapable, wholly or in part of binding themselves by a promise, or of enforcing a promise made to them." These persons are:

1- The Crown and Public Authorities
2- Infants
3- Corporations
4- Persons of unsound mind and a drunken person."

Anson's Principles of the English Law of contract, 22nd Ed., Chap. V.

In Canada, the Federal and Provincial Governments may enter into contracts which have to be considered as being unenforceable because of the technical defect that only the Crown can enforce a contract without action being brought against it by the other party, except by fiat, or permission because of the personal immunity of the Crown form legal proceedings.

What we are concerned with at this time are those classes of persons whose interests are protected by law by being made legally incapable of binding themselves to a contract. Such classes of persons are:

1   Infants

In Canada, all persons, under the age of 18 years are infants or minors. Two classes of contracts with infants which are valid are those which are:

a)   Contracts for necessities.
b)   Contracts for the benefit of the infant.

All other contracts with infants are <u>void</u>, or <u>voidable</u> at his or her option, either before or following, the reaching of his or her majority of 21 years of age. Two classes of voidable contracts are:

a)   Those which are <u>valid unless ratified</u> within a reasonable time after reaching majority, and
b)   Those which are <u>invalid unless ratified</u> within a reasonable time after reaching majority.

2   Mentally Incompetent

A mentally incompetent person's contract is binding, unless it can be shown that, at the time of entering into a contract the person was so insane as to not know what he, or she was doing, and that the other party was fully aware of the person's condition at the time. If these two conditions are proven, the contract is <u>voidable.</u> by the mentally incompetent person, or that person's representative (usually a member of the legal profession)

3   Drunken Persons

If a person, makes a contract while drunk he can afterwards <u>void</u> it, or <u>confirm</u> it. If the contract is confirmed, it is binding. Like a mentally incompetent person, a drunken person is liable for necessities sold and delivered. To be relieved of liability to a contract, a person must be so intoxicated as to be unable to use his reason and the other party must have been aware of this condition at the time the contract was executed.

4   First Nations Persons

First nations persons living on a reservation are wards of the Canadian Government and are thus protected from fraud and deception by being placed in a similar position to infants. If a contract is made, the first nations person can enforce it at his option. *This is in the process of changing as the first nations are gaining control over their land and financial resources.*

5   Corporations

Corporations are artificial persons created by Law. With respect to contracts, evidence of the consent of the corporation is the required seal. When attached to a document a seal indicates the authenticity of the document and expresses the solemn consent of the corporation as to the contents of the document.

The capacity of the corporation is limited by the terms of its incorporation. It cannot use powers which have not been actually conferred by, or are reasonably inferred from the provisions of the Statute which created it. Nor can corporations enter into contracts inconsistent with the objects of incorporation as set out in the Letters Patent and the Companies Act by which it was created.

Contracts which are beyond the powers of a Corporation are <u>void</u> by reason of incapacity to enter into such contracts.

4.3   MUTUALITY

"It is agreed that, in order that a contract may be specifically enforced, there must be mutuality between the parties."
                Anson's Principles of the English Law of Contract, 22nd Ed., Page 515.

"Mutuality of the Minds," or the "Reality of Consent," is the consent expressed both in the offer and the acceptance of it, which must be real and genuine.

Consent may have been given by one, or both parties under circumstances such that there was no real expression of intention. Circumstances could arise from a mistake, revocation, misrepresentation, fraud, duress or undue influences proceed with such a contract would be unfair. To be valid, a contract must have been mutually agreed to by the parties concerned. They must have agreed to identical things and their agreement must be actual and not apparent, predicated upon:

1.   Offer and acceptance <u>without qualification.</u>

2.   Acceptance <u>within a reasonable time</u> following the offer

3.   Acceptance must be in the <u>manner</u> specified.

Circumstances which could affect the fairness of a contract are:

1.   <u>Mistake</u>

A mistake, sufficient to invalidate a contract, is where the parties to it have not meant the same thing as to intention, or have formed erroneous conclusions, concerning the terms and conditions of the proposed contract.

Mistakes which can invalidate a contract are those caused by:

a)   The revocation of an offer under certain conditions, or,

b)   A fraudulent or careless act of a third party, or,

c)   The dishonesty of a party to the contract, or,

d)   A genuine mutual mistake.

2.   <u>Revocation of an Offer</u>

Revocation of an offer may be caused by the death or insanity of the offeror, but if the offer is accepted before such incapacity, a binding contract is affected upon the executors, administrators, guardians of heirs, or assigns of such persons, <u>provided the contract was not for personal services</u>

3.   <u>Misrepresentation</u>

In this context, misrepresentation which may void a contract, is when one party to a contract makes a statement which he believes to be true but, in fact, is not and the other party, believing it to be true and relying on the truth of it, enters into a contract.

Misrepresentation is also the with holding, or non-disclosure, of a material fact by a person under special obligation to disclose the fact because the contract is in the form of a trusteeship, or because the confidential relationship of the parties to the contract.

4.   <u>Fraudulence</u>

Fraudulence will void a contract. In law, fraud is any deception used to cheat or deceive a person, whereby he is induced to part with some legal right without compensation which he might otherwise be due. The willful assertion of facts that are untrue, (and which the asserted knows to be untrue), or the truth of which he does not allow himself to be concerned, used to induce another to enter into a contract to the other's disadvantage, constitutes an act of fraudulence.

The essential elements of fraud are:

a)   A false representation of a material fact.

b)   The representation must concern a past or present fact.

c)   The party making the representation must know the representation to be false.

d)   It must be made with the express intention of having it acted upon by the other party.

e)   The representation must be relied upon by the other party and induce him to act.

f)   The other party must suffer damage.

5.   <u>Duress.</u>

Duress is the illegal act of compelling another, by threat or violence to do something. Physical compulsion or threats of physical injury, will invalidate a legal act such as then signing of a contract.

To again quote Meredith Fleming, Q.C. -

> *"But duress at law does not mean bending to powerful persuasion or heartrending entreaties or threats of being cut off, from work - it means pressure or threat to life, and limb. We are waiting for the first contractor to tell us he was alone in the shack and there was the owner pointing a shotgun at him. If the owner's daughter is no part of the case, we will accept the contractor's brief."*

6.   <u>Undue Influence.</u>

Undue influence consists of taking advantage of a special trust or confidence which is placed by another to cause or induce the other to enter into an unfair contract. A contract so induced is voidable.

7.   <u>Genuine or Mutual Mistake.</u>

Concisely, a mistake is defined as an error, or misunderstanding.

In this context, mistakes may have considerable influence upon the validity of a contract. A mistake by one party, which is a unilateral mistake, may <u>void</u> a contract only if it is fundamental and is known to the other party.

Where the parties merely misunderstood one another, there is a mutual mistake.

If both parties make the same mistake, a common mistake, it may be possible in Law to avoid the contract. To avoid, in the legal sense is to quash, annul, make void, reject as not valid, or put an end to. A mistake in a written contract, such that it does not represent the real intention of the parties may be rectified.

It is generally agreed that, in order that a contract may be specifically enforced, there must be mutuality between the parties.

4.4   LEGAL CONSIDERATION

With the exception of contracts under seal, every contract, whether written or oral, in order to be enforceable requires consideration to support it. Consideration can be defined as:

1.   A promise, or the performance of, an act or forbearance <u>as the price of a promise</u> given by another, or,

2.   The benefit conferred, or the detriment suffered, in return for a promise.

Considerations are of two different kinds, "good" and "valuable."

Good consideration is based upon affection, love, blood relationship, generosity or natural duty. Valuable consideration is where, in Law, it is held that there has to be something given in exchange for an act or promise. A promise to do what one is already bound to do, or a promise based upon a thing already done, is consideration. A past consideration is generally considered as a valuable consideration.

To constitute a valuable consideration there must be a promise to give something of value, or a voluntary gift of something of value. The compromise of a matter in dispute becomes a valuable consideration. A gift, given without something of value given in return, is not a valuable consideration.

It is most likely the courts will not enquire into the sufficiency of a consideration when a contract is founded upon valuable consideration. Nor is it likely the courts will be concerned whether the consideration is adequate, such as whether a "fair" price or fee is being offered or, paid. If the courts are satisfied that the parties to a contract have agreed upon same consideration, they will enforce the contract; <u>for the courts will not "make a person's bargain for him</u>." An exception to this would be proof that the consent to accept insufficient value of a consideration had been procured by fraud, which, of course, would void the contract. A difference in the value of things exchanged maybe evidence of fraud also. Another requirement for a valid consideration is that it is for a <u>new</u> obligation, and not for one already existing. A contractor, having contracted to complete a structure by a given time, would not, after the work has started, be entitled to an offer of a bonus by the Owner to complete the structure by the time set out in the contract. The reason is that the contractor had already contracted to complete the work by the time stipulated in the contract, and he was not offering any new consideration which would entitle him to the bonus offered.

<u>The consideration is the inducement by which the parties to a contract agree to be bound</u>. The principles of consideration are:

1.   Consideration is necessary to the validity of every promise excepting those under seal.

2.   Consideration need not be adequate as to the promise, but must be of some legal value.

3.   The consideration, in itself, must be legal.

4.   The consideration must be either present or future, and not in the past.

5.   The consideration must proceed from the promisee, in Law, one to whom a promise is made.

In conclusion, the consideration is the only test of the actual intention to be bound by contract.

4.5   PENALTIES AND LIQUIDATED DAMAGES

Let us first examine the word "penalties" and the phrase "liquidated damages" in the legal, rather than the literal, sense as to usage.

1.   A penalty, in Law, means punishment, especially a pecuniary fine, a forfeit or fine for a breach of the terms of a bond or contract. In the latter case, the penalty is usually void.

2.   Liquidated means a fixed or predetermined financial assessment.

3.   Damage, in Law, means money that is recoverable for a wrong or an injury, as compensation.

4. <u>Liquidated damages</u>, are the fixed or predetermined amounts of money to be recovered by one party to a contract from the other party who creates a breach of the terms of the contract.

Liquidated Damages stated in the conditions of a contract are usually recoverable without proof of actual loss, provided they cannot be considered as a penalty (owing to being considered absurdly excessive), in which case they are unenforceable.

The purpose of having a condition in a Construction Contract with respect to liquidated damages is to accomplish one, or more, of the following objectives:

a) A stipulated payment to reimburse the Owner for damages anticipated in the event of delay in the completion of a project.

b) A stipulated payment to represent the primary intent of imposing a burden on the Contractor which will be sufficient to deter delay in the completion of the work, which is usually described as "Liquidated Damages" in the General Conditions of the Contract to avoid invalidity.

c) A stipulated payment for the dual purpose of accomplishing both of the objectives outlined in 1 and 2 above.

The following section from a Canadian Government General Conditions of a Contract, is in effect a Liquidated Damage condition:

"Where the Contractor does not complete the work by the day fixed by Article 1 of the Articles of Agreement for the completion of the work, but does complete the work thereafter, he shall pay to the National Capital commission

a) An amount equal to all salaries, wages and travelling expenses paid by the Commission to persons superintending the work during the period of delay,

b) An amount equal to the value to the Commission of the use of the completed work for the period of delay,

c) An amount equal to all other expenses and damages incurred or sustained by the Commission as a result of the work not being completed during the period of delay."

The objective of estimating an amount to reimburse the Owner for actual damages anticipated is within the scope of a liquidated damage clause, as recognized by our Courts. So, also, is the clause (a) above legally recognized as a liquidated damage clause. A payment, in the form of a penalty, intended to impose a burden on the Contractor, as in (b) above, would void the clause if its true nature and intent could be determined. This objective of spurring a Contractor to a greater effort by trying to impress upon him the unprofitable aspects of delays, represents the most frequently encountered purpose of the use of the clause today. A stipulated payment for the purpose of imposing a burden on the Contractor by reason of delay, incorporates the concept of reimbursement of damages which would be difficult to determine, and which would probably be difficult to sustain without the need to impose penalties for delay.

An agreement to pay liquidated damages may well constitute a significant part of the consideration for the contract involved. In arriving at a price for tendering, the Contractor will no doubt, have included the estimated liquidated damages as part of his offer, which, ultimately the Owner will pay; this is particularly true in connection with sizeable contracts for Public Works, with the contracting parties being apparently aware of the risks and benefits inherent in a liquidated-damage clause.

Controversy with respect to the efficacy of the liquidated-damage clause has, been so great that now many contractors are inclined to view this potentially dangerous clause with indifference. A frequently used test for the validity of this clause evolves about the impracticability, or the extreme difficulty in computing the actual damage values. The proof of actual damages incurred by the delay in the completion of work is extremely difficult to establish. The consequence of delay could affect the owner in a number of ways. Included among the problems arising out of delays could be inconvenience, loss of revenues, cost of extended financing, extended costs of supervision, all of which have a real pecuniary value. However, a most significant element in classifying a liquidated-damage clause as a valid provision, or as a penalty, would be the reasonableness of the stipulated payment.

The liquidated-damage clause could be nullified by the Owner, or his Agent, extensively revising the plans, or consenting to an extensive change in them during the course of construction. This extension creates a new contract, nullifying the liquidated damage clause as, the structure is no longer that which the Contractor undertook to build. To retain the liquidated damage clause in force in such a circumstance requires an additional agreement in writing stating the clause is to be retained.

"In many legal systems the parties can agree to pay a penalty, in addition to full damages, in order to prevent or penalize a breach; but in English law, equity would relieve against penalties, cutting them down to the actual damage suffered. This doctrine was taken up and applied by the common law, so that it became the rule in both jurisdictions. The Court will accept as liquidated damages the sum fixed by the parties if it is a genuine pre-estimate of the damage which seems likely to be caused if the breach provided for should occur. The question is one of construction, to be decided upon the terms and inherent circumstances of each particular contract, judged of as at the time of making the contract, not as at the time of breach. Or, again, if, although it is not an estimate of the probable damage, the parties have fixed that sum

because they were agreed in limiting the damages recoverable to an amount less than that which a breach would probably cause, it will similarly be accepted by the court."

Anson's Principles of English Law of Contract, 22nd Ed. Ch. XVIX.

4.6   DISCHARGE OF A CONTRACT

In Law, the word discharge with respect to contracts means:

1   To release from liability or obligation, or,

2   To deprive, to take away, from a right or obligation the force of it.

The discharge of a Construction Contract is by:

1   <u>Specific performance</u>, which is when the Contract is completed according to all the terms and conditions of it, particularly the drawings and specifications, or by,

2   <u>Agreement</u>, by which the parties to the Contract agree to waive all their rights and obligations under the contract by a specified time, or by,

3   <u>Breach</u>, which is the result of nonperformance, (without justification), of one party hindering the other from performing his contractual duties.

More fully, the discharge of a contract may be made by any of the following:

1   <u>By performance</u>, where the parties each performs their separate obligations, or one party may not perform his obligations but arranges for the other party to accept payment of money in lieu, which would be a substituted agreement and a good discharge.

2   <u>By agreement</u>, of the parties to:

    a)   Waive their rights before a breach of the contract, or

    b)   Substitute another contract or alter the terms of the existing contract, or

    c)   Make specific provisions in the terms or condition of the contract for its discharge.

3   <u>Discharge by breach</u>, of contract such as:

    a)   By one party refusing to fulfill his obligations before, or during performance,

b)   By a party making it impossible to complete the contract before performance is due, or during performance, and,

c)   By failure of a party to perform wholly or in part.

4   <u>Impossibilities</u>, created before or during the performance such as repudiation before performance, making it impossible for the other party to commence or continue to perform. Impossibility is an element of breach, refers to 3 (a) and 3 (b) above.

5.   <u>Compulsion</u>, to avoid a discharge by breach is a remedy at Low. If a contract is to be discharged by breach, the Injured party has a number of legal remedies. Most important of these remedies is that the injured party may insist that the contract be performed and may legally request compulsion of performance. It is this axiom which motivates, as we will see later, the inclusion of a Performance Bond in a Construction Contract.

4.7   INTERPRETATION

The interpretation of a contract is the determination of its intention, predicated upon the following rules:

1.   The intention of the contract must be construed for the entire contract. If there is contradiction between what is printed or typewritten and that which is written by hand, the latter will govern.

2.   If a contract is capable of two interpretations, one which would render it void or incapable of performance, and the other valid or capable of performance, the latter interpretation would govern.

3.   Words are given their plain or literal meaning, except where usage may vary their meaning; technical words will be given their technical meaning.

4.   If there is doubt as to the meaning of the contract, the construing of it by both parties will be given weight.

5.   Words are construed most strongly against the party using them.

In deciding upon the validity of agreements from which a vital term has been omitted, the Courts will make a distinction between those agreements where everything to be done, rests on the future (executory contracts), and those where both or one of the parties has performed all or part of the agreed upon obligations (executed contracts). In executory agreements, where everything has yet to be done, the Courts will not make up an omission of a vital term or terms. In a case such as this they will consider no agreement has been reached. In cases where there has been some execution of the work or terms of the agreement, the Courts will determine the equity in what has been done, <u>not in what has yet to be done</u>.

TYPICAL QUESTIONS

1.   What persons are barred from binding themselves to a Contract?
2.   What are corporations, and how may they enter into a Contract?
3.   How fair is a contract with a Governmental Agency?
4.   What is meant by the "Mutuality of the Minds?"
5.   Define mistake.
6.   What constitutes misrepresentation?
7.   What constitutes fraudulence?
8.   What is Legal Consideration?
9.   What are the principles of consideration?
10. Define Liquidated Damages.
11. What effect, if any, has a major change in the plans for a proposed work upon the Liquidated Damage clause?
12. What is meant by the discharge of a construction contract?
13. How may a contract be discharged?
14. What are the usual rules of interpretation of a contract?

REFERENCES

Anger's Digest of Canadian Law, 18th Ed.
Anson's Principles of the English Law of Contract, 22nd Ed.
Encyclopaedia Britannica, 1960 Edition
Fundamentals of Canadian Law - F.A.R. Chapman.
The Law of Contract - Cheshire & Fifoot.

5

FORMS OF CONTRACTS
by Clive E.J. Evans, FRICS, PQS(F) C.Arb.

"English Law recognizes only two kinds of contract, the contract made by deed, i.e. under seal, (which is called a deed or specialty) and the simple contract. The validity of the contract under seal depends upon its form alone. Simple contracts depend on the presence of consideration and, as a rule, need no special form".

Paraphrased from Anson.

5.1   INTRODUCTION

"Simple Contracts", such as a Construction Contract, do not necessarily have to be in writing nor conform to any special form. However, because of the complexity of present day construction, it is essential such a Contract be in writing if the parties to it are to know the nature and extent of the contractual rights or duties conferred or imposed upon them by the contract, as such rights and duties must be determined by the nature of the Contract and the language in which it is expressed.

5.2   LEGAL REQUIREMENTS AS TO FORM

A contract must be set out according to the form and executed in the manner prescribed by law.

Most jurisdictions prescribe the form which certain contracts must take. It may be that particular information may be specified for inclusion, or the requirement may only be that the contract shall be in writing. In general, negotiable instruments such as bank drafts, bank cheques, promissory notes and other similar instruments must be in writing and include the signature of the maker or drawer and an unconditional promise to pay a fixed sum of money. They must also be payable upon demand, or on some fixed date, payable to the bearer or order of the payee and, if a drawee is involved, he must be named.

The Statutes require certain forms of contract to be in writing. These include insurance contracts, contracts of indemnity and contracts coming within the scope of the Statue of Frauds such as contracts of guarantee, contracts of warranty and any of the following:

1.   A special promise by executors or administrators to hold themselves liable for the debts of a deceased person.

2.   Any special promise to answer for debts, defaults, or miscarriages of another person.

3.   Any agreement upon the consideration of marriage.

4.   Any contract of which the terms cannot be executed within a twelve month period.

5.   A contract for the purchase of goods for a price equal to or higher than an amount fixed by Statute.

To be enforceable at law what is to be accomplished by contract must be lawful and not contrary to sound public policy. The principle forms of contract opposed to law or public policy are those which:

1.   Are for the sale of public office, public contracts, or for bribing of public officials.

2.   Tend to deprive the Courts of their jurisdiction.

3.   Condone or compound a crime (a crime being the commission of an act which renders the doer liable to legal punishment).

4.   Tend to encourage litigation.

5.   Are for committing a crime or a tort.

6.   Tend to promote fraud and breach of trust.

7.   Unduly affect the freedom or security of marriage.

8.   Create unreasonable restraint to trade and which tend to suppress competition at letting or sale.

9.   Injure public health and safety.

10.   Involve payment of usurious rate of interest.

11.   Establish unlawful monopolies, trusts, etc.

It will be found that the foregoing will be the foundation for a great many statutes or parts of statutory law. The history of the policy of law, or public policy, which is commonly used to assess the validity of contracts is most obscure. Over the years the policy of law has become more lenient with respect to public policy. Even so, the Courts still maintain it is their duty to consider the public advantage in all cases. An 1875 principle, which is still valid, stated:

"It must not be forgotten that you are not to extend arbitrarily those rules which say that a given contract is void as being against public policy because, if there is one thing which more than another public policy requires, it is that all men of full age and competent understanding shall have the utmost liberty of contracting, and that their contracts when entered into freely and voluntarily shall be held sacred and shall be enforced by Courts of Justice. Therefore, you have this paramount public policy to consider - that you are not lightly to interfere with this freedom of contract."

5.3   IMPORTANT NON-LEGAL CHARACTERISTICS OF A CONTRACT

There are many cases on record in which disputes have arisen between parties to a contract because their rights and liabilities have not been clearly defined. In the case of a oral contract misunderstandings can easily arise. Where the terms and conditions have been reduced to writing no dispute should arise if the documents setting out what is being agreed to have been carefully prepared.

It has been shown that, as a general rule, parties are bound only by the terms to which they have EXPRESSLY agreed. In no sense are they contractually bound by terms contrary to, or inconsistent with, those to which they have expressly agreed; but in certain cases or circumstances, they are not only bound by the express terms of their contract, but also by additional terms which are implied by Law, the nature of the contract and the circumstances in which the contract was entered into.

Therefore, the excellence of a contract is in its ability to withstand attempts to void it. A contract has been poorly prepared if contention or litigation arises out of it because of ambiguity or indefiniteness in its composition.

The following non-legal characteristics are most desirable in a construction contract:

1.   Owners may word contracts as they wish, including injustices which might be just within the Law. Unjust contract terms and conditions give rise to serious contention and possible litigation with added costs to a project. Good faith and confidence alone have no place in the preparation of a contract, the terms and conditions of which should be based on JUSTICE and EQUITY.

2.   In fairness, it is incumbent upon the architect or engineer to point out to intending bidders all or any circumstances which may affect their bids, up to the time of tender closing.

3.   DEFINITENESS in the plans and specifications, which eventually become an integral part of the whole of the Contract Documents, is essential. These should include ALL THINGS having a material bearing on the cost or capacity of performance with respect to the Work. For an architect or engineer to hide behind the phrase "reasonably inferable" is but to admit laziness or inability to prepare these documents properly.

4.   As with indefiniteness, errors in the contract documents can become a source of contention and possible litigation. Therefore, ACCURACY is essential.

5.   CLEARNESS is also essential, for although ambiguities may not void a contract they can be a source of trouble and expense. Contradictions, when found, will be subject to certain rules of interpretation for overcoming the difficulties arising from them:

   a)   An earlier clause in a Construction Contract has precedence over a later clause which is contradictory, unless it is expressly stated that the later clause is an amendment to the earlier one.

   b)   Where there is a conflict between what is specified in the Specifications and the contract, the latter takes precedence.

6.   With a BRIEF contract document, there is a greater chance of becoming informed of its conditions and provision, than there is with a long, repetitious, detailed contract.

7.   The CONVENIENT ARRANGEMENT of content provides easier reading and easier detection of errors, omissions and conflicts.

The Owner has to assume that, when a project is tendered, the Architect or Engineer has most diligently, with both knowledge and good judgment, enquired into the bids and the bidders, to ensure that the accepted contractor is able to complete the Work according to the terms and conditions of ALL of the Contract Documents for the price asked.

On the other hand, the Contractor has every right to expect that the information given in ALL the Contract Documents is sufficiently clear to enable the preparation of an intelligent bid for the contemplated work and that no penalty will accrue for the lack of care or skill in their preparation.

5.4   EQUITY BENEFITS ALL

The function of a Construction Contract is to obtain a completed work, as described by the Contract Documents, of the highest quality at the lowest cost.

This objective must attract the most competent and competitive contractors in relevant fields of construction as well as create circumstances which will encourage Contractors who tender to undertake the Work at the LOWEST REASONABLE PRICE. To accomplish this the Owner must, from the point of view of the Contractor, be as reasonable to do business with as it would be with the best elements of industry.

The Construction Contract should be composed to be as just and as fair to the Contractor and Subcontractors as to the Owner and to provide the contractor with as much protection in the various eventualities which may occur as it does an Owner. Far too frequently, there appears a tendency to draft a Construction Contract to protect an Owner at the expense of the Contractor.

General contractors cannot be held altogether blameless in this regard, since far too often, their contracts with their sub-contractors are inequitable.

In the long run, a just and fair contract will cost less and produce better results than one that is "loaded" against either a Contractor or Subcontractor.

What is equitable in regard to contracts is merely another way of saying that a Construction Contract should reflect those obligations that an Owner is reasonably entitled to expect from a Contractor and should not impose on the Contractor and Subcontractors obligations which cannot be reasonably expected from a Contractor.

"There is no negotiation between the contractor and the owner respecting any provision set out in the instruction to tenders, the general specifications, the general conditions or the actual contract form. This method of settling the form of construction contracts can create serious legal problems for the contractor and impose on him the risk of serious financial loss unless the owner and his architect or engineer fairly differentiate in the contract documents between those matters which should be properly the owner's responsibility and those matters which should be the contractor's responsibility. Unfortunately it has been common practice to place all risks in connection with the work upon the contractor".

RM Sedgewic, Q.C., Tenders and Contracts - Legal Aspects
Successful Management in the Construction Industry by the Canadian Institute of Chartered Accountants

At the time a Contractor (or a Sub-Contractor for that matter) submits a bid for a work, it should be quite clear that the bid is to do the work according to the Contract Documents only, the terms of which should be fixed and well known to both parties to a Contract Agreement. When a bid is accepted there is at that moment a clear-cut contract.

It has been known for an Owner or Contractor, upon accepting a bid, to turn the offer over to a lawyer for the preparation of a contract. Such an action implies that the bidder is committed to a contract for which the terms have not been settled and is also expected to start work immediately. This practice is grossly unfair.

It is to the benefit of all that the relations between Owner and Contractor, and Contractor and Sub-Contractors, be regulated by a contract that is both just and fair to all who may be concerned.

5.5   ELEMENTAL FORMS OF CONTRACT

Before discussing specific forms of Construction Contracts, mention must be made to the following Elemental Forms of Contract, a few of which have already been discussed:

1. As to Origin

   a) <u>Express Contracts</u> which are bilateral or multilateral, in which promises and assent of each party are expressed in speech or writing.

   b) <u>Implied Contracts</u> which are unilateral, where the act of acceptance and the promise are inferred as a matter of fact from the conduct of the parties.

   c) <u>Quasi Contracts</u> are not, strictly speaking, contracts but legal obligations similar to contracts and which are created by implication of law. Quasi contracts are implied by law on the theory that it would be unjust to allow one person to accept benefits of labour or anything of value which belongs to another without refunding or paying for it.

2. As to Participants

   a) <u>Two-Party Contracts</u> are the most common in which only two parties are involved.

   b) <u>Joint Contracts</u> are those in which two or more parties merge, to a greater or lesser degree, their interests to enter into a contract with another party or parties. In a suit under a joint contract all of the promisors must be sued jointly and not separately.

   c) <u>Several Contracts</u> are those in which two or more persons enter into a contract as promisors or promisees but keep their liability more or less separate. A suite under a Several Contract must be brought against each of the promisors or each of the promisees separately.

   d) <u>A Joint and Several Contract</u> has some of the nature of each of the two preceding types. A promisee may sue the promisors either jointly or separately. If a party elects to sue jointly, it must sue all promisors together within the same suit.

   e) <u>Third-Party Beneficiary Contracts</u> are those in which two parties enter into a contract for the protection of the interests of a third party, who is not a direct party to the contract. Most insurance policies and surety bonds are of this form of contract. Third parties may become a party to a suit under such a contract should their interests dictate such action.

3. As to Obligation Status

   a) <u>Bilateral Contracts</u> are those in which one party agrees to perform certain acts in return for which the other party agrees to perform certain acts also.

Agreement by each party to refrain from doing certain acts is also a bilateral contract.

b)   Unilateral Contracts are those in which there is a promise by one party to perform certain acts, provided the other party does certain things, the acceptance to be accomplished by the act.

4.   As to Completion Status

a)   Executory Contracts are those in which an obligation is assumed by one or both parties to do or refrain from doing certain acts at some future time.

b)   Executed Contracts are those in which everything is done at the time of making the contract and no obligation is assumed for future acts by either party.

5.   As to Form

a)   Contract under Seal is one with a seal attached. Under Common Law, a sealed contract is more binding that others and certain materials in sealed contracts cannot be challenged in court. Certain jurisdictions still recognize sealed contracts as superior to others; contracts such as deeds, bonds and contracts of major importance are executed under seal, Construction Contracts for large projects in particular.

b)   Contract of Record is one which is existent because of a court judgment. Unless the judgment is entered by mutual consent, contracts of record are merely quasi contracts.

c)   Simple or Parol Contracts are those which are less formal than sealed contracts, may or may not be in some special form and may be either written or oral, viz:

(i)   Contracts in some specified form are required in some jurisdictions for bills of exchange, promissory notes, etc., which must always be in writing as well as of specified form.

(ii)   In many jurisdictions there are statutes requiring contracts for insurance, surety bonds and the like, to be in writing. Most jurisdictions have statutes concerning frauds which, in most cases, have been predicated upon the English Statue of Frauds of 1677. Such statutes require certain contracts to be in writing, such as a guarantee.

(iii)   Unless there is a legal requirement to the contrary, an oral contract is as binding as a written contract.

5.6   CONTRACT OF AGENCY

In Chapter 2, references were made to the Architect or Engineer being an agent of an Owner. In the Standard Form of Agreement between Client and Architect or Engineer, there are implied functions of an Agent.

Such an agreement may state:

"While work is in progress, the Architect (or Engineer) may, on behalf of and as Agent of the Client, give orders, etc."

An Agent is a person employed by another, the Principal, for the purpose of making contracts between the Principal and third persons. An Agent does not need full contractual capacity to be able to represent and bind its Principal by its acts. The Principal, however, must have contractual capacity, or it cannot employ an Agent. Although a person cannot by contract with another confer rights or impose liabilities upon a third person, they may employ another for the purpose of bringing that person into legal relations with a third person. Such employment is termed Agency.

A Contract of Agency, as with other contracts, is created by the acceptance of an offer. It is an authority given by one party, the Principal, to the other, within the limit of such authority. As a general rule, there must be an express authority given to the Agent, although full contractual capacity is not necessary to enable a person to represent another as Agent. No one can enter into a contract through an Agent which is beyond the capacity of the Principal.

The relationship of Principal and Agent may be created in one of three ways:

1.   By actual or implied authority to contract given by the Principal to the Agent.

2.   By the Principal's ratification of a contract entered into by the Agent on its behalf but without its authority.

3.   By the apparent authority conferred by the Principal on the Agent, although no actual authority might have been given.

An Agent does not incur any personal liability to a person with whom it contracts on behalf of the Principal, provided the agent acts as Agent, names the Principal and remains within the scope of authority. As a general rule, the authority given by the Principal to an Agent is an express authority enabling the Agent to bind the Principal by acts executed within the scope of such authority.

However, the authority of an Agent may also be implied authority. Every Agent, by Law, has implied authority to act according to the reasonable customs and usages related to it's occupation or profession.

5.7 CONTRACT OF GUARANTEE/GUARANTY

In Law, a "condition" with respect to an enforceable contract is a provision, either express or implied, making the existence of a right depend upon a future uncertain event which may or may not occur. <u>It is the vital undertaking in a contract, the breach of which gives a right of redress for damages.</u>

It is usually a condition of a Construction Contract that the Contractor is to remedy, at its expense, defects in the work discovered within a stipulated time, arising out of the use of faulty materials or as the result of poor workmanship. Reference should be made to ARTICLE GC 12.3 - WARRANTY, General Conditions of the Stipulated Price Contract - Canadian Standard Construction Document - CCDC2 - 1994.

Throughout any set of Construction Specifications, there will be found frequent use of the words GUARANTEE or GUARANTY, or WARRANTY, or GUARANTY-WARRANTY with respect to the quality of materials and workmanship. The purpose of this is to ensure that, in the event of defects being discovered, they will be rectified. However, these words have been used interchangeably, which is an error as there is a basic legal distinction between the two words.

In Law, a GUARANTEE is a <u>contract</u> to answer for the payment of some debt, <u>or answer for the performance of some duty,</u> in the event of the failure of another person who is primarily liable for such payment or performance. A valid contract of guarantee must be for a primary liability, present or future and a promise made for a valuable consideration by a third party, the "surety" or "guarantor." The Statute of Frauds stipulates:

"any special promise to answer for the debt, default, or miscarriage of another person" is a guarantee.

This special promise to answer for the obligation of another is the promise of guarantee or suretyship. A guarantee would be collateral or subsidiary promise to answer for the obligation of another, such as the General Contractor guaranteeing the work of a Subcontractor.

"This promise must be distinguished from a contract of indemnity, that is to say, a promise to save another harmless from the result of a transaction into which one enters at the instance of the promisor". (Anson)

A Contract of Guarantee is, therefore, one in which there must always be three parties:

1.   The principal debtor, one who is under obligation to another for service to be rendered, (in our case, the General Contractor).

2.   A creditor, who is the person to whom another is obligated; (in our case, the Owner to whom the General Contractor is obligated to perform according to the conditions of the Construction Contract).

3.   A guarantor or surety, who promises to discharge the debtor's liability if the debtor should fail to do so (the Bonding company).

It would appear that a General Contractor cannot guarantee to the Owner the materials and workmanship which it supplied or performed. It would, however, guarantee the materials and workmanship of its Sub-Contractors, as a guarantor or surety.

In Law, a WARRANTY is a promise in a contract which is collateral or subsidiary to the primary object of the contract, such that a breach of it does not bestow a right to repudiate the contract, but does allow for a justifiable claim for damages. It may be either an express or implied term or collateral promise in a contract and, as such, is less vital than a CONDITION.

"If the parties regard the term essential, it is a condition, its failure entitles the other party to treat the contract as discharged. If they did not regard it as essential, but as subsidiary or collateral, it is a warranty; its failure can only give rise to an action for such damages as have been sustained by the failure of those particular terms. Thus from one point of view a warranty may be regarded as a promise of indemnity against a failure to perform particular term of the contract." (Anson)

A manufacturer's promise to stand by its product is often incorrectly called a guarantee. It is a warranty. Should a product fail to measure up to its intended purpose, or fail to measure up to the manufacturer's claims, then the manufacturer has violated a warranty.

It would appear that a Subcontractor, through the General Contractor, warrants to the Owner all materials, items, and performances with respect to its portion of the Work to be equal to, or better than specified and, as a "condition", promises to rectify existing or developing defects for the period stated in the contract. The General Contractor, on the other hand, guarantees the work of Subcontractors, while warranting what it itself has supplied or has done with its own resources. The General Contractor, by the conditions of the Construction Contract it has entered into with an Owner, warrants the entire work.

5.8   CONCLUSION

The interpretation of a contract is the determination of its intent, which is predicated upon the following rules:

1.   The intention must be construed from the entire contract - all of the documents comprising it. If there is a contradiction between what is printed and what is typewritten, the latter will govern. What has been written by hand takes precedence over all.

2.   If a contract is capable of two interpretations, one which would render it void or incapable of performance and the other valid or capable of performance, the latter interpretation would govern.

3.   Words are given their plain or literal meaning, except where usage may vary their meaning and technical words will be given their technical meaning.

4.   If there is doubt as to the meaning of a contract, the construing of it by both parties will be given weight.

5.   Words are construed most strongly against the party using them.

> *"When parties have entered into a contract and a question arises as to the nature or extent of the contractual rights or duties conferred or imposed upon them by the contract, this must in general be determined by a consideration of the nature of the contract and the language in which it is expressed."*
>
> *His Honour Mr. Chief Justice Gordon, Australia.*

TYPICAL QUESTIONS

1. What forms of contracts must be in writing?
2. What are five (5) forms of contract that are contrary to public policy?
3. Describe at least three (3) of the most important non-legal characteristics of a contract.
4. What has the Contractor the right to expect when asked to tender for a contract?
5. What is the function of a Construction Contract?
6. What are:
    a. Express contracts?
    b. Quasi contracts?
    c: A Joint and Several Contract?
7. Define a contract under seal.
8. What is meant by Contract of Record?
9. What is the Contract of Agency?
10. What is the relationship between Principal and Agent?
11. Describe the Law of Guarantee.
12. What is the difference between a guarantee and a warranty?

REFERENCES

Anger's Digest of Canadian Law, 18th Ed.

Anson's Principles of English Law of Contract, 22nd Ed.

Canadian Standard Construction Document CCDC2 - 1994 Stipulated Price Contract.

Encyclopaedia Britannica.

Fundamental of Canadian Law - F.A.R. Chapman.

The Law of Contract - Cheshire & Fifoot.

RAIC Standard Form of Agreement Between Client and Architect.

6

CONSTRUCTION CONTRACTS
by Clive E.J. Evans, FRICS, PQS(F), C.Arb.

6.1   INTRODUCTION

The cost of preparing the documents which comprise a Construction Contract will vary according to the size, nature and importance of the contemplated Work. Small construction projects may need only sketchy and generalized plans and specifications which would, in all probability, effect possible savings by their use as compared to the preparation of plans and specifications complete in every detail.

Sizeable projects involving large sums of money require accurate cost estimates before construction can be approved, much less started. Such cost estimates can only be accurately determined from complete and detailed proposed Contract Documents.

Before examining the various forms of Construction Contracts and the documents they might comprise, let us first consider construction of a project without a Construction Contract.

6.2   CONSTRUCTION BY THE DIRECT EMPLOYMENT OF LABOUR

This method of construction is independent of any contract.

The responsibility for both the actual construction of a Work, and the actual cost of it, become the responsibility of an organization which must be created for the purpose of Construction by Direct Employment of Labour. The success of this organization will be dependent upon its efficiency. Except for possible adverse local conditions, there appears to be no reason why such as organization, established on a sound business basis could not produce results comparable to those of a highly qualified contractor.

The principal factor governing the success of Constructing by the Direct Employment of Labour method is the creation of an efficient construction organization. The owner becomes greatly involved as it purchases ALL materials required for the Work, pays ALL wages of ALL employees engaged for the WORK and, either directly or through an employee, supervises and co-ordinates the Work. In this manner the work is performed by the forces of the Owner. The Owner must directly assume all obligations with respect to permits, fees, etc. and all responsibilities and liabilities inherent in the business of construction.

The principal advantage of this method of construction is the flexibility of the operation of the organization and the control over the performance of the Work that can be exercised directly by the Owner.

Construction can be started before the plans and specifications have been completed in all details, avoiding delays inherent in starting and completing work let to contract. Materials and equipment which the Owner particularly wants can be provided without detailed plans and specifications. Any change in plans can be incorporated into the Work easily and at minimum costs. It is also possible under certain circumstances to utilize a part of the construction force for maintenance after completion of the Work.

It has been long debated whether the Owner, by this method of construction, avoids the expense of overhead costs usual to a contractor's organization. Work that is usually performed by that part of a contractor's organization, the costs of which are charged to overhead expense, must be performed by some one on behalf of the Owner. Such costs must be considered as part of the total cost of construction. The question the Owner must resolve is whether it is qualified and equipped to perform the functions of purchasing, accounting, supervising, etc. otherwise executed by the Contractor.

A distinct disadvantage of the Direct Employment of Labour method of construction is the necessity for the Owner to assemble and retain an organization comparable to that of a good contractor.

In normal times, qualified workers, lead-hands, superintendents, etc., will not accept temporary employment, (such as this method of construction implies), unless the rates of pay are higher than the going wage.

Good supervision is the key to good construction at reasonable cost. Only those familiar with the needs of construction are able to purchase for them so that delays are avoided and the purchases are economical.

If a well organized force of construction personnel is to be assembled for one project only, the cost of this organization will be substantial. With such an organization there is always the problem of providing enough work to utilize all personnel to the fullest advantage and of retaining them until their responsibilities have been fully discharged.

It would appear that no clear comparison can be made between the cost of constructing a Work by contract and the cost by direct employment. It is believed by many that the costs of construction are usually lower when the work is let to contract.

Finally, another disadvantage is the need to purchase new equipment for a Work, which is likely to be a "one shot" enterprise and then having to dispose of it, probably at a loss, when the Work is completed.

6.3   CONTRACT AT A FIXED PRICE

The most common method of letting work by contract is by soliciting competitive tenders with fixed prices.

These fixed price tenders may be either Lump, or Stipulated, Sum (or the summation of extensions of unit prices on each of a number of scheduled items which together constitute the whole of the Work). These fixed price contracts are unsecured-cost agreements, as the difference in the price tendered and the contractor's actual costs represent the profit or loss.

This form of contract is usually used for the construction of all manner of structures, highways and roads, sewer and water distribution systems, the supply and installation of all sorts of mechanical equipment, etc. This FIXED PRICE form of contract is most widely used in connection with the construction of Public Works, as it enables decisions to be readily reached as to whether to proceed with the work once the "actual" cost is known.

In Canada, government is by Law rather than by individuals. This establishes not only the importance of legislative bodies with respect to Public Works, but creates the basic difference between Private and Public Works. Public Works are those works constructed, maintained and renovated for the use of both a Public Service and the Public generally, at public expense and under public control.

Canadian Federal and Provincial Statutes, and Municipal By-laws governing contracts for Public Works are framed to prevent patronage, collusion and fraud. This legislation either specifically, or by inference, requires a Public Service to accept the lowest, but not necessarily the best, offer.

Before any public work can be performed by either the forces of the Public Service or by contractors on its behalf, it must, as a general rule, be approved by competent authority and the costs for the Work included in the estimates of the fiscal year in which the work is to be done.

A Fixed Price Contract places the interests of the Owner and the Contractor in conflict.

The Owner is interested in securing the best quality of materials and workmanship for the price to be paid. The Contractor is primarily concerned in carrying out the Work as economically as possible, often at the expense of quality of materials and labour. If the Contractor is reputable and experienced, its tender, if based on well prepared plans and specifications, will allow sufficient profit to perform the Work satisfactorily. However, if the Contractor is either unreliable or inexperienced and places profit before reputation, its tender is likely to create a loss if the work is to be performed satisfactorily. It is essential that the Owner is protected from the improper award of a Construction Contract.

The tender price is but one element in a good contract. Important as the tender price may be, the Contractor's financial responsibility, its competence to perform the work and the adequacy of its plant are also of major importance.

There are three (3) forms of Fixed Price Contract in wide use today:-

1. STIPULATED PRICE CONTRACT - Standard Construction Document, CCDC 2 - 1994

This form of contract is also known as the Firm Price or Fixed Sum. The difference in the price tendered and the Contractor's actual costs represents its profit or loss. A Contractor working under this form of contract, no doubt obtained by highly competitive bidding procedures, will generally oppose any attempt to deviate from the requirements of the original plans and specifications, except where it is evident that a profit in "extras" is possible. This form of contract encourages claims for extras which, far too frequently, result in considerable contention.

A Stipulated Price Contract will often include provision for unit prices applicable to incidental additions to, or deletions from, the original contract requirements. These unit prices most often concern excavation, concrete, reinforcing steel, formwork, etc. and are made effective when site conditions require variations from the original contract requirements.

2. UNIT PRICE CONTRACT, Standard Construction Document CCDC 4 - 1982

This form of contract is used most frequently for engineering works such as roads, sewer and water facilities, landscaping, etc.

Quantities are shown in a schedule for each separate item of work, which the bidder prices. It is frequently stipulated that such quantities are estimated only and that they are likely to change according to the actual requirements of the work. It may be further stipulated that the contractor will be paid for only actual quantities of materials supplied and work performed, and is barred from recovery of any loss of anticipated profit, loss by damage, etc., arising out of difference between estimated and actual quantities, unless the contract contains a specific agreement to the contrary.

This form of a contract sometimes provides the means of adjusting the unit rates if large differences in quantities occur. Adjustment is usually in the form of a reduction in the unit price when the quantities shown in the contract schedule are exceeded by a certain percent and conversely, the unit price rate is increased when the estimated quantities are reduced by a specified percentage.

A contractor's losses arising out of this form of contract are usually the result of:

a)   A drastic reduction in the estimated quantities without compensating adjustment of the unit price rate and

b)   Errors in pricing the individual units of work.

3.   COMBINED LUMP SUM AND UNIT PRICE CONTRACTS

It is not unusual to combine the two previous forms of contracts for a particular project. For example, the structure and its auxiliary services may be included in one contract, with the structure to be constructed according to the terms of a Lump Sum Contract, while the auxiliary services, roads, sewers, water service, etc. are to be constructed according to the terms of a Unit Price Contract.

6.4   ADVANTAGES AND DISADVANTAGES FROM THE OWNER'S VIEW POINT

The most important advantages of the **Fixed Price Contract** are:-

1.   Competitive tenders can be received.
2.   Time-honoured and well-recognized method.
3.   Once tenders are received, the final cost is known (except for the cost of subsequent change).
4.   Owner knows at time of bidding exactly what he is getting.
5.   Value of work could be more than fixed price during bad economic times (profit for Owner).
6.   Contractors more inclined to complete the project faster.

The outstanding disadvantages of the **Fixed Price Contract** are:-

1.   Need to prepare complete drawings and specifications (takes time).
2.   Exclusions of small contractors on large projects (could also be an advantage).
3.   No involvement by Contractor during design stage.
4.   Low bidder not necessarily the best.
5.   Changes cost more.
6.   Changes can result in claims for extension of time.
7.   Contractor may cut corners (conflict of interest).
8.   Owner pays costs of competitive bidding.
9.   Owner does not benefit from improved methods during construction.
10.   Progress payments may be unbalanced (front end loading).
11.   Drawings may be poor resulting in higher prices.
12.   Group of contractors may form a price ring.

13. High inflation risk (not a good market condition).
14. Site inspection of the work is a necessity.
15. If price is too low then the work may be finished late.
16. High risk may result in too high price, or too few bids.
17. Owner does not get full credit for any work delayed.
18. Low bidder may end up in financial difficulty, (resulting in additional expenses to the Owner. Wise Owner will consider the low bidder's financial adequacy, amount of equipment he possesses, his experience and prior performance. Also whether the bid is realistic). Some public authorities require TENDERS to be "prequalified".
19. Owner has no say on who works on the job, i.e. workers or sub-trades.
20. Owner has little control over prompt payment to material suppliers or sub-trades.
21. Owner cannot make changes to the specified job unless the right is reserved in the contract.
22. Owner has no guarantee that the lump sum price will be within the preliminary budget which was established before the working drawings were prepared.

The main Advantages of a **Unit Price Contract** are:

1. Bid competitively even when drawings are incomplete.
2. More practical method for site work and heavy construction work.
3. Easy to make changes.
4. Start work earlier.
5. Know what each item is costing.
6. Final total cost can be controlled.
7. Pay exactly for quantity of work done.
8. Easy to break down into sub-contracts (if more than one contractor on the job).
9. No hidden contingency sums to cover mistakes in quantities.
10. Usually no payment for lost profit due to lower "actual quantities."
11. Reduces the possibility of "front end loading" on payment applications.

The main Disadvantages of a **Unit Price Contract** are:

1. Owner has to decide on items of work and estimate approximate quantities.
2. Final cost not known until close to completion of construction.
3. Danger of receiving unbalanced tenders.
4. Not suitable for building projects (too many items of work).
5. Requires complete control of work at the site.
6. More work to check field measurements and payment administration.
7. If actual quantities are much smaller than estimated, some contracts may provide for the unit to be renegotiated.

8.   Missing items - unit prices will have to be negotiated.

9.   Completion times may vary with the quantity of work.

6.5   COMPETITIVE BIDDING

Unsecured contracts are competitively bid contracts drawn up on a fixed price basis. Used almost exclusively for the construction of Public Works, they are also used for the execution of Private Work.

Competitive bidding is usually initiated by:-

1.   Private invitation to several selected contractors to submit tenders for a proposed project.

2.   A general invitation advertised publicly to stimulate the widest possible contractor interest in a proposed work.

Most contractual agencies for Public Works are required by statute to advertise publicly for tenders for a proposed Public Work.

Intelligent bids take time to be accurately prepared. The costs of compiling estimates for a project will vary among contractors bidding for the work.

The bidding costs of securing contracts by competitive bidding have been estimated to be from 2% to 4% of the bid price. Such costs are of concern to all associated with the Construction Industry, particularly the Owner and the Contractor.

There have been many suggestions as to how to reduce costs in competitive bidding, one of which is to use secured-cost forms of construction contracts.

Much has been written about the precedent - setting Ron Engineering case, the judgment in which concluded that not one contract, but two contracts are executed in the traditional tendering process. Contract A is the Tender Contract which must be distinguished from Contract B, the Construction Contract. Many in the industry are still wondering at the logic, if any, that led the judge in this case to render such opinion. Nonetheless, the precedents set continue in force today. In summary they are:

1.   Contract A is automatically created upon the submission of the tender.

2.   Contract A was breached by the contractor (Ron Engineering) when it refused to enter into the construction contract, Contract B.

3.   Ron Engineering's tendered price of $2,748,000 was some 19% below the second tenderer's price of $3,380,000. However, no mistake in Ron's tendered price was apparent. (Note that it is not clear what constitutes an apparent mistake.)

4.   The mistake was entirely the fault of Ron Engineering. Canadian Courts now take a more technical approach when interpreting tenders to protect the integrity of the tendering system.

6.6   SECURED-COST CONTRACTS

Secured-cost contracts are somewhat similar to the Direct Employment of Labour method of construction; an "actual cost of construction" method. The profit consideration is fixed, or may vary with the cost of the work, but never is a profit lost. The three most prevalent forms of secured-cost contracts are:

1.   Cost Plus Percentage or Fixed Fee

This form of contract is one which pays the Contractor the cost of materials, labour, etc., with an additional payment in the form of an agreed percentage of the actual cost of the work to cover the Contractor's supervision of the work, overhead costs and profit. By this form of contract the Owner stands to benefit from any savings effected by the contractor, and has the assurance it need not pay an extravagant profit to the Contractor. It also has the assurance it need not pay abnormal amounts for unforeseen contingencies which might arise during the progress of the work.

This form of contract is frequently used in connection with the construction of hazardous or experimental works, since an unsecured-cost contract would be impracticable. This form of contract permits work to start before the final completion of the plans and specifications and allows variation to requirements without opposition by the contractor and prolonged negotiation in respect to them.

However, this form of contract provides no incentive for economical and efficient operations by contractors; rather the converse is most likely to occur, since the contractor's profit will be proportional to the total cost of the work.

2.   The Cost Plus Fixed Sum

This form of contract is superior to the Cost Plus Percentage or Fixed Fee form of contract, since the contractor's profit is a fixed sum, agreed upon as the result of negotiation but, like the Cost Plus Percentage or Fixed Fee form of contract, there is no incentive for the contractor to keep costs down.

However, by this form of contract, the contractor is unable to profit by any increase in cost and benefits most by being economical and efficient in its operations. The Owner could, therefore, benefit also.

3.   The Cost Plus a Variable Premium, or Cost Plus Fixed Sum with Bonus or Penalty

These forms of contracts are those by which the Contractor, with the Owner's Architect or Engineer, estimates a reasonable cost and duration of time for a project and undertakes to execute it at cost plus a fixed sum or fee for overhead and profit. Such a contract usually provides a condition that, should the Contractor effect a reduction in costs or duration of time, it will receive in addition - an agreed upon percentage of the savings as a bonus. Conversely, should the estimated project costs, or the duration of time to perform the work be exceeded - the Contractor is penalized an agreed upon percentage of the increase of costs and a penalty sum for delay in completion of the work.

One advantage of this form of contract is that the Owner can determine the final cost of the project almost as closely as with a Lump Sum contract. If the cost of the work is less than estimated, the owner benefits by the saving to the extent agreed upon. However, should the cost of the work exceed the estimate, then the Contractor must bear its share of the additional costs. The same rules govern with respect to the duration of time to perform the Work.

One major disadvantage of this form of contract is that the estimate of cost may be too high, or the estimated duration of time too long. Such conditions would permit the contractor to gain an unfair advantage over the Owner.

In addition to the forgoing contract forms, the following forms of secured-cost contracts have also found favour in connection with commercial and industrial projects of a complex nature:-

1.   The Cost Plus a Guaranteed Maximum Price

This form of contract is one by which a maximum limit is placed on the cost of a project to the Owner. The contractor is compensated for actual cost plus an agreed upon fee. Should the total cost of the project exceed the maximum limit, the contractor is held responsible for the additional costs and receives no compensation beyond the agreed ceiling price.

2.   Cost Plus a Sliding Scale Fee

This is a variant of the Cost Plus Fixed Fee contract and provides for a change in the Contractor's fee proportionately to the actual costs, according to a sliding scale of fixed fees. It is usual to establish the fee scale by negotiation so as to provide for an increase in the fee proportionate to the reduction of the estimated costs.

6.7   MANAGEMENT CONTRACTS

Often an Owner wishing to have an important and complex project constructed will want the direct supervision of the actual construction performed by a contractor with considerable experience in the particular type of work contemplated. The contractor so engaged is, in effect, the <u>professional manager of the contract.</u> The basic objectives of this form of contract are to:-

1.   Engage the managing contractor during the early stages of design so that its knowledge, skill and experience may be used gainfully.

2.   Start work earlier than is usually possible with Lump Sum contracts by having the managing contractor engage other contractors to actually perform the work as approved by the Owner.

3.   Provide a qualified Management Group, employed by the managing contractor to supervise all phases of the execution of the contemplated work.

It is essential that the management contractor is the professional manager working with the Owner's Architect or Engineer as part of the design team. It is also essential, for the efficacy of the role, that the managing contractor is not to participate in any part of actual construction, since management and actual construction work are separate identities.

It has also become common for firms and even individuals to establish themselves as Project Managers who not only manage construction, but are also responsible for engaging and controlling the consultants, on behalf of the Owner.

The Construction Management system of construction uses variations of the above. Often the manager employs the site superintendent in a similar manner to a general contractor and also hires or provides miscellaneous labour to execute interface work and operate site equipment and temporary facilities. It is not unusual for general contractors to act in this type of arrangement with the building owner.

6.8   THE ARTICLES OF AGREEMENT

The purpose of the Articles of Agreement in a Construction Contract is to formally record the intentions of the signatories with respect to what has been agreed upon. It is the formal record of the Mutuality of the Minds, or the Reality of Consent mentioned previously; refer to Chapter 4.

It is essential to include among the Articles of Agreement only such matter required for the administration of the contract. The Agreement should not include matters referring to the technical aspects of the work. It should contain only those matters which would be neither necessary to the field staff, nor need to be disclosed to others to conduct the business of the contract. The best form of an agreement is one which outlines the character of the contract.

The length of the Agreement, or the volume and nature of its content, will vary from one contractual authority to another. The preparation of the Articles of Agreement, both as to content and form, should be by the Owner and its Solicitor. It has been held that neither the Architect nor Engineer can be considered as a legal authority and should therefore not prepare the Agreement.

The Articles of Agreement will indicate the form of contract which has been entered into by the Owner and the Contractor and will be more fully discussed in the following chapter.

TYPICAL QUESTIONS

1.   What are the advantages and disadvantages of the direct employment of labour method of constructing a work?
2.   What are the advantages and disadvantages of constructing a Work by contract?
3.   Can the cost of the contractor's overhead be saved by the direct employment of labour method? Explain fully.
4.   What are unsecured-cost contracts? Name them.
5.   What are the advantages of secured-cost contracts?
6.   List, and explain three (3) secured-cost forms of contract.
7.   What effect does unrestricted competition in bidding have on construction costs?
8.   What are the advantages and disadvantages of cost plus fixed sum form of contract.
9.   What is the difference between a cost plus fixed sum form of contract and the cost plus a percentage form?
10.   What type of construction requires the use of the fixed sum form of contract in nearly all cases? Why?

REFERENCES

Building Construction Handbook - Merritt.
Contracts, Specifications and engineering Relations - Mead, Mead and Akerman.
Engineering Contracts and Specifications - R. W. Abbott.
Engineering Law - Laidlaw, Young and Dick.

7

TENDERING AND CONTRACT EXECUTION
by Clive E.J. Evans, FRICS, PQS(F), C.Arb.

7.1　THE INVITATION TO TENDER

The Invitation to Tender may be sent privately to a selected number of contractors, and/or may be publicly advertised. It is usually limited to sufficient information necessary to enable a prospective bidder to judge whether the work is within its capacity, whether it has the necessary qualifications and whether it will have time to prepare a bid.

The several parts which consistently appear in the Invitation to Bid are:-

1.　Project Identification, which identifies the agency, organization, owner, architect or engineer issuing the documents, including full name and address, telephone number, and date of issue of the invitation.

2.　Time and Place, when and where proposals will be received, when and where they will be opened and whether their opening will be private or public.

3.　Description of the Work describing the major characteristics of the construction, with any description of the project type and size, to give the bidder a guide as to whether the project is within its construction ability and financial capacity.

4.　Types of Proposal Required: whether Lump Sum or Unit Price bids are required. Details in this regard are more fully given in the Instructions to Bidders.

5.　Bid Surety Requirements, whether a bid surety is required and if so the nature of the security. Full details in this regard are usually contained in the Instructions to Bidders.

6.　The Right to Reject Proposals, is usually stated in the invitation.

7.　Procurement of Documents describes where they may be examined and obtained, describes charges, deposits and refunds concerning the procurement.

7.2 TENDER/CONTRACT DOCUMENTS

The following items usually comprise the Tender Documents and subsequently become the Contract Documents when an Owner accepts the tender of a contractor.

1. <u>Instructions to Bidders:</u> the general instructions for tendering informing bidders of the manner in which they must submit their tenders to qualify for consideration and what security must accompany the bid. (The Instruction to Bidders do not form part of the Contract Documents)

2. <u>Form of Tender:</u> the blank form which when completed by Bidders becomes the Offer.

3. <u>Articles of Agreement:</u> are the Construction Agreement or Indenture.

4. <u>General Conditions of Contract:</u> briefly referred to as the General Conditions.

5. <u>Terms of Payment:</u> may be a separate document to supplement any conditions set out in the General Conditions of the Contract and should be included in the Articles of Agreement.

6. <u>Supplementary Conditions:</u> amend or amplify the General Conditions of a Standard Form of Contract.

7. <u>Special Conditions:</u> such as a separate document setting, out Labour Conditions are usually included in the Contract Documents for Public Works.

8. <u>Specifications:</u> may be listed in an Index attached to the Form of Tender but which should be listed in the Articles of Agreement.

9. <u>Drawings, Details and Schedules:</u> listed in an Index attached to the Form of Tender and also listed in the Articles of Agreement.

10. <u>Construction Schedule Requirements:</u>

11. <u>Addenda:</u> issued prior to bid closing and post bid addenda.

12. <u>Definitions:</u> apply equally to all Contract Documents.

This list may not be complete to some contractual authorities and may be too extensive for others.

7.3   INSTRUCTIONS TO BIDDERS

The requirements with which a bidder must comply during tendering are contained in the Instructions to Bidders. These instructions may include the following:-

1.   Project Identification: by title or name

2.   Bid Surety: which must accompany the tender

This surety is normally required to be in the form of a bid bond. Certified cheques have also been used. The bond ensures the bidder will enter into a contract if its tender is accepted. Failure to enter into a contract results in forfeiture of the bond to help defray the costs of the Owner's having to accept a higher tender proposal in order to engage a Contractor.

Note: A bid bond does NOT commit the surety to issuing any further bonds. If a Labour and Material Payment Bond and / or Performance Bond is to be required a "consent to surety" which commits the issuer of the bid bond to issue the subsequent bonds should be requested.

3.   Documents stating whether documents may be issued to others than General Contractors and whether partial sets may be issued. Information about the availability of documents, their cost, mailing charges and responsibilities for partial sets should also be included. The conditions and requirements governing the return of drawings and specifications by both General and Sub-Contractors should be given including the time for their return and refund of deposits.

4.   Site Examination: should be mandatory and the bidder informed that it will be deemed to have examined the site of the work at it's own risk and expense.

5.   Basis of Proposal: when appropriate, detailed outline of work separation under each form of proposal should be given and the acceptable combinations described. The Invitation to Bid should indicate the forms of proposals, such as separation for segregated contracts. The Instructions to Bidders should clearly set out the scope of each proposal, the conditions under which combined and alternative proposals will be considered for award and the conditions under which assignments, if any, will be made.

6.   Substitution of Materials: Bidders should be informed of the requirements and procedures under which proposed substitution of materials and methods may be considered for approval. Included, when applicable, will be a pre-bid date after which requests for substitution will no longer be considered. Approvals before tender closing should be made known to ALL THOSE TAKING OUT DRAWINGS AND SPECIFICATIONS.

7.   Discrepancies and Ambiguities: when discovered must be resolved. The Instructions to Bidder should give detailed instructions in this regard, particularly to whom to address enquiries, the manner in which enquiries are to be made and how replies, in the form of addenda will be issued.

8.   Preparation of the Proposal: the Bidders should be told how the proposals are to be prepared, including instructions as to how to fill out printed Forms of Tender when these are used. Explicit instructions concerning signatures should also be given.

9.   Identification and Submission of Proposal: the Bidders should be informed how to identify their proposals. Instructions should be given regarding the submission of the completed proposal, including date, time, place, and name of person to receive proposal, and clear information concerning the disposition of late proposals.

10.   Modification of Proposal: if it is permissible to change a proposal after submittal, but before the opening of tenders, bidders should be informed of the procedures and time limits concerning such modifications.

11.   Withdrawal of Proposal: it should be stated whether a bidder can or cannot withdraw their proposal, if it is possible to withdraw then the conditions in this regard should be also stated, particularly with respect to forfeiture of bid bond. The time limit on the Owner's holding proposals before withdrawal is permitted, should be stated also. The conditions under which the bid surety may be forfeited should also be described, including a time limit within which legal action may not be taken.

12.   Disqualification of Proposals: it is necessary to inform bidders of those conditions under which tenders may be disqualified.

13.   Opening of Proposals: the bidder should be told the time and place for the opening of proposals.

14.   Award of Contract: the procedure under which an Owner will award a contract, including consideration of alternatives and unit prices should be clearly described. If alternatives are to be accepted in a definite order then the Instructions should so state this order of precedence. If appropriate the Instructions may contain the reservation for the Owner to waive irregularities in a proposal.

15.   Return of Surety: the length of time that a bid surety may be retained should be noted in the Instructions and the conditions under which it will be returned to unsuccessful bidders should also be described.

16.   Execution of Contract: the requirements and conditions of the execution of the contract, including the preparation, examination, and signing of the contract agreement should be noted.

17.   Subcontractor Listing: the conditions relating to the acceptance and listing of subcontractors may be explained, indicating the manner in which they are to be listed in the Tender Form. There may be information about the importance that such a list might have in evaluating the bid.

To comply with an Article in the General Conditions of Contract, which instructs the Contractor to include Cash Allowances in the Contract Price, the Instruction to Bidders may give information regarding such allowances as Contingency, Brick, Pile Inspection, Concrete Testing, etc.

The Instructions to Bidders must be considered the conditions governing the submission of a bid, proposal or tender.

7.4   THE FORMS OF TENDER OR PROPOSAL FORM

This Form is usually prepared by the Owner in the form of a letter from the bidder to the prospective Owner. It contains blank spaces that are to be filled in by the bidder regarding the bidders legal name and address, the bid amount, contract duration, acknowledgment of receipt of addenda, and a place for their signature and seal. The signature of the bidder indicates agreement to all provisions and conditions of all the documents which will comprise the contract.

THE FORM OF TENDER IS NOT A PART OF THE INSTRUCTIONS TO BIDDERS, THE TWO ARE SEPARATE BUT RELATED ENTITIES.

7.5   THE ARTICLES OF AGREEMENT

There has been widely diversified opinion as to what should be covered by the Articles of Agreement of a Construction Contract. The present Canadian Standard Form of Agreement Between the Owner and the Contractor has evolved from many years of discussion between various committees of the Committee of Canadian Architectural Councils, the Association of Consulting Engineers of Canada, the Canadian Council of Professional Engineers, the Canadian Construction Association and Construction Specifications Canada.

The Title Clause of the Articles of Agreement should record the date of the Agreement, and the names of the parties.

The Title Clause should be concluded with a statement such as: -
"That the parties agree as follows......"

The Contractor's Undertaking, is usually set out in the first Article following the Title Clause of the Agreement. This undertaking should establish the required completion dates with respect to work.

In addition to the required completion date of the Work, there may be recorded the stipulation with respect to Liquidated Damages.

Also included in the contractor's Undertaking is the agreement by the Contractor to perform the work according to the Drawings, Specifications and General Conditions of the Contract.

It is important that the Owner's Consultant be formally stated.

The Inclusion and Precedence of Specific Documents.

The Articles of Agreement should list the various documents which, in total, would be the Contract Documents. By the terms of the Articles of Agreement both the Owner and the Contractor are bound to the terms and conditions contained in them. It is most important that the Agreement clearly indicates all of the documents which are intended to comprise the contract in its entirety.

The signing of the Agreement only does not constitute a good contract even though it may be valid. The necessity of both parties to the contract to sign All documents in an equal number of copies as of the Agreement should not be overlooked.

To avoid contention as to the precedence of the contract documents, most authorities recommend that the order of their seniority be stipulated in the Agreement.

It should be borne in mind, that in all cases of litigation, the Courts will be first guided by what has been definitely expressed in the Contract Documents rather than what may be inferred from them.

Consideration: Of primary importance to a Contract is the extent of the Consideration and the nature of it. It is most generally stipulated that the Owner will pay, the Contractor the tender price or offer, for performing the work as set out in the Agreement. It is usually a condition that payment shall be made in the lawful money of Canada and shall be subject to additions and deductions provided for in the Contract Documents.

It is this Article of a Construction Agreement which should indicate the form of the contract, either by inference or by description. If only a single amount is given the contract would be a form of a Fixed Price Contract.

Commencement and Completion of the Work.

The required completion date of a Work is relatively easy to establish, even considering the factors involved. Unless it is a condition of the Agreement that the Contractor starts work within a specified time following the award of the contract, to arbitrarily set a completion date is poor practice, particularly if there is a liquidated damage clause in the contract.

The duration of time that may be required to complete a project can be determined within relatively close limits. Once the duration of the project is estimated satisfactorily, the date the Work may be completed can be established once it is known when work will actually start.

The start of the work is that date, in time, when the Contractor is informed by the Owner that its tender has been accepted and it is instructed to proceed with the work. Although the Contractor may be instructed to start work at once some time might elapse before the actual physical work can be started. It is for this reason some Tender Forms may include the following condition:

"I/WE understand that this work is to be completed within - calendar days. If this tender is accepted, I/WE agree to start within - calendar days of notification of contract award and to work vigorously and continuously to complete this work, in all its parts, no later than - calendar days following."

From this a reasonably realistic completion date may be established. It is for this reason that a contractual agency or an owner will establish as a condition of the offer to be made, a time limit with respect to considering an offer. If, as is customary, a maximum of 30 days is allowed for the consideration of an offer, then this period of 30 days could become a factor in determining the dates of not only commencing the work, but the date of completion also.

It is not until the Owner has accepted the tender and has informed the successful bidder, that the Consultant can direct that work shall commence.

The Consultant should have the responsibility of general supervision and direction of a Work, but the Contractor must have complete control of his organization. The Consultant, therefore, is usually made responsible for:-

1. Direction as to when the work should physically start.
2. Direction as to staging or phasing the work.
3. Ensuring that the progress of the work does not endanger the interest and safety of the Public.
4. The extension of time of completion if circumstances warrant it.
5. Determining whether the rate of progress is satisfactory, and ascertaining whether the required completion date can be attained.

Manner of Payment

The Agreement should stipulate the manner in which the Contractor is to be paid and also state the annual rate of interest to apply where failure to make payment occurs.

It is generally agreed that payments to the Contractor will be made regularly in an amount equal to a stipulated percentage of the total value of the work completed at the time of payment. This percentage payable may range from 85% to 95% of the value of the completed work, depending upon what is set out in the Agreement, or a supplemental document outlining the Terms of Payment. The balance withheld is referred to as the holdback. Holdback is NOT for the following commonly mistaken purposes.

1.   An inducement to have the Contractor perform as is required of it.

2.   Protection against overpayment during the progress of the work arising out of erroneous certificates. Such overpayments are adjusted in the Final Certificate.

Such a procedure is to ensure that provision is made for payments of liens, which are claims made against the property of the project by unpaid subcontractors and suppliers for monies owing them.

Progress Payment Certificates issued by the Consultant should be the basis for regular payments. Such certificates are provisional only as all necessary adjustments in the accounting are made in the Final Payment Certificate. In preparing Progress Payment Certificates a cost breakdown, item by item, is necessary to relate the physical value to the true monetary value in each case. It is frequently specified in the Contract Documents that:-

"The Contractor shall submit with the first Progress Claim for work, performed, a Cost Breakdown of the Contract Price, listing by sub-trades the total cost of each, the sums of which shall equal the aggregate sum of the Contract."

From the standpoint of the Owner, it is perhaps even more useful to insist that the Contractor's breakdown of the contract price be submitted before the Contract is executed.

The cost breakdown is essential if equitable payments are to be made to both the Contractor and its Subcontractors. It must be remembered that periodical payments are for completed and acceptable work at the time of submission of the Progress Claims.

Beginning with the second Payment Certificate, the Contractor should submit with each Progress Claim a Statutory Declaration to the effect it has paid outstanding claims against it from the proceeds of previous payment received.

The payment of the Final Payment Certificate may be withheld for any period of time stipulated in the Articles of Agreement, or as may be required by Law, to ensure payment of outstanding claims against the Contractor. This, however, can be obviated by the posting of a Labour and Material Payment Bond, discussed in a later Chapter.

It should be noted that the payment of the final Payment Certificate does not relieve the Contractor of obligations or guarantees and warranties specified in the Contract Documents.

Liens

A Lien is the right to hold another's property as a security for debt or performance of a duty or obligation. It is a form, called a "claim for lien", which has been designed by the provisions of Provincial Statues (known as Mechanics', Builder's or Construction Lien Act) and which commences an action upon its being registered.

A Lien Act may be defined as a piece of legislation intended to give rights of claim to those whose work, services, or materials have been provided to the Owner, enhancing the value of the land, or works upon the land. The Act establishes the right for payment for such work, services or materials, by attachment to the property of a lien for the value owing.

The manner by which liens may be finally settled are usually described in the Articles of Agreement and the General Conditions of the Contract.

7.6   BINDING SUCCESSORS

In order that there is assurance the performance of a Construction Contract is continued, it is not unusual to make the contract binding not only to the parties themselves but to their respective heirs, executors, administrators or successors.

7.7   DATING AND PLACING

Preceding the signatures of the parties to a contract, it is customary to state the parties have signed and affixed their seals, if it be a contract under seal, on the "date above written" which is the date appearing in the title clause of the agreement. It is not recommended to date the document twice as it is possible the dates may not agree. The "place of execution" of the contract is of greatest importance, as the law applicable to the contract may be held to be that of the place where the Work is executed.

7.8 GOVERNING LAW

The Law governing the Contract should be stated and is often, but not necessarily, the Law of the Place of the Work.

7.9 LANGUAGE

The Language in which the Contract is drawn should be agreed to. Where bi-lingual contracts are drawn the language taking precedence <u>must</u> be stated.

7.10 SIGNATURES, SEALS AND WITNESSING

The draft of an agreement before execution is merely a document. If it has been signed by the parties it becomes an instrument. If it is sealed it becomes a deed.

The execution is the act of the parties signing the document as a visible means of their acceptance of it and a true expression of their contract.

Seals, when used, are merely wafers stuck to the documents at the proper place, even before the signatures of the parties have been made. Theoretically the signer should place their finger on the seal and say something like "I deliver this as my act and deed". Corporations, when contracting, must affix their corporate, seal as this is equivalent to witnessing the signatures of its officers.

It is customary to have the parties sign the agreement in the order as listed in its title clause, thereby preserving the doctrine of "offeree" and "offeror".

Witnessing of signatures should be so arranged to make clear which signature a witness is witnessing. To facilitate the tracing of witness, should it arise, the address and occupations of the witnesses should be indicated.

The addresses of the parties and the Consultant should also form part of the Articles for the purposes of delivery and receipt of Notices in writing.

7.11 TIME, TENDER CLOSING

Controversy sometimes arises over the interpretation of the closing time for a tender. The question will arise: *"Is that a late tender?"*

The answer turns upon the wording of the tender documents; depending upon how the documents are worded, the two key interpretations can be:

1.   It must be received not later than the stated closing time; or,

2.   It may be received at the stated closing time plus 59 seconds.

Two recent court rulings, one in British Columbia and the other in Ontario, have addressed this issue.

1.   In *Smith Bros and Wilson v. British Columbia Hydro and Power Authority and Kingston Construction Ltd.* in the Supreme Court of British Columbia by Justice D.W. Shaw, time according to the Advertisement and the Instructions to Tenderers was set out as follows:

   1.   the Advertisement to tender used the expression:

   "B.C. Hydro will receive tenders until 11:00 a.m. local time..."

   2.   the Instructions to Tenderers said:
   "Closing Time — Tenderers shall deliver their Tenders... not later than 11:00 a.m. local time ... (The "closing time"), and Tenders which are delivered after closing time will not be considered."

As Justice Shaw read both the Advertisement and the Instructions, nothing implies that "11:00 a.m. local time" means the time according to B.C. Hydro's clock. There is nothing to suggest that if B.C. Hydro's clock is inaccurate that it will nonetheless prevail over accurate time. He did however note that *"There is some evidence of custom that generally the clock used by the party receiving tenders will govern. But none of that evidence goes so far as to establish that on a close disputed call, an inaccurate clock will prevail over accurate time. While a provision to cover that situation could be included in the Advertisement and the Invitation to Tender, none was used in the present case."*

He also found that *"When the Smith Bros. tender was delivered, it was almost immediately stamped by the Widmer clock. At that time, both the clock and the stamp read 11:01 a.m. The conclusion I draw, based upon Mr. Lee's report, is that the tender was received after 11:00 a.m. and before 11:01 a.m. actual time."*

Kingston Construction (the second bidder who was awarded the contract) submitted that whatever may have been B.C. Hydro's policy, it cannot change the clear provisions of the Advertisement and the Instructions to Tenderers. The words in each document are *"until 11:00 a.m."* and *"not later than 11:00 a.m."* respectively.

Justice Shaw concluded, *"In my opinion, one cannot read into the quoted words that the time for delivery of tenders will extend past 11:00 a.m. until almost 11:01 a.m."*

2.   In *Bradscot (MCL) Ltd. v. Hamilton-Wentworth Catholic School Board* heard by Justice Somers of the Ontario Court of Justice (General Division) it was determined that the tender submitted thirty seconds after the time of closing was not late. The tender documents stated *"Friday May 8, 1998 at 1:00 p.m."* as the deadline. The Owner's Instructions to Tenderers made it emphatically clear that bids not received by the time stated *"WILL NOT be accepted by the owner."* The official clock was a digital one, but it showed the hours and minutes only and did not record the seconds. According to the watch of the representative from Bradscot (MCL) Ltd., the second bidder, the time that the tender of the low bid was submitted was 30 seconds past 1:00 p.m. The President of the Ontario General Contractors' Association stated in a letter: *"In our opinion any tender received after the instant of 1:00 ... is late... One thing for sure contractors understand the tender that is even one second late, is late, and should not be considered."* The Board's Architect offered the opinion that where the bid closing time is stated to be 1:00 p.m., any bid received at 1:00 p.m. was delivered on time, and for a delivery to be late the clock would have to register 1:01 p.m.

Justice Somers reviewed the decision in *Smith Bros and Wilson v. British Columbia Hydro and Power Authority* but did not find it particularly helpful as the clear provisions and particular words in that matter were "not later than 11:00 a.m." Justice Somers noted that the relevant bid deadline in the matter was set as "Friday, May 8, 1998 *at* 1:00 p.m." Justice Somers then concluded: *"In my opinion when it is stated that some deed be done 'at 2:00 p.m.' the time is for that minute and the act is not overdue until the minute hand has moved off the 12 hand to the :01 position."*

Clearly the answer is in the wording of the tender documents. *"Before and not later than"* clearly has a different legal meaning than "*at.*" Bidders, typically are always waiting for one last, lower price or final adjustment. Submitting your tender prior to the stated closing time is the only certain way to avoid this problem.

TYPICAL QUESTIONS

1. List the usual documents which might comprise a Construction Contract.
2. What is the purpose of the Invitation to Bid?
3. What should the Invitation to Bid contain?
4. What are the Instructions to Bidders?
5. What are eight (8) of these instructions?
6. What is the Form of Tender?
7. What does a completed Form of Tender signify?
8. What is the purpose of a Construction Agreement?
9. What matters may be covered in the Agreement?
10. What is meant by the "Contractor's Undertaking?"
11. Why should the precedence of the Contract Documents by specified?
12. What is meant by the Contract Completion Date and how may it be established?
13. How are payments usually made to the Contractor?

REFERENCES

As for Chapter 6, to which is now added: CSI Manual of Practice - Construction Specifications Institute (USA)

CCDC Document 23 - A Guide to calling Bids and Awarding Contracts.

THE GENERAL CONDITIONS OF A CONSTRUCTION CONTRACT
by Clive E.J. Evans, FRICS, PQS(F) C.Arb.

8.1   INTRODUCTION

Reference is made through this Chapter to Standard Construction Document CCDC 2, 1994, Stipulated Price Contract.

When both parties have signed the Articles of Agreement, it signifies that:

a.   The Owner has formally accepted the offer of the Contractor, and

b.   Both parties agreed to the terms and conditions of the General Conditions of the Contract, to what has been specified in the Specifications and to what has been shown on the Drawings which will have been listed in the Agreement (Article A-3 - Contract Documents).

8.2   THE STANDARD CONSTRUCTION DOCUMENT CCDC 2 - 1994

Standard Construction Document CCDC 2 - 1994, which is a standard Stipulated Price Contract was prepared and published by the Canadian Construction Documents Committee, comprised of representatives of:

1.   The Association of Consulting Engineers of Canada (ACEC)

2.   Canadian Construction Association (CCA)

3.   The Canadian Council of Professional Engineers (CCPE)

4.   The Committee of Canadian Architectural Councils (CCAC)

5.   Construction Specifications Canada (CSC)

This committee is responsible for the development and publication of Canadian Standard Construction Documents for use by Owners, the Design Professions and Contractors.

8.3   THE OBJECTS OF THE GENERAL CONDITIONS

The objects of any set of General Conditions to a Construction Contract are:

1.   To clearly identify throughout that the contract is between two (2) parties only; the Owner and the Contractor.

2.   To ensure that both parties to the Contract are reasonably protected under the Contract without undue bias in favour of either party.

3.   To clearly state that the Contractor is totally responsible for performing all the work under the Contract in accordance with the requirements of the Contract Documents and that none of these responsibilities are to be transferred to the Consultant.

4.   To ensure that the Contractor is not required to assume the Consultant's design responsibilities.

5.   To ensure that the Consultant is not required to be the guarantor of the Contractor's work and the Contractor is not required to be responsible for the Consultant's work.

8.4   MATTERS TO BE CONSIDERED IN THE GENERAL CONDITIONS

The nature of the material which should be included in the General Conditions is governed by both the nature and extent of the contemplated work. Also the "General Conditions" may vary from one project location to another, or from one Owner to another.

Regardless of variations, the type of material contained in the "General Conditions" has, by usage, become more or less standard, as exemplified by Standard Construction Documents currently in use. The long use of such forms is accomplished by precedence in the courts in the establishment of terms. These terms are familiar to the contractor, consultant, Quantity Surveyor and specification writer, resulting in a ready understanding of their meaning.

A standard document provides a certain assurance that all major contractual requirements have been included in the contract. Nevertheless if the work is more complex, "General Conditions" are likely to become complex through the use of SUPPLEMENTARY GENERAL CONDITIONS which amend the "General Conditions" <u>as may be required for a particular project.</u>

The Supplementary General Conditions, like the "General Conditions", are non-technical in nature. Conditions related to technical matters are included in DIVISION 1 of the Specifications, of which mention will be made in a later Chapter.

In general there appear to be nine (9) classes of subject matter which are likely to be found in any set of "General Conditions".

1. **Definition of the intent** of the contract documents and their relationship to one another.

2. **Definitions of special words used and of ordinary words used in a special sense,** together with the complete wording or phrases for abbreviations appearing in the documents.

3. Listing and defining the **rights reserved for,** or assigned to the **Owner, Consultant, Contractor and it's Subcontractors.**

4. **Listing and defining the responsibilities of Owner, Consultant, Contractor and it's Subcontractors.**

5. **Requirements as to bonds, insurance** or other financial protection required by the Owner.

6. **Listing and defining the authority assigned to each of the Owner, Consultant, and the Contractor.**

7. **Particular measures to be taken to ensure the protection of both property and persons.**

8. **The legal arrangements** and procedures which should be known to all parties of the contract, including Subcontractors.

9. **The business arrangements** and procedures which should be known to the parties to the contract.

It is not unusual to find a set of "General Conditions" in which the foregoing material will be grouped in specific divisions, as is customary with Specifications. Such a set of "General Conditions" is the Conditions of Contract (International) for Works of Civil Engineering Construction. In most cases the foregoing material is contained in Articles placed in sequence in the document. The Articles could be grouped sequentially as follows:-

1. Intent of the Contract Documents

2. Definitions

3. Bonds and Financial Requirement

4. Payments and Particular Reports

5.   Modifications of Contractual Relations

6.   Business Details

7.   Conduct of the Work

8.   Completion and Acceptance of the Work

If you will examine the indices of various Standard Forms of "General Conditions" comparing one another, you will note there will be variances in setting out the material of the conditions illustrating the different points of view held by different contractual authorities.

Regardless of how the "General Conditions" are set out, whether as in a Standard Form or not, governing a particular Construction Contract they are for that particular contract ONLY.

8.5   DEFINITION OF TERMS

Because so many words used in Contract Documents have special meanings and other words have inexact meaning when used in ordinary conversation, it is essential they be given precise meanings with respect to the contract in which they appear. The definitions should be carefully studied to avoid misunderstanding.

Among the terms it is most desirable to define is the phrase - "The Intent of the Contract Documents". This definition may be given in either the "General Conditions", or the "Supplementary General Conditions", preferably the former.

GC 1.1.3 (CCDC 2 - 1994) states; "The Contract Documents are complementary and what is required by any one shall be as binding as if required by all."

GC 1.1.1 (CCDC 2 - 1994) which defines the intent of the Contract Documents is predicated by GC 1.1.3 above. GC 1.1.1 states; "The intent of the Contract Documents is to include the labour, products and services necessary for the performance of the Work in accordance with these documents. It is not intended, however, that the Contractor shall supply products or perform work not consistent with, governed by or properly inferable from the Contract Documents."

In interpreting the contract documents, words describing materials or work which shall have well-known technical or trade meaning, unless otherwise specifically defined in the contract documents, shall be construed in accordance with such well-known meaning recognized by architects, engineers and the trades.

Refer to GC 1.1.4, CCDC 2 - 1994.

THE FOLLOWING TERMS ARE THOSE MOST FREQUENTLY DEFINED IN CONTRACT DOCUMENTS OF A CONSTRUCTION CONTRACT:-

1. <u>Contract</u>, meaning the agreement between the Owner and the Contractor.

2. <u>Contract Documents</u>, meaning those documents listed in the Articles of Agreement which comprise the contract.

3. <u>Owner</u>, the person or entity who awards the contract for the Work.

4. <u>Consultant - (the Architect or Engineer)</u> Too much emphasis cannot be placed upon the need to properly define the Consultant. Not only should the Owner's Consultant be properly designated, but the full scope of duties, responsibilities and authority should be fully defined. Without proper authority no one may act on behalf of the Owner with respect to changes to the original contract requirements; make quasi-judicial (resembling judicial) decisions with respect to the acceptability of the Contractor's work nor interpret the intent of the Plans and Specifications. Proper definitions in this regard will prevent attempts to exercise unwarranted authority, to the benefit of both the Owner and the Contractor. It is suggested Chapter 2 be reviewed at this time, together with - "The Contract of Agency" outlined in Chapter 5. Reference should be made also to General Conditions Part 2 - Administration of the Contract CCDC 2 - 1994.

5. <u>Contractor</u>, meaning the party agreeing to perform the work according to the Contract Documents.

6. <u>Sub-Contractor</u>, the person, firm or corporation, other than the Contractor, who is to furnish labour, materials, and perform work under the direction and supervision of the Contractor.

7. <u>The Project</u>, being the total construction.

8. <u>The Work</u>, being the total construction and related services required by the Contract Documents.

9. <u>Products</u>, meaning those materials, machinery, equipment and fixtures forming the work.

10. <u>Other Contractor</u>, meaning another party employed by the Owner for work other than that required by the Contract Documents.

11. <u>Place of the Work</u>, designating the site of the Building or Project.

12. <u>Time</u>, defining Contract Time as stated in the Agreement for substantial performance as certified by the Consultant; the term day as meaning calendar day and what shall be a working day.

13.   <u>Substantial Performance</u> as defined in a statute, such as a Builder's Lien Act.

14.   <u>Total Performance</u>, defined as meaning the entire-work having been performed as required by the contract Documents and certified by the Consultant.

15.   <u>Changes</u>, being revisions to the Work within the scope of the Contract.

The Definition of Terms is certainly not limited to the foregoing, which are some of the most common definitions to be found in various forms of General and Supplemental General Conditions. Definitions of terms in any contract should be given careful study as they exert considerable influence upon the execution of the work and the administration of the contract.

8.6   PLANS AND SPECIFICATIONS

There are responsibilities which the Consultant has towards the Contractor.

1.   It must provide any additional written or graphic instructions concerning the execution of the work. Such additional information should not be inconsistent with the execution of the work and should be promptly issued to avoid delay in the progress of the work. No additional work should be done by the Contractor without drawings or instructions, or both.

2.   It is usually required to provide the Contractor, free of charge, all copies of plans and specifications reasonably necessary for the execution of the Work.

3.   It may require of the Contractor a specified number of particular shop or setting drawings, or manufacturers' brochures, necessary for the execution of the work by the various trades. The Contractor is required to submit such promptly to prevent delays in its own or sub-trades' work. In turn the Consultant must act upon such submission with reasonable promptness also.

4.   It is usually required of the Contractor that it keep on the site of the Work one set of all drawings and specifications in good order for use by the Consultant.

8.7   CONTRACTOR TO SATISFY HIMSELF OF CONDITIONS

It is generally stipulated in the Instructions to Bidders that a Bidder, in preparing a bid, is to visit the site of the work before submitting the tender. The purpose of this is to ensure that the Contractor has made itself fully acquainted with all site conditions which may affect its performance of the Work, and that it has prepared it's tender accordingly. Usually a Bidder is required to state in it's proposal that such examination was made.

Although the Consultant may have done it's best to prepare the Drawings and the Specifications, it cannot warrant the results. For this reason, the Contractor should have satisfied itself by personal inspection, examination, computation and tests, that it is practical to perform the Work, and that any quantities scheduled in the Specifications are reasonably accurate.

It has been held in Law that the Owner does not warrant that site conditions are fit to do the work, nor that they will continue to be fit. If a Contractor fails to make it's own examination and enters into a Contract, signifying it's willingness to assume all risks, it's failure to examine and investigate before submitting a tender could have disastrous results.

Circumstances could occur which could relieve the contractor of liability in this regard such as encountering, during excavation, obstacles that were previously unknown to either party of the act. In such case the contractor may gain relief from liability and would likely be compensated if circumstances are justifiable.

8.8   WHAT IS TO BE PROVIDED BY THE CONTRACTOR

It is usually a Condition of a Construction Contract that, unless otherwise specified, all workmanship, equipment, materials, and articles incorporated into a Work are new and of the best of their respective kinds for the purpose intended. However, the Owner usually reserves the right to insist that the Contractor give personal superintendent to the work, or have at the site of the work at all times competent foremen or superintendents. Such superintendent must be to the satisfaction of the Owner. Refer to GC 3.7 - CCDC 2 - 1994.

8.9   AUTHORITY OF THE CONSULTANT

The status of the Consultant with respect to the execution of a Construction Contract is most important. The General Conditions most usually define this status as related to:-

1.   Date of Substantial Performance

2.   Certification of Total Performance

3.   Authority to issue additional instructions

4.   Authority in respect to deciding questions arising under the Contract Documents

5.   Authority to stop the progress of the work

6.   Making changes by altering, adding to or deducting from the Work

7.   Issuance of Certificates of Payment

8.   Inspection of work in progress

9.   Issuance of Certificate of acceptance of work completed.

Such definitions are predicated upon the fact that the Consultant will be acting as an Agent of the Owner, and their authority extends only to the limit of such Agency, whose limits must be defined.

When the Owner has engaged a Consultant to administer the Contract, and superintend the Contractor's performance of the work, the Owner:-

1.   Should provide the Consultant all necessary legal advice and service, except when the Consultant is acting as judge of the performance of the Contract, or is rendering a decision concerning the interests of the Owner and the Contractor.

2.   Should not give orders to a Contractor, or Sub-Contractor, particularly in person. All such orders should be given by the Consultant to avoid confusion and misunderstanding of an order given directly by the Owner. Orders given directly by the Owner could be misconstrued as an "Extra". It has been held in Law, in cases of this nature, that a verbal order given by the Owner to a Contractor or Sub-contractor is a waiver of any special requirement to the form of an order, which is usually stipulated to be in writing.

The authority of the Consultant, is not unlimited, being only within the limits set out in the terms and conditions of the contract. For a Consultant to assume authority which has not been expressly conferred upon it, or which cannot be reasonably inferred, makes it liable for all which might ensue from unwarranted assumptions.

It must be expected, however, that decisions given by the Consultant will be final, provided such are not unreasonable, arbitrary, oppressive, acts of bad faith, or fraudulent.

8.10   CONSULTANT'S REVIEW OF WORK IN PROGRESS

It is axiomatic that all work be reviewed for compliance with all terms and conditions of the contract. The procedures for this function if not specified in the General Conditions, should be specified elsewhere in the Contract Documents.

Reference should be made to GC 2.3, CCDC 2 - 1994

8.11   DEFECTS AND THEIR CORRECTION

In addition to being required to remedy defects within a stated period following the "substantial completion" of the Work, a condition of the Contract may stipulate as follows:-

1.   Progress Payments will be withheld until all defects have been corrected.

2.   If the work is defective and the Owner considers it expedient to accept it, an amount equal to the value of the defective work, or an estimated amount to correct it, together with reasonable allowances for damages, may be deducted from what is owing the Contractor.

3.   For a period one (1) year from the date of Substantial Completion of the work, the Contractor is to remedy, at it's own expense, such defects which may appear in the work, even though the Final Certificate has been issued and the Contractor has been paid in full. Refer to GC 12.2 and 12.3, CCDC 2, 1994.

There usually is stated in the Specifications for certain work, that Warranty-Guarantees are required relative to the quality of materials and workmanship, and that during a specified period defective work arising out of inferior materials or workmanship is to be rectified at the Contractor's expense.

It should also be noted that the time required for the necessary rectification of defects is not valid reason for extending the specified item for the completion of the work. Therefore, defects could become a source of liability for liquidated Damages.

8.12   GUARANTEES AND WARRANTIES

The terms of "guarantee" and "warranty" are often and mistakenly used interchangeably to describe a manufacturer's responsibility after completion of construction. In legal usage, a warranty is an absolute liability on the part of the warrantor and the contract is void unless it is strictly and literally performed, while a guarantee is a promise, entirely collateral to the original contract. In other words, a warranty binds a party to terms of another's contract. A good example of a type of guarantee is a performance bond which acts as a third party promise that a contractor will or has performed in accordance with the terms of the contract with an owner.

8.13   ALTERATIONS

There are usually two Articles of the General Conditions of a Construction Contract which are of importance. First, there, is the matter of alterations or variations to the original contract requirements, which shall be discussed now. Secondly, there is the matter of "Extras" and "Credits" to the, contract value which shall be discussed immediately following.

The Consultant is not empowered to make any alteration or variation to the original plans and specifications, unless authority to do so has been conferred upon it. Such authority, is usually established in the General Conditions of the Contract. Refer to GC 6.1, CCDC 2 1994.

The most common alterations are those arising from:-

1.   Changes to foundation design to suit unusual site conditions, which were either unknown, or overlooked during the planning of a project.

2.   Changes implemented to correct errors, omissions, conflicts, and to clarify ambiguities in the plans and specifications.

3.   Changes which have resulted in either a function or requirement; such an a change in use and occupancy.

4.   Changes to comply with the requirements of some legal authority, such as the regulations of a Hydro-Electric Power Commission.

There are certain well-established rules:

1.   The authority to make alterations to vary the requirements of the contract, once it has been entered into, must be clearly defined. For either party to act without such authority being agreed upon would be to act with personal discretion and risk, and the party so proceeding would be liable for the consequences which could include voiding the contract.

2.   The person authorized to alter or vary the original requirements of the contract should direct such changes in writing. Should a contractor proceed to effect a change without written authority to do so, it proceeds at its discretion and risk, and must suffer the consequences.

3.   If the changes are so great as to completely alter the original intent of the work, the contract may be considered void, relieving the contractor of all obligations. In such

circumstances the contractor is entitled to be compensated for the work the completed under the terms of the contract before it was voided.

4. Changes which make the work more difficult, require the use of materials of better quality than those specified, or requiring work to be done under unfavourable conditions do not provide grounds for voiding the contract. However, the contractor may be entitled to be compensated for additional costs, depending upon the circumstances.

5. The reduction of quantities, particularly those of a Unit Price with Schedule of Quantities form of contract is not sufficient grounds to claim for damages, or loss of anticipated profit.

In all cases of dispute arising out of changes, the Courts will examine the extent and nature of the changes, and the conduct of the parties to the contract with respect to the execution of the changes.

8.14   "EXTRAS" OR "CREDITS"

Changes which are additions to the originally required work often result in an ultimate additional cost to the Owner, and deletions often result in a reduction of the contract value. We are not concerned with the manner by which changes are valued, this being an estimating function of Quantity Surveying. We are, however, concerned with certain legal aspects regarding "extras" and "credits" to the construction contract.

It has been held in Law that there can be no claim for "extras" arising out of additional work performed which is considered to be indispensably necessary to the completion of the whole of the work as intended even if:

1. The indispensably necessary work has not been particularly specified.

2. Such work has not been shown on the Drawings.

3. Such work has been understated.

4. The Consultant's estimate of cost is in error.

5. Such work, ruled indispensable is impracticable, but not impossible.

6. The quantities shown in the contract schedule are different from those upon which the tender was based.

Unless specific instructions in writing by the Consultant are given, the supply of better materials, or the supply of materials or work not particularly specified or implied, cannot be a claim for an "extra".

Unless the Consultant has been granted authority as an Agent of the Owner, orders given by it do not constitute a claim for "extras". **Recovery of compensation for "extras" can only be made according to the terms of the contract.** Refer to GC 6.2 and 6.3, CCDC 2 - 1994.

Where it is a condition of the contract that the Consultant is the sole judge of questions arising out of the interpretation of the plans and specifications, there can be no claim for "extras" when the Consultant holds the work to be required by the plans and specifications.

Unless a change has been effected upon receipt of a written order to do so, **there can be no claim for an extra, unless the change is beyond the terms of the contract.**

Adjustments to the contract value resulting from changes in the work are usually determined by the methods set out in the General Conditions of the Contract and communicated by means of a change order.

It should be noted that any unauthorized change to the contract may void guaranty bonds, and for this reason only authorized changes are allowed.

Usually the General Conditions will contain provisions for the collection of damages from the Contractor for it's failure to complete the work by the time fixed by the terms of the Contract.

These damages, which were discussed in Chapter 4, are liquidated damages, which in effect, represent a penalty.

Damages can be collected by the Contractor for the following acts by the Owner or it's representative:-

1.   Failure to give the site of the work over to the Contractor at an agreed time.

2.   Failure to supply plans and specifications and addenda related to them.

3.   Failure to supply promised materials, equipment, etc., which the Contractor has taken into account in preparing it's tender.

4.   Failure to negotiate and mutually agree upon a revision of the Contract Completion Date, when negotiating "extras" to the contract. A contractor failing to include in it's proposal for an "extra" for an extension of the Completion Date, could be placing itself in jeopardy.

8.15   TIME IS OF THE ESSENCE

This clause is used to ensure that the conditions with respect to the time the work is to be completed are not overlooked. The clause is only effective when it is not inconsistent with other terms of the contract and the particulars of a specific case. Refer to definition 14 and GC 6.5, CCDC 2 - 1994.

8.16   RESPONSIBILITY OF THE CONTRACTOR

Responsibilities of the Contractor to the Owner, apart from complying with the plans and specifications, are usually of two kinds:

1.   Those which, normally are the responsibility of the Owner but which, have been delegated to and accepted by the Contractor as may be prescribed by Federal or Provincial statues or municipal By-laws or other authority, which are related to Public Liability and Property Damage, and,

2.   Those which are solely the responsibility of the Contractor.

In the first case, the General Conditions of the Contract may state that the contractor is:-

1.   Responsible for the procurement of all necessary permits, etc., which may be required for the construction of the work, and,

2.   To indemnify, that is to provide security against loss or damage, and save harmless the Owner from and against all claims, demands, losses, costs, etc., which could be attributable to the Contractor's actions.

The following definitions of words are given to assist in understanding what is to follow:-

1.   INDEMNIFY - to make good, or promise to make good any or all loss suffered by a person as a result of an act, or default of another, to protect and secure against legal responsibility.

2.   INDEMNITY is a collateral (subordinately connected: attendant or secondary: incidental) contract or SECURITY to prevent a person from suffering loss resulting from damage sustained, an undertaking to remunerate another for loss or to protect him against liability.

3.   LIABILITY is the condition of being responsible for a possible loss, or an actual loss.

This inclusion of the **save or hold harmless** clauses in construction contracts is becoming an increasingly popular practice. Depending upon its scope, this clause will protect the Owner to some degree, from claims arising or in connection with the construction of the project. The save or hold harmless clause may take different forms which in substance, require that the Contractor bear the cost of defending all legal proceedings, and pay any judgment involving a suit against the Owner by a separate contractor contending it was damaged by the Owner's Contractor.

Some contracts contain save and hold harmless conditions that particularly specify that the Contractor will indemnify both itself and the Owner from any loss or damage owing to personal injury or loss to any person, or damage to property, as the result of Subcontractor's negligence while executing it's portion of the Contract. Such conditions do not absolve the Contractor from indemnifying the Owner from any loss or damage because of personal injury to any person, or damage to property, as the result of the Contractor's negligence, during the execution of the contract.

Other construction contracts may stipulate, in substance, that the Contractor shall indemnify the Owner against any loss or damage owing to personal injury to any person or damage to property, arising out of the construction of the Work which may be attributable to the Contractor's negligence while executing the contract.

There have been contracts which have stipulated, in substance, that the contractor indemnify the Owner against any loss or damage because of personal injury to any person or damage to property during the construction of the Work. This clause is dangerous, if it makes no mention of negligence on the part of the Contractor, or of the Contractor solely, or by persons employed by it, including sub-contractors. The following clause is in this category, and is classic:-

"The Contractor agrees to indemnity and save harmless the Owner, Consultant, their Agents and Employees, from and against all loss and expense (including costs and attorney's fees) by reason of liability for damages because personal injury, including death at any time resulting therefrom, sustained by any person or persons or on account of damage to property, including loss of use thereof, regardless of negligence of the Contractor and whether caused by or contributed to by said Owner, Consultant, their Agents, Employees or others."

Such a condition makes the Contractor liable for all defects and deficiencies in the consultant's plans and specifications! Such a condition is not enforceable.

If indemnification is required of the Contractor, then in terms of Equity, the Owner should indemnify the Contractor with respect to loss or wages sustained by the Contractor arising out the Owner's responsibility such as:

1.   The lack of, or defect in, title to, the site of the Work, or,

2.   Infringement, or alleged infringement, of any patent or invention in executing anything for the purposes of the contract for which the model, plan or design was supplied by the Owner to the Contractor.

The second case of responsibility comprises those matters which rest solely with the Contractor as the requirement to protect the Work while under construction. The requirements in this regard, exclusive of Fire Insurance and protection against the elements and other hazards, are usually:-

1. The Contractor is to maintain adequate protection of ALL the work from damage. He is to take all reasonable precautions to protect the Owner's property from all damage or injury arising in connection with the contract.

2. The contractor is to make good any damage or injury to the Work resulting from the lack of reasonable protective precautions.

3. The Contractor shall adequately protect adjacent property as required both by Law and the terms and conditions of the Contract Documents.

The Contractor should not be held responsible or any damage or loss to the Work arising out of defective plans and specifications, (or caused by the Owner, it's Agents or Employees), provided the Contractor has exercised reasonable precautions against such loss.

8.17   INSURANCE - GENERALLY

The General Conditions of a Construction Contract will usually require a Contractor to maintain various types of Insurance during the construction of the Work. The most usual forms of Insurance are:

1. **Contractor's Liability Insurance:**

    a)   Insurance which will protect the Contractor and the Owner jointly from, claims under the provision of Worker's Compensation Acts of the various Provinces.

    b)   Insurance against liabilities or damage in respect of injuries to persons, including injuries resulting in death, and in respect of loss and/or damage to property arising out of the performance of the work (known as Property Damage and Public Liability).

2. **Insurance Against the Elements and Other Hazards**

    a)   Fire Insurance

    b)   Boiler and Machinery Insurance covering all pressure vessels, such as boilers, air compressors, etc., used in connection with the work.

    c)   Builder's Risk Insurance, which covers not only what has been incorporated into the work, but provides coverage for materials stored at the site of the work, including concrete forms in place, form lumber at the site of the work, temporary structures, equipment, supplies, etc., all incidental to the construction of the Work.

8.18   CONSTRUCTION BONDS

Construction bonds are sureties which are specified by the Owner to ensure that the successful bidder will enter into a contract, the Contractor will perform as agreed, and the costs of all labour and materials entering into the work will be paid by the Contractor.

1.   A Bid-Bond - is required to ensure that the successful bidder will enter into a contract for which he has submitted a tender. (Refer to Chapter 7, Article 7.3).

2.   A Performance Bond - is an instrument issued by a Bonding Company, .1 guaranteeing that the Contractor will faithfully perform according to the terms and conditions of the contract, and, .2 that in default of the Contractor, the Bonding Company, referred to as the Surety, will indemnify and reimburse the Owner for any loss suffered through the failure of the Contractor to complete the work contracted for and described in the Bond.

3.   A Labour and Materials Payment Bond - is an instrument issued by a Bonding Company that guarantees that payment will be made for labour and materials supplied in connection with the construction of the work.

It is usually stipulated in the Bond that the Contractor and the Surety Company bind themselves, their heirs, executors, administrators, successors and assigns, jointly and severally, for payment up to the amount of the bond if there is default in the payment for labour and materials entering into the Work.

There is need for such a bond. Private construction could result in heavy claims being brought against the Owner for work and materials secured, but not paid for, by the General Contractor. Sudden materials shortages or faulty estimates of labour requirements by the Contractor could result in charges being presented to the Owner in the form of liens against the property for payment, should the Contractor default in payment of these charges.

The costs incurred for the procurement of these Bonds may be included in the bid price or be authorized as an extra to the bid price. In either case the costs are paid by the Owner.

8.19 RIGHTS TO TERMINATE THE CONTRACT

Both the Owner and the Contractor have separate rights to terminate the Contract under certain conditions.

The Owner has the right to cancel or terminate a Construction Contract if:

1.   The Contractor defaults, delays in starting the work or fails to diligently execute any portion of it, following adequate notice of such default or delay issued by the Consultant.

2.   The Contractor has failed to complete the work by the required Contract Completion Date.

3.   The Contractor has become insolvent.

4.   The Contractor has declared bankruptcy.

5.   The Contractor has abandoned the work.

6.   The Contractor has made an assignment of the Contract without consent of the Owner.

7.   The Contractor has otherwise failed to comply with any of the terms and conditions of the contract.

The Contractor has the right to suspend the Work, or to terminate the Contract if:-

1.   The Owner should be adjudged, bankrupt or becomes insolvent.

2.   Work is stopped under an order of any Court of Law or other Public Authority through no act or fault of the Contractor, or anyone employed by it, including Sub-Contractors.

3.   The Consultant fails to issue a certificate of payment for work satisfactorily performed according to the terms and conditions of the Contract.

4.   The Owner fails to pay the Contractor within a stipulated time any sum certified by the Consultant, or awarded by arbitration.

5.   Written notice is given within a stipulated time addressed to the Owner and Consultant that the Contractor intends to stop work owing to the foregoing circumstances.

The subject of termination of a contract before it is completed, is one which should always be referred to a competent legal adviser.

TYPICAL QUESTIONS

1.   What does the signing of the Articles of Agreement of a Construction Contract signify?
2.   What is the object of the General Conditions?
3.   List five (5) separate matters which should be considered in the General Conditions.
4.   Define "Intent of the Contract Documents".
5.   Define (a)   Contractor
                (b)   Consultant in the context of this paper
                (c)   Sub-Contractor
                (d)   Surety or Security
6.   What do you consider to be an "order"?
7.   What are the responsibilities of the Consultant and the Contractor with respect to the plans and specifications?
8.   Why should the Contractor visit the site of the Work?
9.   What must the Contractor provide?
10.   What is the status of the Consultant with respect to the execution of a Construction Contract?
11.   Is the authority of the Consultant unlimited? If not, why not?
12.   What should be specified concerning the rectification of defects?
13.   What is the difference between maintenance and rectification of defects?
14.   What are the origins of Alterations?
15.   State three (3) rules governing alterations.
16.   What are "extras" and "credits"?
17.   Who is the judge of questions arising out of the interpretation of the plans and specifications? Why?
18.   What effect could an unauthorized alteration have?
19.   What acts of omission by the Owner prevent a collection of damages arising out of delays?
20.   List the responsibilities of the Contractor.
21.   What is meant by "save or hold harmless"?
22.   List insurance cover which may be required by a Contract.
23.   Describe Construction Bonds.

REFERENCES

The A.I.A - Contract Forms and the Law - Parker and Adams.

Building Construction Handbook - Merritt.

Canadian Building Contracts - Immanuel Goldsmith, LL.B. (Lond.)

Civil Engineering Construction - International Federation of Consulting Engineers (FIDIC).

Conditions of Contract (International) for Works of Contracts, Specifications and Engineering Relations - Mead, Mead and Akerman.

Engineering Contracts and Specifications - Robert Abbett.

Legal Aspects of Architectural Practice, 2nd Edition - Ontario Association of Architects.

Manual of Practice - Construction Specifications Institute.

CCDC 2 - 1994.

CONSTRUCTION SPECIFICATIONS GENERALLY
by Claude Lawrenson, RSW, RHI

"It is generally accepted that someone must supervise and manage the construction of a project. The Owner, his representative, or the Contractor must regulate the construction of a project throughout. The Specifications can, and must, assign the required coordinating responsibility."

G..W. Slee - SPECIFICATION ASSOCIATE, June, 1963.

9.1. INTRODUCTION

The Specifications are the working and technical documents of a Construction Contract, and are included in the Tender Documents to allow all bidders to prepare their tenders on an equal basis. They are the written material, complementing the Drawings, which have been put into documentary form for inclusion among the Contract Documents. Upon the award of a Construction Contract, they become the enforceable rules which will govern the technical requirements and details of the whole of the Work. The Specifications describe and specify the type and quality of materials to be incorporated in the work, items of equipment to be installed, the quality of workmanship required, and manners of application or methods of installation.

In checking the Specifications, three things should always be kept in mind:

1. No matter how the Specification content is composed, no one phrase, clause, section or division is without meaning with respect to the intent of the Specification for the whole of the Work.

2. As neither the Architect, Engineer, nor Specification Writer is gifted with omnipotent infallibility, the Drawings and Specifications should be continually checked for inadvertent errors, omissions, conflicts and ambiguities. If at all possible, such defects should be corrected before the contract award. Defective Drawings and Specifications leave bidding contractors no alternative but to include contingent sums in their bids. These hidden costs are ultimately borne by the Owner, to the enhancement of the Architect's or Engineer's Fee. Further, such defects usually result in costly changes being made after the award of a contract, again at the expense of the Owner, and further enhancing the Architect's or Engineer's Fee (which is usually a percentage of the total cost of a completed project.)

3.   Defective Specifications often result in serious contention during the course of construction in respect to interpretation and application.

Regardless of the quality of the Specifications, the onus is on the Contractor (and the Subcontractors), to determine for themselves the quantity and quality of the work specified. Great as this Contractor's responsibility may be, it is no excuse for poorly prepared Drawings and Specifications.

9.2   THE OBJECT OF THE SPECIFICATIONS

The primary objective of the Specifications is to communicate proper, clear and concise information supplementary and complementary to the drawings, to permit competitive bidding for a contract upon an equal basis. From a Contractor's point of view, the Specifications must provide well-defined scopes of the work of the various trades to enable all who is bidding to bid intelligently, as the tenders of each must be the result of their own estimates of the quantities and the quality of the work they must accomplish.

9.3   THE CONSTITUENT ELEMENTS OF THE SPECIFICATIONS

As a document, the Construction Specifications published today is becoming a Project Manual, which usually consists of three separate major parts:

1.   The Bidding and Contract Documents are usually listed in DIVISION 0 of the Project Manual and could consist of separate sections such as:

Section 00010 - Pre-Bid Information

Section 00100 - Instructions to Bidders

Section 00200 - Information Available to Bidders

Section 00300 - Bid/Tender Forms

Section 00400 - Supplements to Bid/Tender Forms

Section 00500 - Agreement Forms

Section 00600 - Bonds and Certificates

Section 00700 - General Conditions of the Contract

Section 00800 - Supplementary Conditions

Section 00900 - Drawings and Schedules

Section 00950 - Addenda and Modifications

Such sections are included in a Project Manual in the interest of standardization and coordination between items of documentation. It has been recommended that titles and terminology be fixed and listed in the sequence above.

2. General Non-Technical Requirements are usually set out in the first Division of the documented Specifications.

3. The Technical Requirements of the Work follow in numerical sequence of Divisions and Sections of Divisions, setting out general technical information, detailed requirements and instructions related to specific subjects, or trade by a trade basis, e.g., excavating, roofing, masonry, etc.

The General Non-Technical Requirements may be captioned, Project General Requirements, General Contract Work, etc. It has been recommended as standard practice to set these out as, DIVISION 1 - GENERAL REQUIREMENTS, with separate Sections for each of the following as may be required for a particular project:

Summary of Work
Allowances
Special Project Procedures
Coordination
Field Engineering
Regulatory Requirements
Abbreviations and Symbols
Identification Systems
Alternates/Alternatives
Measurement and Payment
Project Meetings
Submittals
Quality Control
Construction Facilities and Temporary Controls
Material and Equipment
Starting of Systems
Testing, Adjusting and Balancing of Systems
Contract Closeout
Final Cleaning

9.4   THE FORMAT FOR CONSTRUCTION SPECIFICATIONS

Since the end of World War II there has been a great expansion in Architectural, Structural and Engineering Construction. There has also been a parallel advance in the technology of construction. These have given rise to and have encouraged the growth of subcontractors performing specialized work, requiring particular skills and technology. It is not now unusual to find 95 per cent of a Work being constructed by Subcontractors. This condition has required Architects, Engineers and Specification Writers to set out specifications in such a manner that would not only permit specialist trades to easily determine the requirements related to their specialties, but would also allow the General Contractor to properly coordinate Subcontractors and properly manage a project.

As a result of a survey made in 1959 in both Canada and the United States, it was found that there was no universally uniform practice of arranging specifications. The survey revealed specification arrangements had been haphazardly developed by various regions of the countries for use within those regions only, with no one arrangement uniformly similar to another. Each arrangement differed considerably as to basic ideas and reflected regional and parochial practices.   The greatest weakness found was the extent of disagreement, even among acknowledged experts, as to the functions and purpose of the various parts of a Construction Specification. In fact, there appeared be no universal agreement on what constituted a set of specifications.

Out of a mass of conflicting practices and opinions has evolved a logical, simple and flexible arrangement of Construction Specifications which has now wide acceptance. This arrangement was developed jointly by the Construction Specifications Institute (U.S.A.) and Construction Specifications Canada (formerly the Specification Writers Association of Canada), is referred to as the 16-division CSI Master format; which is Part 1 of the Uniform Construction Index, published by CSI and CSC and supported by the Association of Consulting Engineers of Canada, the Canadian Construction Association, the Canadian Institute of Quantity Surveyors, and the Royal Architectural Institute of Canada

The 16-division Specification Format has proved beneficial to Architects, Engineers, Specification Writers, Quantity Surveyors, Contractors and material Suppliers, making it easier for each to perform his function in the construction of a Work.

Subsequent to the publishing of the Uniform Construction Index (UCI) in 1972, the Master format, a Master List of Section Titles and Numbers, was published in June 1978. To the original 16 divisions CSI Specification Format, was added, - DIVISION 0 - BIDDING AND CONTRACT REQUIREMENTS referred to previously.

Arising out of the development of the UCI has been the evolution of the CSI Three Part Section Format. A review of various guide and master specifications, published for use by Specification Writers in preparing master specifications for a specific office, or specific project specifications, shows there has been considerable effort to develop consistency of arrangement or format from one Section to another. The three main groups of the Three Part Section Format represent an irreducible minimum for practical purposes.

With the Three Part Section Format the user of specifications will find a particular bit of information in the same location of the specification, regardless of the author of the specifications. The consistency of the Three Part Section Format presentation of data permits the specification reader to ascertain information of significance to him expressed (hopefully) in clear, concise and readable language.

The Section of a Division provides for recognition of a basic unit of work, e.g., masonry, dampproofing, etc. The content of a Section must clearly indicate all that is required to be known about that basic unit, e.g.,

1.   What is the product?

2.   How is it to be incorporated into the Work?

3.   What interrelationships have existed, do exist, or will exist with the remainder of the project or with any portion of the project?

With the CSI Three Part Section Format, the function of each part can be described briefly as follows:

PART 1 - covers those general areas of concern which precede and follow the Work and which define the scope of the Work

PART 2 - defines in detail the materials, products, equipment, systems, fixtures, etc. which are to be incorporated into the Work

PART 3 - describes in detail the manner in which items covered by PART 2 are to be incorporated into the Work.

The CSI Specification Formats allows:

1.   Suppliers and Contractors to estimate costs more easily, and to prepare bids more accurately and more competitively.

2.   Architects, Engineers and Contractors to control the construction of a Work more easily.

3.   Architects and Engineers to have greater assurance that the intent of their plans and specifications is being accomplished.

4.   Architects, Engineers and Specification Writers to translate design criteria more easily and more accurately.

In spite of the wide acceptance of the CSI Format there are still far too many reactionaries whose credo appears to be - "What was good enough for Queen Victoria is good enough for you lad."

Requirements to be covered in the Specifications ideally should be set out according to the CSI Format.

9.5   IDEAS TO BE COVERED IN THE SPECIFICATIONS

Construction Specifications are written either by the Architect or Engineer, or the Specification Writer, as technical instructions to Contractors for the construction of the whole of the Work. Contractors, in turn, must use them as a guide for the purchase of materials, as a basis for agreements with their Sub- Contractors, and as rules governing the construction of the Work.

As mentioned previously, modern building embraces many trades and specialties. Each requires particular instructions peculiar to the trade or specialty concerned. Such instruction should be written in the language of the trade concerned. Therefore, it is not unusual to find in either the Supplementary Conditions of a Construction Contract, or in Division 1 of the Specifications the following:

For convenience of reference, and to facilitate the letting of contracts and subcontracts, these specifications are separated into title Divisions and sections. The separation into Divisions and Sections within the specifications shall not require the Architect (or Engineer) to determine what Part of the work shall be done by any subtrade, or to decide any limits of Contract between Contractor and his sub-trades."

From this it should be noted that the Architect or Engineer does not establish subcontracts and that they should not delineate trade responsibilities. These decisions rest with the Contractor.

Separations as set out in the CSI Format of Construction Specifications permit a General Contractor who may be tendering upon particular work, the opportunity to determine what Sections of the Work they would be performing, and what work they should subcontract to specialist sub-trades.

Regardless of the format of the Construction Specifications, there are certain fundamentals which should be incorporated into them.

1.   Use of appropriate language - "The idiom of the trade."

2.   Clearness as to all details

3.   Brevity, sufficiently comprehensive as to set out what is intended without ambiguity.

4.   Reasonableness as to a requirement.

The contractual authority can only assume that all contractors have made themselves familiar with all conditions governing the performance of the Work. The old legal axiom, - "ignorance of the Law is no excuse," is equally applicable to the knowledge of the contents of ALL the contract documents.

9.6   EXTENT OF THE WORK - THE SCOPE OF THE WORK

It is essential that the Extent of the Work be defined in each Section of each Division of the Construction Specifications. This is necessary to ensure that there is an equitable basis for contractual agreements between General Contractors and Subcontractors.

It would not be necessary to enumerate all of the various parts of the work if the Drawings completely showed all of the Work in graphic detail. Such enumeration, when used, is often dangerously incomplete and contains the most irresponsible "grandfather" or "weasel" clause: - Work includes, but is not necessarily limited to the following: -

Such a clause usually results in serious contention during the course of the work, as contractors have been known to have interpreted it as a means to secure payment for work done which was neither shown, particularly specified nor enumerated, though ruled by the Architect or Engineer to have been "reasonably inferable" as indispensably necessary, another "weasel" clause.

Mention should be made of related work not particularly within the scope of a Division or Section of a Division of the Specifications. This is to enable the Contractor to better determine what work is to be omitted insofar as a particular Division or Section is concerned. It may be, for example, a requirement of DIVISION 3 - CONCRETE - that concrete bases for mechanical or electrical equipment are to be constructed by whomever is performing the work specified in the Division. Unless it is particularly specified in Division 15 that it is the responsibility of this Division to supply anchor bolts, provide all location details, including dimensions, to whomever is to construct the bases, it is likely there will be a dispute as it is possible the mechanical sub-trade will not have made proper provisions concerning them.

In checking the Scope of the Work, and Enumerated Work Not Included, with the complementary Drawings, a bidding Contractor would be well advised to make certain:

1.   That the Drawings and Specifications indicate what is required to accomplish the intended work. The discovery of what might appear to be a discrepancy, or that which appears to be ambiguous, should be referred to the responsible Architect or Engineer immediately.

2.   That, where it is specified only materials are to be supplied, he determines whether there is a provision in the Specifications for their installation or application. Often the

Mechanical and Electrical Divisions of the Specifications will specify that certain controls are to be supplied, with no mention as to who is to be responsible for their installation: or the electrical trade is to wire to and connect to controls "to be supplied by others with `others' not defined." Such ambiguity could be most contentious and costly.

ARTICLE GC 3.2 - CONSTRUCTION BY OWNER OR OTHER CONTRACTORS -General Conditions of Stipulated Price Contract Canadian Standard Construction Document CCDC 2 1994 establishes the right of the Owner to let separate contracts in connection with a particular project of which the Work in a particular Contract may be a part. In such a case the Extent of the Work should indicate: -

1.   What part of the project, related to the Contractor's undertaking has been let or is to be let another contractor.

2.   That the Contractor is to coordinate his work with that of other contractors.

3.   That, where the work of other contractors must be done so as not to impede the Contractor in his work, the Contractor must inform the Architect or Engineer of the interference by others in his work. Failure to send such a notification could leave the contractor solely responsible for added costs which could be attributable to the interference by other contractors.

The conditions set out in the previously mentioned ARTICLE GC 3.2.3 refer to what is commonly known as Segregated Contracts. With Segregated Contracts, each Prime Contractor is entirely responsible for the coordination of this particular contract. The coordination of several Segregated Contracts should be the responsibility of the Owner. Such contracts can easily, result in confusion and contention, with a lack of overall cooperation, because contractors forced to work with others not of their choosing often resist working as a team. Among the conditions of the General Requirements, DIVISION 1 of the Specifications, there will be found items related to the Extent of the Work such as: -

1.   The safety measures to be taken and the employment of safety personnel.

2.   Works Office to be provided for the use of the Contractor and the Architect or Engineer separately.

3.   Temporary structures such as storage shed, office of sub-trades, etc.

4.   Temporary, facilities such as electric power and light, sewer, water supply and telephone.

5.   The supply and maintenance of temporary heat for construction purposes.

6.   Temporary enclosures of the building.

7.   Erection of boarding around the site of the work.

8.   Access roads and vehicular parking.

9.   Warning lights and barricades for excavations.

10.   Requirements related to construction work being performed in cold weather.

11.   Protection of the work, including precautions relative to overloading, and the drilling of beams for pipe sleeves, etc.

12.   Cash and Contingency Allowances according to the General Conditions of the Contract.

13.   Independent Inspection and Testing.

14.   Layout out of the Work.

15.   Work to be performed according to the directions of manufacturers where applicable.

16.   Submission of Shop Drawings.

The foregoing list is not complete by any means. It does serve, however, to illustrate that the extent of work of any project is not confined to the technical Divisions and Sections of the Specifications entirely. Therefore, the content of DIVISION 1, with respect to the extent of work cannot be ignored.

9.7   DRAWINGS, AS RELATED TO THE SPECIFICATIONS

Although this chapter is primarily concerned with Construction Specifications, we cannot overlook the project drawings.

It must always be remembered that the Drawings and Specifications are COMPLEMENTARY; that together they are intended to fully describe the whole of the Work and what is called for in one shall be as called for in the other.

Like the Specifications, the Drawings are included among the Contract Documents and are listed with the Specifications in the Contract Agreement. Like the Specifications, the Drawings become valid upon the award of the Contract and the details delineated in them are, therefore, enforceable.

During the progress of construction the drawings may be revised from time to time to graphically describe variations to the original contract requirements. It should always be remembered that a Drawing of a later date takes precedence over a Drawing of an earlier date.

There should never be any doubt concerning that which has been specified in the Specifications or shown on the Drawings. This is not always the case, however. It should be always expected that unless the Drawings and Specifications ACTUALLY and not THEORETICALLY, details the full scope of the Work, there are likely to be omissions by Bidders of items desired by the Owner, the Architect or Engineer. It may also be expected that there may be efforts to have the Contractor pay for items omitted from either the Drawings or Specifications. Such efforts are not only unjust, but give rise to serious contention, to the detriment of both the Owner and the Contractor.

9.8   INTERPRETATION RULES

In cases of doubt as to meaning, it is generally accepted that the Architect or Engineer should authoritatively interpret the drawings and specifications for, having prepared them, should be best able to define their intent. ARTICLE GC 2.2 - ROLE OF THE CONSULTANT - General Conditions of the Stipulated Price Contract - CCDC 2 - Architects - 1994 - indicates in paragraph 2.2.6:

"The CONSULTANT will be, in the first instance, the interpreter of the requirements of the Contract Documents and shall make findings as to the performance thereunder by both parties to the Contract, except with respect to GC 5.1 - FINANCING INFORMATION REQUIRED OF THE OWNER. Interpretations and findings of the CONSULTANT shall be consistent with the intent of the Contract Documents. When making such interpretations and findings, the CONSULTANT will not show partiality to either the OWNER or the CONTRACTOR."

Therefore, any interpretation made with respect to the intent of the Drawings and Specifications must be governed primarily by the Conditions of the Construction Contract. Also, in the matter of interpretation, it has long been held in Law that a Contractor is not required to do better or be more careful than could be in all circumstances expected and no more should be demanded than is necessary to comply with the intent of the plans, Specifications and the General Conditions of the Contract.

Nevertheless, Contractors and their Quantity Surveyors or Estimators will, by necessity, be required to make their own interpretations in the preparation of tenders. Such interpretations should be governed by the customary general rules of interpretation usually set out in the General Conditions or Supplementary General Conditions of a Construction Contract.

These rules usually are:

1. Description of materials and methods in words, phrases and abbreviations, which when so applied will have well known technical meaning and will be the "idiom," or the language of construction as in the Specifications and on the Drawings.

   Each trade has an "idiom" of its own. The wording of the Drawings and Specifications should conform to these trade "idioms."

   When the wording of these documents departs from general usage, it may become necessary to seek clarifications as to meaning. To be able to read these documents properly, or to properly communicate their intent, all those reading or preparing these documents must have adequate knowledge of the language of construction.

2. Written dimensions take precedence over those scaled; large scale Drawings take precedence over those of a smaller scale; supplementary Drawings and Specifications supersede those issued previously. Discrepancies between figured dimensions on the Drawings must be referred to the Architect or Engineer, as such could have considerable influence upon the structural integrity of a Work.

3. Architectural Drawings take precedence over all other Drawings.

4. Specifications shall govern over Drawings. In cases of conflict between Drawings and Specifications as to the description of materials or methods, the specifications shall govern.

5. In conflict between the Drawings, or Specifications and the General Conditions of the Contract the General Conditions shall govern.

It has been frequently stated much information can be given in writing without the necessity of reference to the Drawings. This is a "loaded" statement. It can never be taken for granted that the dimensions, say, either shown on the Drawings or specified in the Specifications are separately the sole dimensions. Both the drawings and the specifications must be read together to ensure, that their intent is understood fully.

The use of the word "exact," as applied to dimensions either given on the Drawings or Specified in the Specifications, often results in controversy. The use of the word "exact" is to alert the contractor to the importance of maintaining the indicated dimension to very close tolerances. Whenever the word "exact" is used, in this sense, then acceptable deviation from the indicated dimension should be given as a plus or minus "X" mm. Such a tolerance description would remove all doubt as to the degree of accuracy required. Where no tolerance is given, with respect to the use of the word "exact," the Architect or Engineer should be required to state, in writing, the degree of accuracy governing the "exact" dimension.

9.9   SHOP DRAWINGS

The purpose of specifying a requirement for Shop or Setting Drawings, and Manufacturers' Brochures, is to ensure that items to be fabricated, equipment to be installed, etc., conform to the specified requirements. It is generally inferred that the checking of these by the Architect or Engineer is gratuitous, is for general arrangement only, and that the review of them in no way relieves a Contractor of the responsibility as to their accuracy or efficaciousness. One important provision frequently overlooked is that the Architect's or Engineer's review of these submissions is not to be construed as an authority to substitute other items for those particularly specified. It is the Contractor's responsibility to field check all dimensions of shop or setting drawings. Any failure to do so makes the Contractor liable for all necessary corrections to rectify errors.

9.10   INCLUSION OF SPECIFICATION STANDARDS

Reference to Standards or Codes or both will be made throughout the Contract Documents particularly the Specifications. Such reference usually states that the referenced standards are to be the latest editions at the time of their application. These referenced standards are specifications prepared and published by a recognized technical society, or other specialized or competent group, for the purpose of setting the minimum level of performance, quality, safety, or other attributes of materials or items.

The following is a partial list of such recognized standard writing authorities:

AFT	Air Filter Institute
AGA	American Gas Association
ASME	American Society of Mechanical Engineers
ASCE	American Society of Civil Engineers.
ASHRAE	American Society of Heating, Refrigeration and Air-Conditioning Engineers
ASTM	American Society for Testing Materials
ANSI	American National Standards Institute
API	American Petroleum Institute
ACI	American Concrete Institute
CGSB	Canadian Government Specifications Board
CFUA	Canadian Fire Underwriters' Association
CISC	Canadian Institute of Steel Construction
CSA	Canadian Standards Association
DBIU	Dominion Board of Insurance Underwriters
IRB	Institute of Radiator and Boiler Manufacturers
NBFU	National Board of Fire Underwriters (US)
NBC	National Building Code, Canada
NFPA	National Fire Protective Association (US)
NEMA	National Electrical Manufacturer's Association (US)
CGA	Canadian Gas Association

| ULC | Underwriters' Laboratories of Canada |
| AMCA | Air Moving and Conditioning Association |

9.11   BEGINNING AND SEQUENCE OF OPERATIONS

It has been long held that an Architect or Engineer should administer the construction of a project which they have designed.

It is also generally accepted that the safety, suitability and economy of any structure depends upon the design, skill and judgment of the Architect or Engineer and the success with which the intent of the Drawings and Specifications has been carried out.

It has been long accepted that the Contractor is the expert in construction. Otherwise, he or she should not be in the business of building.

An Architect or Engineer, while he or she may be sufficiently qualified and competent to perform actual construction supervision he should not do so, for he or she, best serves their employer's interests by certifying to the acceptability of the Contractor's work. The inspection of the Contractor's work is by far the most important single function of an Architect or Engineer following the award of a Construction Contract. (Refer to Chapter 18.)

The coordination of materials, labour and equipment necessary to construct the Work is the sole responsibility of the Contractor. However, coordination of the Work should not be confused with the beginning of the Work and the sequence of operations to accomplish it. Commencement of work and sequence of operations is a function of work for its orderly progress. It is frequently a condition of a Construction Contract that such scheduling must be to the approval of the Architect or Engineer. Refer to Article GC 3.5, CCDC 2 - 1994.

It should be noted that the CSI Format for Construction Specifications is arranged in such a manner as to conform to a great extent with the usual procedure of actual construction. It is usual for the General Conditions, to state that the Contractor must permit the Architect or Engineer to have access to the Work at all times, and provide them with all information concerning the work which they may require or request. This condition is to enable the Architect to perform the following functions related to the beginning and sequence of the work:

1.   It is usually specified that the Architect or Engineer will establish building lines and a bench mark.

2.   It may be specified that the Architect or Engineer will outline working areas.

3.   It may be specified that the Contractor will be governed by the direction of Architect or Engineer with regard to the sequence of operation.

9.12   PROTECTION OF WORKS AND SERVICES

Of concern are the specified requirements predicated upon the General Conditions of the Contract which hold the contractor to be liable for all damage to the Work, to the property of others and to persons while carrying out the Work. That these requirements are generally covered by the Contractor's Liability Insurance is not quite enough for the Contractor having assumed the Owner's responsibility and liability for damage to the property of others and injury to persons is required by Municipal, Provincial and Federal legislation to comply with certain safety regulations. The fact the Contractor has assumed the Owner's liability in this regard does not relieve the Owner from being responsible of being certain that the Contractor has done, or is doing all that is required in this regard.

A typical specification with respect to the protection of work would be: -

"Maintain and protect any water, sewer, gas, electric, steam, or other piping and services encountered, and immediately notify the proper authorities and see that they take whatever measures are necessary before proceeding further with the work."

Specifications concerning the protection of works and services are usually set out in DIVISION 1 - General Requirements of the Specifications.

9.13   CAPACITY OR REQUIRED PERFORMANCE

The purpose of transposing design criteria to the Specifications is to provide particular information required by the suppliers of materials or equipment as to the minimum performance requirements of the design. Such particulars, when specified, are enforceable.

It should be noted that although the Contractor is considered to be the expert in construction. The Contractor is not the design authority. Although, as a general rule the Contractor is given a relatively free hand in the methods they choose to construct a Work, the Specifications must contain conditions governing the manner by which particular materials, equipment, etc., are to be incorporated in the Work. Any deviations from specific instructions transfer liability in the event of failures. This not only applies to methods of construction but to the supply of materials, equipment, etc., not meeting required capacity or performance. The structural integrity of work may be imperilled, or the expected performance of the equipment is affected by deviation from what had been specified. The cost to rectify such instances must be borne by those who deviated.

When no deviation from the specification has occurred and the expected capacity or performance has not been achieved, the failure to secure the expected performance may be the result of faulty design or specification which is certainly not the responsibility of the Contractor.

9.14   DESIGN REQUIREMENTS

Normally all design requirements, not set out in mandatory building codes, are established by the Owner's Architect or Engineer. As a consequence it is not necessary to include designing rules in the Specifications.

However the various Provincial statues and Regulation of the Workers' Compensation Boards make it mandatory that falsework for concrete forms and concrete forms for multi tiered buildings and structures are designed and their construction supervised, by a Professional Engineer. This design authority need not be the Architect or Engineer who designed a total project and is usually employed by the Contractor. Construction safety by the Contractor is also addressed in GC 3.6 - Construction Safety.

However, where it may be necessary for the Contractor to design details for his working drawings, the Specifications should contain sufficient design criteria to enable him to do so.

9.15   CLASSIFICATION RULES

Work or material to be incorporated into a Work should be classified. It is this subject which causes considerable contention between the Contractor and the Architect or Engineer whenever ambiguity in this regard exists in the Specifications.

The classification of each type of material to be incorporated into the Work should be clearly specified. Where authoritative standards exist, governing the quality of materials, these should be specified also. As one example, copper piping may be required to conform to any one of three classifications. Type K, Type L or Type M. Therefore, careful reading of the Specifications is essential to avoid the supply and installation of materials not conforming to specified material classifications. It could prove costly to a Contractor to replace materials installed which do not conform to a specified classification.

One of the most contentious items in this regard is the classification of excavated material as to what constitutes "earth" and what constitutes "rock." The reason for this contention is the fact there appears to be no universally accepted definition in this regard. It is suggested the following definitions would be good guides:

Earth Excavation, shall apply to the removal and disposal of earth, muck, muskeg, clay, hardpan, shale, silts, sands, quicksand, gravel, and any other materials which can be removed by hand, with heavy power grading or earth moving equipment.

Rock Excavation, shall apply to the removal and disposal of boulders with a minimum volume of one cubic metre (1.3 cu. yd.) rock in-situ, concrete and masonry foundations which cannot be removed by heavy power grading or earth moving equipment having a cubic capacity in excess of 7.6 cubic metres (10 cu. yd.) which shall require drilling and blasting, or drilling only, to facilitate removal.

Classification of materials is essential for intelligent bidding. Unless the Quantity Surveyor is aware of what may be particularly required, one can only guess, and "guesstimates" are irresponsible.

9.16   ESTIMATING RULES

The method of measurement should be given in each case where payment is predicated upon measured quantities. Again, because of varying practices throughout Canada, it has been difficult to establish universally acceptable uniform methods of measurements. For example, in determining volumes of earth work one authority may use the "average end area method," while another may use the "prismoidal method" in calculating volumes of excavation. Regardless of the method used to determine a quantity, the contractor estimates, or is paid on the basis of quantity measurements, such as cubic yards, square feet, gallons, etc. (m^3, m^2, L, etc.)

Much is being done by the Canadian Institute of Quantity Surveyors to establish uniform methods of measurement. This Institute has prescribed the following General Principles with respect to methods of measurement: -

1.   Schedules of Quantities shall not only describe materials and workmanship briefly, but shall   accurately represent the quantities of work to be executed also.

2.   The CIQS Method of Measurement, whilst it aims at providing uniform units of measurement, is a definition of principle rather than an inflexible document.   In particular and exceptional cases the Quantity Surveyor is expected to use their discretion and to adopt special methods, provided the principles of measurement laid down are observed and the intention is made clear to   the estimator. If it is in the interests of accurate and practical estimating, he may give more detailed information than is demanded by strict adherence to the document.

3.   Unless otherwise stated all work shall be measured net as fixed in place.

4.   In giving dimensions the order should   be consistent and generally in the sequence of length, width, and height.

In every case, the Specifications should disclose the manner of calculating quantities. As a general rule, each item of a schedule of quantities should be based upon the delivery, unloading, hoisting, all labour of installing, fitting or placing into position all materials, as well as establishing the rules of measurement.

Regardless of the skill of the Quantity Surveyor, or Estimator, they can be assisted, or hampered by the quality of the Specifications. All applicable rules governing the classification of materials, dimensions and proportions, and the methods of measurement should be most clearly defined by the Architect or Engineer and the Specification Writer. Where there is any doubt in this regard, failure to seek clarification could prove costly to the Contractor.

9.17   QUALITY OF MATERIALS

It has been estimated by Construction Specifications Canada that at least 80 new construction products are entering upon the market daily, while 20 products are being withdrawn at the same time. For this reason the Architect or Engineer, and the Specification Writer must be most careful in the selection and quality of materials to be incorporated into a Work. Such a condition makes it imperative that Contractors and their Quantity Surveyors and Estimators are fully informed.

Either the General or Supplementary Conditions of the Contract, or Instructions to Bidders should emphatically state that a bidder is to base the tender upon the original Drawings, Specifications and Addenda issued before closing of tenders and that he or she is to make no allowance for possible substitution in the future of the specified materials, methods or equipment.

However, if there is provision permitting the use of approved equivalents or alternatives, either before or after the award of the contract, then terms, and conditions governing approvals for these should be clearly stated.

The Architect or Engineer, and the Specification Writer have selected materials, both as to quality and kind, methods of installation and types of equipment to the satisfaction of the Owner, and have specified accordingly.

Since Architects or Engineers may be held responsible for the success or failure of the drawings and Specifications they produce, they alone must have the final word concerning the materials or equipment used.

To provide some element of competition for manufacturers and suppliers, the specifications may frequently name one, two, or more products followed by the term "or equal," or "approved equal." The use of the term should alert a Contractor, the Quantity Surveyor or Estimator, that there is a possibility products other than those specified may be permitted. The use of the "or equal" term can result in serious controversy if conditions governing the use of "equivalents" or "alternatives" are not clearly defined.

Should the Contractor incorporate into the work materials which have neither been specified nor approved, he or she does so at their own discretion and risk, and could be required to take immediate action to correct, or remove authorized materials at his own expense. Certification of acceptance for Progress Payment can be withheld in cases of this nature until all remedy has been affected and found to be acceptable.

It is considered essential that the rules governing the acceptance or rejection of any class of material should be most clearly set out in the Specifications. If it is required there is to be submission of material samples for the approval of the Architect or Engineer the procedures should be clearly stated, and the Contractor should be conversant with both the General Conditions of the Contract and the Specifications.

Because of the increasing complexity of modern building, with the increasing refinement of design, more than ever is consideration being given to the quality of materials to be used in a Work and the rules and conditions governing this quality are being more particularly specified.

9.18   QUALITY OF WORKMANSHIP

The need for speed has now become one of the most important factors in construction. In fact today, so much emphasis is being placed upon speedy construction that the few really skilled workmen available are finding it more and more difficult to avoid sacrificing quality workmanship.

The least acceptable quality of workmanship should be particularly specified. While it might be desirable to obtain better than what has been specified, efforts to do so could work a hardship on a Contractor. It has been held in Law that contractors are not required to do better or be more careful than could be in all circumstances expected of them. Therefore, the quality of workmanship should be clearly defined in the Specifications. It is essential, if contention and litigation are to be avoided, the positive rules for judging the quality of workmanship should be specified also. A perusal of any set of Specifications will reveal it contains clauses particularly spelling out the requirements for workmanship and installation. Such conditions enable the Architect or Engineer to have defective workmanship remedied at the Contractor's expense.

It is not unusual to find in the Specifications conditions concerning the quality of materials and workmanship, that where no particular reference to requirements is specified, it may be specified the best quality of each is expected, which is generally taken to mean that where there are no specific requirements "common practice" shall prevail.

"Common practice" is the summation of the experience of all persons from all phases of the Construction Industry, which varies from one locality to another. Because of the complexity of modern building, the multiplicity of materials performing identical functions, and the rapidity, with which new construction products are being developed and marketed, there are many instances where no "common practice" exists.

Construction techniques are constantly changing. New products with different methods of application and installation are quickly replacing the old and building codes, regulations, etc., are being constantly amended. For these reasons it is necessary to have up-to-date knowledge and experience to determine what might constitute "common practice."

Since it is held that a contractor is not required to do better or more carefully than could be in all circumstances expected, the Architect or Engineer who wants the best possible construction, should draw and specify accordingly.

9.19 METHODS OF CONSTRUCTION

Special instructions, or particular standards may be specified for specialized work or fabrication. Usually such specifications make it mandatory that the Contractor check and verify all dimensions. Invariably it is the responsibility of the Contractor to maintain "on site" dimensions.

Whether fabrication of a component to be incorporated into the work is done at a shop or at the site, such fabrication is most likely to be governed by a particular specification or standards. Specialized trades such as structural steel, boiler making, etc., are not only governed by statutory regulations codes, standards, etc., but may be under the jurisdiction of an independent inspection and testing laboratory appointed by the Architect or Engineer, which is likely required to conduct not only shop inspection and tests of fabrication, but field inspection as well.

It is considered to be the responsibility of the Architect or Engineer to specify methods with respect to such things as mix designs for concrete, the design and location of construction, control and expansion joints in concrete work, methods of compaction of earth fill and the desired result, the mixes for asphalt and the method of application, etc.

9.20 DISPOSAL OR UTILIZATION OF REMOVED MATERIAL

The disposal of material or re-use of it should be clearly specified. If there should be doubt or ambiguity the Owner should be questioned, preferably before the close of tenders.

9.21 CLEAN UP

The cleanup of the debris of construction is the General Contractor's responsibility. It is an annoying housekeeping chore, but is necessary to reduce fire hazards, prevent possible damage to newly completed work, and remove possible causes' injury to workmen.

The general requirements in this regard will be usually found in the General Conditions of the Contract, e.g. - ARTICLE GC 3.14 - CLEAN UP - Stipulated Price Contract - Canadian Standard Construction Document - CCDC2 - 1994.

Although a clean house is to everyone's benefit on a construction site, it is most surprising how much resistance is experienced whenever attempts are made to enforce compliance with the cleaning up requirements of a construction Contract.

9.22   SUMMATION

The complexity of modern building requires Drawings and Specifications containing the most advanced knowledge of materials, engineering principles, and methods of construction. Such Drawings and Specifications can only be produced by highly skilled Architects, Engineers and Specification Writers. The more intricate the project, the more necessary it becomes for these persons to rely upon specialists.

Since a Contractor must interpret the Drawings and Specifications for their own use, and must expect that their requirements will be enforced, they must have good knowledge of the legal requirements of contract forms and the technical requirements of the Drawings and Specifications. The Contractor must have a comprehensive knowledge with respect to the physical properties of the materials of construction and the best methods for their application, as well as the most advanced methods of administration of construction if he or she is to succeed.

TYPICAL QUESTIONS

1. What are the Specifications?
2. Define the Object of the Specifications.
3. What are the advantages of a standard specification format such as the CSI Format for Construction Specifications?
4. What fundamental ideas should be covered in the Specifications?
5. Why is it necessary to outline a scope of the work?
6. What may be included in the Scope of the Work?
7.   What is the intent of the contract documents?
8. What are some of the "Rules of Interpretation?"
9. What is the purpose of Shop Drawings?
10. What is the responsibility of the Contractor with respect to shop drawings?
11. What is the purpose of reference standards?
12. Who is responsible for the coordination of the work?
13. What functions may the Architect or Engineer perform in connection with the sequence of work operations?
14. What governs the Contractor's responsibility with respect to the protection of work and services?
15. Why should dimensions and proportions be specified?
16. What is meant by "capacity or required performance?"
17. Why are classification rules necessary?
18. Define   (a) earth excavation,
                   (b) rock excavation.
19. What are "estimating rules?" and Why should they be specified?
20. Why should the quality of materials and workmanship be specified?
21. What is meant by "common practice?"
22. What methods of construction should be particularly specified?

REFERENCES

R.W. Abbott - Engineers Contracts and Specifications

Chesley Ayers - An Introduction to Specifications

Canadian Construction Association - A Guide to Contract Management

Canadian Institute of Quantity Surveyors - Method of Measurement of Construction Works

Construction Specifications Canada - Specification Guide Studies

Construction Specifications Institute - Manual of Practice and Specification Series

Norman Foster - Construction Estimates from Take-off to Bid

Prof. Mervyn W.A Jones - The Specifier and Building Science

Mead, Mead and Ackerman - Contracts, Specifications and Engineering Relations

Hans W. Meier - Construction Specifications Handbook

F.C. Merritt - Building Construction Handbook

Harold J. Rosen - Construction Specifications Writing

Parker, Gay and MacQuire - Materials and Methods of Architectural Construction

Canadian Construction Documents Committee - Stipulated Price Contract - Canadian Standard Construction Document CCDC 2 - 1994

Construction Specification Institute and Construction Specifications Canada, Uniform Construction Index and Master format.

Construction Specifications Canada - Construction Specifier's Handbook

10

ARBITRATION
by Kenneth M. Macdonald, PQS, FRICS, C.Arb.

An arbitration is the reference of a dispute or difference between not less than two persons for determination after hearing both sides in a judicial manner by another person or persons, other than a court of competent jurisdiction.

W.M.H. Gill - Evidence and Procedure in Arbitration

10.1   INTRODUCTION

Alternative Dispute Resolution (ADR) is becoming increasingly popular as an alternative to our legal system where litigation is often lengthy and expensive. Arbitration is one form of ADR.

The concept of arbitration has been around for centuries and is now fairly tightly controlled by statutory acts in Canada. The Acts are Provincial and while they vary the broad principles are the same.

Construction disputes are inevitable as no matter how carefully a contract is written the parties may place a different interpretation on its terms and conditions. The performance of the parties to the contract may fall short of the requirements of the contract and irrespective of the reason, delays, allegations over workmanship, extra work claims, claims for non-performance and similar disputes arise. It is rare for a construction dispute to involve complex legal issues as they more likely involve evaluation of facts and the interpretation of the terms and conditions of the contract. They can however involve large sums of money.

Construction disputes seem to fall naturally to ADR including arbitration where the privacy of arbitration appeals in particular to professionals. The allegation is made in some disputes that the Architect or Engineer was deficient in performing their duties and that they were thereby responsible for structural deficiencies, inefficient facilities, etc. Allegations, such as these, when made public could ruin a professional career.

The main advantages to arbitration are the speed by which disputes can be resolved and the probable lower cost than litigation. It is possible, depending to some extent on the complexity of the matter in dispute, for an arbitration to be convened, a decision reached and an award made within weeks from the time the dispute arose. There have been other cases, however, where arbitration lasted for years incurring a substantial cost before an award was made.

It should be noted that an individual appointed to settle a dispute by virtue of their expertise - such as an appraiser or valuer - is not an arbitrator. The dispute is being settled on the basis of the individual's expertise and not on their interpretation of evidence.

10.2 THE ARBITRATION ACTS

Consensual arbitration in Canada is governed by Acts of the various Territorial and Provincial Legislatures. The Acts set out the procedures to be followed in an arbitration and define the circumstances when court intervention can occur. Where there is no express agreement between the parties to the arbitration the acts will often dictate the terms of the arbitration.

It is essential that an arbitrator be aware of the relevant legislation and be comfortable working within its framework when an arbitration takes place.

An arbitration can only take place with the consent of the parties and this consent is very often a separate agreement to submit all disputes to arbitration, in some cases drawn up with a named arbitrator long before any dispute occurs.

A "submission" is defined as "A written agreement between two or more parties to submit present or future differences to arbitration". This "agreement to refer" or "submission" must be in writing. An agreement which intends to circumvent the jurisdiction of the courts is contrary to public policy and is void.

When the parties to a dispute agree upon a submission, or reference to arbitration, such agreement is predicated on the provisions of the governing Provincial Statute which may be necessarily part of the submission or reference. Such provisions may be:

1.   If no other mode of reference is provided, the reference shall be to a single arbitrator.

2.   If reference is made to two arbitrators they may appoint a third person to act as umpire or chairman of the arbitration tribunal at any time within the period during which they have power to make an award.

3.   If any arbitrator refuses to act, or is incapable of acting or dies, the party or parties, or arbitrators who made the appointment, may make another appointment to fill the vacancy. This power may be exercised from time to time as vacancies occur.

4.   The submission shall not be revoked by the death of either one or both the parties.

5.   The arbitration award shall be delivered to any of the parties requiring it.

6. The arbitrators shall make their award in writing and within a stipulated time (dependent on the complexity of the arbitration). They may on the request of a party to the arbitration, extend the length of time for making the award.

7. If arbitrators have allowed their time or extended time to expire without having made an award, or have delivered to any party to the submission, or to the umpire, a notice in writing that they cannot agree, the umpire shall decide the matter instead of the arbitrators and the decision for all purposes shall be the decision of the arbitrators.

8. When acting singly, the umpire shall make the award within the stipulated time after the completion date, or, postponed date, fixed by the arbitrators and may from time to time prolong the period within which to make the award.

9. The parties to a reference, and persons claiming through them, shall, subject to any legal objection, submit to examination by the arbitrators, on oath or affirmation, matters relevant to the dispute and shall be required to produce before the arbitrators all books, deeds, papers, accounts, writing and documents and things in their possession or power which may be required or called for, and do all other things which during the proceedings on the reference the arbitrators may require.

10. The witnesses on the reference shall be examined under oath or affirmation.

11. The award made by the arbitrators or by a majority of them or by the umpire shall be binding on all parties and persons claiming under them, unless set aside by a court of competent jurisdiction.

12. The costs of the reference and award shall be at the discretion of the arbitrators or umpire, who may direct to and by whom and the manner in which such costs are to be paid.

10.3   CCDC - 2, 1994

The Consultant named under the contract must always exercise judicial functions in the interpretation of the terms and conditions of a Construction Contract to ensure that the Contractor is performing according to the terms and conditions of that contract.

Matters of architecture or engineering judgement are the responsibility of the Consultant who is the proper person to determine whether the intent of the contract documents has been satisfied. This judgement requires not only the exercise of technical knowledge but the exercise of fairness and common sense. The necessity for a Consultant to perform a judicial function in the legal sense should be eliminated as far as possible. The Consultant should however be granted sufficient authority to make the necessary decision that would hasten the completion of the work with the proviso that such decisions are subject to appeal either by a mediated settlement, arbitration or litigation.

When the Consultant is the exclusive judge of all matters relating to the construction of work under a contract, including the conditions of contract, specifications, drawings, acceptance of work and the certification for payments of accounts to the contractor the Consultant is acting in an administrative capacity as Agent of the Owner rather than in a judicial capacity.

Consultants are not immune from the consequences of their acts as Architect or Engineer, they only become immune when performing those particular and limited functions which require them to act in the capacity of a judge. In the role of arbitrator and in that role alone is the cloak of immunity.

CCDC - 2 provides a three level dispute settling mechanism under GC 8.2 whereby arbitration is resorted to after negotiation and mediation have failed. The failure is recorded formally by the Project Mediator and transmitted formally to the disputing parties thereby ending the mediation. It is from the date of the Project Mediator's termination that either party may elect within 10 Working Days to require the other party or parties to submit the dispute to arbitration. Failure to require the other party to submit to arbitration within the specified 10 working days causes forfeiture of the right. Thereafter the dispute can only be settled by litigation unless a further consensual agreement is made.

The timetable laid down under GC 8.2 is specific in its requirements relating to dispute resolution and should be clearly understood by both parties. In addition to the CCDC - 2 document there are CCDC - 20, "A guide to the use of CCDC - 2 - 1994 Stipulated Price Contract" and CCDC - 40, "Rules for Mediation and Arbitration of Construction Disputes", two documents which provide the necessary amplification of the dispute resolution process. These documents are written in a more "user friendly" way than the more formal legal prose of arbitration statutes and contain specifics that are not normally found in legislation, e.g. 13.1 - Notice of Meetings.

It should be noted that the provisions of the Provincial Lien Acts still apply and that the initiation of judicial proceedings does not constitute a waiver of any right to proceed by way of arbitration under GC 8.2.6 to adjudicate the merits of the claim upon which the lien is based.

Only those persons who are competent to enter into a valid contract are competent to make a submission to arbitration. Corporations may submit their rights to arbitration, but in so doing must conform to the same requirements governing their competency to enter into binding contracts.

10.4   ARBITRATORS

Arbitrators come from all walks of life putting aside their daily work to preside over hearings of disputes arising from the execution of daily business conduct. They sit as judges, selected by the parties to the disputes. The awards they render are binding and can be enforced as if they had been decisions of a Court of Law. These persons are arbitrators, with one thing in common, they are usually recognized as experts in their own particular professions or vocations.

The arbitrator's role as discussed previously, is quasi-judicial in nature. The decisions rendered represent the arbitrator's judgement of the rights of the parties to the disputes. Strict rules of evidence need not always apply, but they should be the guiding principles in hearing evidence that may be material to the determination of a dispute. The arbitrator or arbitrators should not hear arguments or evidence from one party without giving the other party an opportunity for comment or rebuttal. They are the final judge of matters brought before the arbitration. The provisions of the prevailing Arbitration Acts do not allow the decision of an arbitrator, or board of arbitrators to be reviewed by the courts, unless the procedures were unfair, partial or fraudulent. The limited grounds for setting aside an award are as follows:

1.   A party entered into the arbitration agreement while under a legal incapacity.

2.   The arbitration agreement is invalid or has ceased to exist.

3.   The award deals with a dispute that the arbitration agreement does not cover or contains a decision on a matter that is beyond the scope of the agreement.

4.   The composition of the tribunal was not in accordance with the arbitration agreement or, if the agreement did not deal with that matter, was not in accordance with the applicable statute.

5.   The subject-matter of the dispute is not capable of being the subject of arbitration under the applicable Provincial statutes.

6.   An applicant was not treated equally and fairly, was not given an opportunity to present a case or to respond to another party's case, or was not given proper notice of the arbitration or of the appointment of an arbitrator.

7.   The procedures followed in the arbitration did not comply with the applicable Provincial Act.

8.   An arbitrator has committed a corrupt or fraudulent act or there is a reasonable apprehension of bias.

9.   The award was obtained by fraud.

The authority of an arbitrator to hear and adjudicate upon any particular dispute exists only by virtue of the agreement of the parties to the dispute. The arbitrator is empowered with only that authority that has been conferred by the disputants. The extent and limitations of an arbitrator's authority are to be found in:

1.   The demand or notice requiring arbitration and the statement in reply to the demand.

2.   The arbitration clause of the contract from which the dispute arose.

3.   The "submission" or "agreement to refer" wherein existing disputes between parties not having a prior agreement to arbitrate may be resolved by arbitration on the basis of the statement setting out the issue of dispute.

4.   The rules of procedure, as established by the parties of the dispute according to the statutory requirements of the place in which the dispute arose.

In construction disputes the expertise of the arbitrator is an advantage to the parties, as many cases not only involve a question of law, but also questions of fact, such as:

1.   Was the constructed work defective?

2.   Were substituted materials equal in quality to those specified?

3.   Did the completed work conform to the inferable intent of the Contract Documents?

4.   Was the additional work being claimed for, and completed as ordered within the terms and conditions of the contract?

5.   Were the costs excessive?

6.   Who was responsible for any defects or failures - the Consultant, Contractor or Owner?

In such controversies the expert "lay judge", the arbitrator, be they an Architect, Engineer or Quantity Surveyor, can assess evidence and weight testimony as there is usually no need to explain to them the meaning of technical terms or technical reports. Such an arbitrator should be able to grasp the essentials of a complicated dispute arising out of a construction contract, and readily comprehend the testimony of an "expert witness". There is no reason to think that because an Architect, Engineer or Quantity Surveyor has limited legal training they could not be qualified to be an arbitrator. The qualifications an arbitrator requires are integrity, sound judgement, and specialized knowledge, which are the expected qualifications of any reputable and experienced Architect, Engineer or Quantity Surveyor. In the case where the Arbitrator is not trained in law and where matters of law arise the parties may have their legal counsel prepare submissions to the Arbitrator or they may agree that the Arbitrator engage independent legal counsel to receive an opinion. In both of these ways issues of law can easily be dealt with by an Arbitrator not fully versed in the law. It is important to remember that whether through submissions by the party's legal counsel or by independent legal counsel the decision is left to the Arbitrator.

10.5   APPOINTMENT OF ARBITRATORS

The parties to a dispute are able to choose their own arbitrator or arbitrators as the case may be. If the parties cannot agree on a single arbitrator it is usual for them to select one each and for the arbitrators to select a third who shall be the chairman. The appointment of the arbitrator must conform to the terms of reference set out in the "submission" or the "agreement to refer". It must also conform to the relevant Provincial Statute. If the appointment is made without this conformity it will be deemed to be an irregular appointment and any award made could be declared invalid by a court.

In most circumstances, it follows that no person can be appointed as arbitrator if they have a direct interest in the matter or have an ongoing business relationship with either party to the dispute. The only time such an appointment would be allowed is if the Arbitrator fully disclosed the relationships within the arbitration agreement and both parties accepted the appointment after such disclosure. In any case where there is a reasonable apprehension of bias the person cannot be appointed as an appointment of this nature would certainly be declared invalid by a court.

10.6   APPOINTMENT or REMOVAL OF AN ARBITRATOR BY THE COURTS

There is provision in the different statutes to allow appointment of arbitrators, for example the BC Commercial Arbitration Act which states:

"Appointment of arbitrator by court

17.   (1) Where an arbitration agreement provides for

(a)   the appointment of a single arbitrator, and the parties, after a dispute has arisen, cannot concur in the appointment of the arbitrator, or

(b)   an arbitrator or another person to appoint an arbitrator, and the arbitrator or that person neglects or refuses to make the appointment, a party may serve written notice on the other party, the arbitrator or the other person, as the case may be, to concur in the appointment of a single arbitrator or to appoint an arbitrator.

(2)   Where the appointment is not made within 7 days after the notice is served under subsection

(1),   the court shall, on application of the party who gave the notice, appoint an arbitrator, and an arbitrator so appointed has the same powers and duties as though he were appointed under the arbitration agreement.

(3)   Where an arbitrator refuses to act, is incapable of acting or dies, and

(a)   the arbitration agreement does not provide a means of filling the vacancy that has occurred, or

(b)   the arbitration agreement provides a means of filling the vacancy, but a qualified person has not filled the vacancy

(i)   within the time provided for in the agreement, or

(ii)   where no time has been provided for, within a reasonable time, the court may, on the application of any party, appoint an arbitrator, and an arbitrator so appointed has the same powers and duties as though he were appointed under the arbitration agreement.

As with the appointment of an Arbitrator, there is provision in the different statutes to allow appointment of arbitrators, for example the BC Commercial Arbitration Act which states:

18.   (1)   The court may, on the application of a party to an arbitration, remove an arbitrator who

(a)   commits an arbitral error, or

(b)   unduly delays in proceeding with the arbitration or the making of his award.

(2)   Where the court makes an order under subsection (1) and the grounds for removal   consist of

(a)   corrupt or fraudulent conduct, or

(b)   undue delay in proceeding with the arbitration or in the making of his award,   the court may order that the arbitrator

(c)   receive no remuneration for his services, and

(d)   pay all or part of the costs, as determined by the court, that the parties to the arbitration have incurred up to the date that the order removing him was made.

(3)   Subject to subsection (4), where a court makes an order under subsection (1), it may, where the parties have not agreed in the appointment of another arbitrator to replace the one who was removed, appoint another arbitrator to act in the place of the arbitrator who was removed, and an arbitrator so

appointed has the same powers and duties as though he were appointed under the arbitration agreement.

(4)   Where

(a)   an arbitration agreement includes a provision that names the arbitrator, and that arbitrator is removed under subsection (1), and

(b)   the parties to the arbitration agreement do not, within 30 days after the removal, agree on another arbitrator to take his place, the arbitration proceeding is stayed, and the parties may take any other proceedings to resolve the dispute that they could have taken but for the arbitration agreement."

It is not necessary for the appointment of the arbitrator to be in writing but it is the recommended practice and the documentation should be properly executed by the relevant parties. Where there is more than one arbitrator each member of the board should be provided with a copy of the appointment of the other members. The appointment should include copies of the contract under which the dispute arose and the submission or agreement to refer.

The arbitrator should ensure that the terms of the appointment include details of the fees payable and any arrangements concerning how and when the fees are to be paid. The arrangements to pay any other costs or expenses should also be clarified and recorded in the appointment.

10.7   ARBITRATORS' AUTHORITY AND DUTIES

Arbitration tribunals derive their authority from the relevant statute supplemented by the submission or agreement to refer. Any award which exceeded the powers would not be binding on the parties to the dispute and would be set aside by a court.

An arbitration tribunal is required to act in a judicial manner, proceedings, while less formal than court, must be conducted accordingly and must be fair to all parties without bias and without reason to question their integrity or impartiality. The authority and duties must be discharged with honesty and justice in accordance with the evidence presented and the law.

The powers and duties usually include:

1.   To confirm acceptance of the appointment to the parties concerned.

2.   To be certain that a right to arbitrate does exist in fact and that the dispute is within the scope of the submission.

3.   To ensure that any act required of the tribunal is performed.

4.   To make an award within the stipulated time or, if empowered by the terms of the submission, to enlarge upon the time in which to make an award. The time must be enlarged prior to the expiration of the originally specified time. (A court may order the enlargement of the time at any time prior to the award being made).

5.   To provide to the parties to an arbitration unbiased personal judgment; for this reason arbitrators must not allow others to take part in their deliberations nor delegate the duty in this respect to anyone else.

6.   To appoint, if necessary, a Clerk to assist in the administrative duties of the arbitration. The parties to the dispute may also consent to have such professional assistance as considered necessary by the tribunal.

7.   To attend all meetings of the arbitration hearing, unless the submission indicates otherwise. Consent of the parties is required to allow an arbitrator to be absent from a hearing but this is not considered to be good practice and the neglect of an arbitrator to attend a meeting is considered to be misconduct.

8.   To be present at all deliberations regarding the arbitration. The absence of any one arbitrator could render an award invalid.

9.   To give sufficient prior notice to the parties of all meetings or hearings. If proper notice has been given, the arbitrator may, at his discretion, proceed in the absence of a party so notified. It is considered good practice to advise in the notice, (if not contrary to the submission), that the hearing will proceed in the absence of the party so notified. Where proper notice has been given, the arbitrator is justified in proceeding and an award made in such circumstances is valid.

10.   The submission may provide that the parties are not entitled to be represented by legal counsel. The parties may agree that no legal assistance shall be permitted in the discussions and the determination of the dispute. It is within the rights of an arbitrator to refuse to hear counsel unless otherwise provided for in the submission. If the counsel of one party is denied the opportunity to present his client's case an equal denial must be extended to the other party.

11.   To take evidence in each case where consistent with the conditions and provisions of the submission. It is important that the evidence of the parties be given in the presence of each other.

12.   To administer the oath or affirmation to the parties and witnesses. This must be in a form that is binding upon the consciences of each individual sworn.

13.   To disclose their personal knowledge and skill related to the subject of a dispute to both parties in order that the parties may give weight to any decision. This statement can be made at any time up to and after the award.

10.8   THE HEARING

The consensual arbitration process allows the parties in dispute great latitude in determining the procedure by which arbitration is undertaken. The arbitrator is however the sole authority in controlling the process running the hearing like a judge in a courtroom in addition to being the sole judge of fact and law for the parties.

The arbitrator takes control of the proceedings making any required decisions on procedure relating to adjournment, production and disclosures or exclusion of witnesses. The first meeting should be a preliminary one to ensure both parties and their representatives clearly understand the matters in dispute and to establish and clarify the procedure to be followed in the arbitration. Among the matters which could be discussed are the following:

1.   The nature of the dispute.

2.   If known, the amount that is in dispute.

3.   The time needed for the arbitration and tentative dates when all participants are available.

4.   The facts upon which the parties can agree.

5.   The facts upon which the parties do not agree.

6.   Whether either party will use a lawyer or other advocate.

7.   Whether pleadings are necessary.

8.   The dates for filing or exchanging any documents or pleadings.

9.   The number of witnesses each party will call.

10.   Whether the arbitrator is to attend at the scene of the dispute, or to take a view.

11.   When, where and who is to attend such a viewing.

12.   Whether someone is required to record the arbitration proceeding, and who will bear the expense.

13.   Whether any special assistance may be required, e.g. legal advice, translators, experts; and who will pay for them.

14.   Whether it is necessary to "state a case" to the courts.

It is at this preliminary meeting that the arbitrator's jurisdiction and appointment must be confirmed and any question of possible bias dealt with. It is also useful to ensure that all parties have the same clear idea of the issue or issues in dispute. The preliminary meeting might well be dispensed with in a relatively minor arbitration but the above issues should then be dealt with at the commencement of the first hearing. The hearing should follow the pattern set down in the traditional court process with the claimant making an opening statement outlining the overall position, the remedy being sought and the kind of evidence that will be introduced.

The claimant then proceeds to present the witnesses or evidence and the respondent is given the opportunity to cross-examine these witnesses as they complete their evidence. The claimant is then given the opportunity to re-examine the witness to clarify anything arising from the cross-examination but is not allowed to introduce any new evidence.

A similar process is followed allowing the respondent to present the overall position and to call witnesses or present evidence with cross-examination and clarification allowed as with the claimant.

The claimant then summarizes the case based on the facts proven and provides legal reasons why the arbitrator should rule for the claimant. This summary or "argument" can be based on past cases or decisions, statutes, equity, common sense and facts established during the hearing. The respondent is then given a similar opportunity to "defend" the opposing position based on similar criteria to that of the claimant.

The claimant usually makes a "reply" in which the opportunity is given to meet any of the issues raised by the respondent in the "reply" to the original argument. No new issues may be raised at this time.

The arbitrator generally has the power to order the attendance of witnesses and the presentation of documents relevant to the case but it is not the arbitrator's duty to seek evidence which is not presented. The seeking of evidence during a hearing would likely be construed as a breach of impartiality putting the arbitrator's position at risk due to perceived bias.

The arbitrator will advise the parties at the conclusion of the hearings when they may expect to receive the award. There are no statutory requirements for the arbitrator to give reasons for the award and if they are required by the parties in dispute this should be clarified at this time.

An alternative procedure at the hearings is frequently adopted and has come to be known as "boardroom procedure". This is a less formal procedure although the pattern of presentation follows that described above while following an agreed agenda of specific issues. The arbitrator therefore hears all the evidence on each issue separately but does not make any award until completion of the hearing. The layout of the room is less like a court and the parties can be made to feel more relaxed without the pressure of feeling they have to perform as on stage. It is a procedure more in line with business meetings taking place on a daily basis.

10.9   THE AWARD

The award represents the judicial opinion of the arbitrator based on the evidence presented at the hearings. It should be clear and concise and should be duly signed. It should deal with all matters submitted and should contain no reference or opinion with any other matter.

The relief awarded must be consistent with the submission, should be equitable and can direct specific performance, monetary damages or a combination of the two. It may also grant injunctive relief under a contract preventing the continuance by a party of actions which would lead to a breach of contract.

The arbitrator's task is complete when the award is delivered but the obligation of confidentiality remains in perpetuity. The arbitrator does not become involved in any subsequent litigation associated with the dispute.

The award of an arbitrator is final in that it is not subject to appeal on its merits and the evidence cannot be reviewed or reassessed as in an appeal to a higher court.

The award may be appealed to the Appeal Court of the Provincial jurisdiction but only on the grounds of natural justice being denied. The court will not upset or re-open the award unless it finds that there has been bias, fraud, collusion or that the proceedings were conducted improperly as discussed earlier in this chapter.

11

EVIDENCE IN ARBITRATION
by Kenneth M. Macdonald, PQS, FRICS, C.Arb.

11.1   INTRODUCTION

Arbitration has been demonstrated to be an alternative method of resolving disputes by the interpretation of the governing contract and statute and by the evaluation of the facts and other evidence presented. The process has been likened to the court process but usually in a much less formal manner; this informality extends to the taking of evidence at the hearings.

11.2   EVIDENCE

The law of evidence is complex and based mainly on the exclusion of certain evidence. In an arbitration it is up to the arbitrator to decide on the admissibility or non-admissibility of any evidence. The standard rule should be that if the evidence is relevant it is admissible and if it is irrelevant it is inadmissible. The arbitrator is interested in making findings of fact based on the evidence presented after that evidence has been considered and evaluated. The evidence to be considered is restricted to that presented at the hearings and the arbitrator must not take into consideration any evidence or information not presented, no matter what its source, including the arbitrator's own personal knowledge.

Evidence is something which establishes or tends to establish a fact, it can be a photograph or other document or it can be personal testimony from an individual who witnessed an event. The arbitrator having decided evidence is admissible has to decide how credible the evidence is and this requires an understanding of the concepts known as "weight", "burden of proof" and "standard of proof".

The weighting of evidence by the arbitrator is necessary as there might well be evidence which is contradictory; the arbitrator must decide which evidence is more credible and can therefore be relied upon. It is based on this weighting of the evidence that an arbitrator will make his findings of fact.

The burden of proof lies with the claimant and the claimant must therefore present evidence to prove entitlement to an award. This proof can include proving the contractual agreement between the parties, breaches of that agreement and any subsequent damages. Where the respondent alleges that the claimant failed to mitigate the damages the burden of proof shifts to the respondent.

The standard of proof required varies from that required in a court of law; it is sufficient to prove an issue or point on the "balance of probabilities". It follows therefore that if an issue is undecided on the "balance of probabilities" the claimant has failed to prove the case.

11.3   TYPES OF EVIDENCE

There are basically three types of evidence in arbitration - oral evidence, documentary evidence and physical evidence.

1.   Oral evidence is that given in person by a witness, usually as testimony under oath or affirmation.

2.   Documentary evidence is the provision of documents to prove facts. The documents may be letters or contracts but they can also include sworn affidavits and, though it is desirable to have the original documents before the arbitration, it is acceptable in many jurisdictions to allow copies to be entered as exhibits. This relieves the arbitrator of the responsibility associated with original documentation upon completion of the arbitration.

3.   Physical evidence is the production of objects that have a direct relevance to the issue. It can also take the form of an adjournment to a site to allow the arbitrator to see physical evidence for himself.

It should be noted that no one can be compelled to give evidence or produce evidence at an arbitration that would not be required to be produced in a court of law. In some jurisdictions the parties may apply to have the evidence taken down in writing.

Evidence presented at arbitration may be described differently while still coming under the classifications above.

1.   Direct evidence is evidence which proves a fact at issue, it can be oral or documentary.

2.   Circumstantial evidence is evidence which allows a conclusion to be drawn. The conclusion must be a reasonable one.

3.   Hearsay evidence is evidence of a fact not actually perceived by a witness but proved by the witness to have been stated by another person. It can also be documentary evidence by way of minutes of meetings.

4.   Opinion evidence is evidence provided by an expert in an effort to assist the arbitrator to draw inferences from the facts contained in the evidence presented. Opinion evidence from a lay person is limited to common matters such as sobriety, distance, time, temperature or size.

11.4   THE EXPERT WITNESS

An expert can be defined as one who is skilled, or one who has special knowledge. An expert is a person selected by either of the parties to the dispute, or by the arbitrator, to give an opinion on some point at issue with which they are most particularly knowledgeable. A person must pass a recognized standard as to qualification and be able to give testimony on matters not within common knowledge to be distinguished as an expert.

An expert may also be defined as one who has special knowledge or skill and is particularly recognized as a specialist or authority in their vocation or profession. "Expertise", however, is an evaluation or assessment by an expert, such being referred to as expert opinion.

To give testimony in a Court of Law, an "Expert" must prove their qualification as to expertise.   Proof of qualification of experts usually follows examination as of ordinary witnesses; by direct examination, cross-examination and re-examination, before being ruled by the presiding Judge as qualified to give admissible opinion evidence. An arbitrator would be well advised to follow the usual legal procedure in establishing the validity of an "expert", particularly with respect to their qualifications as related to the dispute being heard.

An arbitrator may not have sufficient knowledge of a matter in dispute and as a result may require specialised, expert assistance to determine the cause and nature of a dispute in order that a proper award may be made. An arbitrator who did not have the necessary expertise to adjudicate fairly would be remiss if expert testimony was not sought. The expert retained by the arbitrator should be made available to both parties in the dispute, this availability would however not extend to assisting either party in pursuing the case against the other party.

The parties to a construction dispute - particularly lawyers in their employ - are likely also to need expert assistance to fully comprehend and pursue issues arising out of construction technology and methodology. The expert assistance would be required to:

1.   Provide expert counselling with respect to technical details which may be involved.

2.   Assist in the preparation of the case for presentation to arbitration.

3.   Assist in the examination and cross examination of technical witnesses by the lawyer employed by the party who is also employing the expert.

4.   Testifying as an expert witness.

The time to challenge the admission of expert testimony is immediately after the statement of qualifications and before the giving of testimony.

It follows that the utilization of expert witnesses before and during the arbitration can be critical to the success of the parties. The opinion built up by the expert must be based on careful consideration of all available facts, deducing the logical conclusion that can be drawn from the facts. It is not unreasonable to assume that the results of an arbitration may depend on the opinions expressed by expert witnesses who are unlikely to venture opinions that cannot be substantiated as they will be subject to very close examination by the experts retained by the other party. The expert is often also required to assist in carefully framing the questions to be put to opposing experts in such a fashion as to solicit direct answers without any alternative answer. Many technical lawsuits and arbitrations have been won by lawyers in cross-examination of an opposing witness having been well advised by competent experts. Construction disputes usually require the services of several experts and it is not uncommon for them to be as active in the preparation and presentation of the case as the legal advisors. The disputants and their legal advisors must therefore ensure that the experts retained are truly experts, that their credentials and expertise will be acknowledged and that they are fully prepared to give their evidence and be cross examined. In the final analysis the expert witness will be selected on the basis of how well they will perform under the heat of direct examination, cross examination and re-examination of testimony.

11.5   RULES OF EVIDENCE

The arbitrator's duty to apply the strict rules of evidence is, as distinct from the duty of a judge, normally undefined. It therefore usually follows that the rules of evidence at an arbitration are not as strictly applied as they would be in court but it is advisable to generally adhere as much as possible to the rules. The parties to the arbitration should discuss any particular opinions they have on the application of the rules of evidence when establishing the jurisdiction of the arbitrator. The informality of arbitration and the expeditious settlement of issues are promoted advantages for choosing arbitration over litigation, this combined with the lay arbitrator's likely unfamiliarity with the rules is a strong argument for not strictly applying the rules of evidence.

The procedure for taking evidence usually follows the procedure used in a court of law and is as follows:

1.   The party who began the Arbitration, the plaintiff, calls his witnesses in order. Each witness is first examined by the party by whom he is called. This is called direct examination or examination-in-chief.
2.   Such witnesses are liable to be cross-examined by the other side.
3.   Finally they may be re-examined by the party by whom first called.
4.   When the plaintiff's case is completed, the other side calls its witnesses and the foregoing procedure is adopted for the other side.
5.   In certain circumstances, such as the introduction of new evidence by the other side, the party who began is allowed to bring forward further evidence as rebuttal.

The examination-in-chief must be confined to the matters bearing on the main issue of the dispute and a witness must not be asked leading questions, i.e. questions suggesting the answer the person putting the question wishes or expects to receive, or suggesting disputed facts about which the witness is to testify. The rule regarding leading questions is not applied where questions asked are simply introductory and form no part of the real substance of the enquiry, or where they relate to matters which, though material, are not disputed.

It is normally during the examination in chief that the introduction of documentary evidence takes place as the witness can factually establish the validity and identity of the document.

The main relaxation to the rules usually applies to the admissibility of hearsay evidence which would normally be inadmissible in a court of law. The relaxation of the rules does not permit any relaxation in the obligations of the arbitrator nor does it change the legal rights of the parties. The arbitrator must therefore:

1.	allow all evidence which is relevant to the issue or issues in dispute;
2.	critically evaluate all the evidence and base the award on convincing and relevant evidence;
3.	conduct the process in a way that is both fair and just.

It can be seen that as important as the Rules of Evidence are it is more important that the arbitrator is able to evaluate and weigh the evidence taken in order to make a just award.

12

BUILDING CODES AND BY-LAWS
by Claude Lawrenson, RSW, RHI and Evan B. Stregger, PQS(F), AScT, C.Arb.

1. *If a builder build a house for a man and do not make its construction firm and the house which he as built collapse and cause the death of the owner of the house - that builder shall be put to death.*

2. *If it cause the death of the son of the owner of the house - they shall put to death a son of that builder.*

3. *If it cause the death of a slave of the owner of the house - he shall give to the owner of the house a slave of equal value.*

4. *If it destroy property, he shall restore whatever it destroyed, and because he did not make the house which he built firm and it collapsed, he shall rebuild the house that collapsed at his own expense.*

5. *If a builder build a house for a man and do not make its construction meet the requirements and a wall fall in, that builder shall strengthen the wall at his own expense.*

From the Code of Laws of HAMMURABI, King of Babylonia (2000 BC)
(translated by R.F. Harper - Code of Hammurabi)

12.1   INTRODUCTION

No one may design, or construct a building, or construct facilities servicing a building or buildings, anywhere in Canada, without conforming to certain statutory rules and regulations governing both design and construction. This also applies to the alteration, repair, moving or demolition of buildings are also governed by regulations of a similar nature.

Statutory rules, regulating design and construction have been enacted by Federal, Provincial, and Municipal legislative authority, predicated upon the jurisdiction granted by the British North America Act, and various Federal and Provincial Statutes.

We are concerned, primarily, with Building Codes, and statutory regulations which are enforced by Municipal or other authority, which are frequently referred to as codes or building by-laws. These codes or by-laws, adopted or enacted by a provincial legislature or municipal corporation, is a set of minimum provisions respecting the safety of buildings with reference to public health, fire protection and structural sufficiency. Failure to comply with the requirements of these codes and by-laws may result in penalties being imposed.

At the municipal level the use of land, and the erection, alteration or use of buildings may be governed by a Zoning By- Law. The purpose of this form of by-law is to regulate land use for the benefit of all property owners within the corporate limits of the municipality enacting such a by-law.

> *"It is an accepted principle that the ownership of land is exclusive but not absolute; each owner may use his property to the exclusion of all others, but he must use it with due respect to the limitations imposed by society. In a sense, the group, or community, has certain rights in each parcel of land ownership, that must be respected in its utilization."*

> *Urban Land Economics, Chap. 14 - R.U. Ratcliff*

Anyone deciding to build a structure of any kind, therefore, must not only design and construct it according to the design and construction criteria of applicable building by-laws or codes, but must conform also to the use and occupancy regulations prescribed in the applicable Zoning By-Law, where such is in force.

12.2   BUILDING CODES - GENERALLY

As the primary purpose of any building code or by-law is to protect public health, safety and welfare, to protect workmen engaged in construction, rather than to safeguard financial interests, trade union privileges, or traditional building materials and methods, essentially any worthwhile building code or by-law should:

1.   Permit the use of any material or method that complies with the <u>minimum</u> of accepted performance standards related to the material or method.

2.   Adopt, by reference, other building codes or nationally accepted performance standards.

3.   Provide the right to appeal and obtain legal remedy for any grievance caused by the requirements of a building code or by-law or the enforcement of them.

4.   Be subjected to periodic review for up-to-date revisions of it.

Most building codes and building by-laws include all of these elements, with the exception of specific provision for redress of grievances. Such remedy can, however, be had by virtue of the provisions of the various provincial Municipal Acts.

12.3 THE NATIONAL BUILDING CODE OF CANADA

Under the British North America Act and its successor the Constitution Act, responsibility for building regulation in Canada rests with the provinces and territories. In the past, this responsibility was generally delegated to municipalities.

Not surprisingly, this lead to a multiplicity of regulations, developed as each municipality tried to deal with its own needs, making it very difficult for designers, product manufacturers and contractors to conduct business in more than one region.

Although the majority of municipal authorities had available to them excellent professional and technical talent, these sources, for various reasons were not sufficiently employed by the municipal authorities to consider all aspects, principles and safety criteria needed for safe and healthful structures as related to the use and occupancy of them. Codes of the individual municipalities were found to be copies of existing codes of other municipalities with no consideration having been given to their applicability to individual localities. They were full of inept revisions, inconsistencies and antiquated requirements.

To resolve this situation the Department of Finance, in 1937, asked the National Research Council (NRC) to develop a model building regulation that could be adopted by all municipalities in Canada. The result of that initiative was the publication of the first edition of the National Building Code of Canada in 1941.

The post-war construction boom resulted in demand for a revised NBC. In 1948, NRC created the Associate Committee on the National Building Code to update and maintain the document and to provide for a broader input. The Associate Committee revised the Code in 1953 and has published new versions about every five years since. The NBC 1995 is the 11th edition.

In 1956, NRC created the Associate Committee on the National Fire Code which produced the first edition of the National Fire Code in 1963. The two Associate Committees were disbanded in October 1991 and replaced by the Canadian Commission on Building and Fire Codes (CCBFC).

From its beginning in 1941 the National Building Code was and remains an advisory document, applicable throughout Canada. It has no legal standing until it has been adopted in whole, or in part, by a provincial or municipal government having jurisdiction. The National Building Code is only a set of **MINIMUM** requirements respecting the safety of buildings with reference to public health, fire protection, and structural sufficiency.

12.4 COMPOSITION OF NATIONAL BUILDING CODE OF CANADA

The National Building Code is published as a set of minimum standards for the use of provincial and municipal governments. However, unless adopted by the governing agency, the NBC has no legal standing. Each governing agency may adopt new or future editions of the NBC either in whole, or in part with modifications as it sees fit. Therefore, all persons affected by the Code must first establish the version adopted by the governing authority prior to proceeding with design or construction.

The National Building Code of Canada comprises the following Parts, Sections:

Part 1 - Scope and Definitions

Throughout the Code certain words appear in italics. These words are defined in Part 1 which also contains a list of abbreviations.

The definitions of certain words and phrases which appear in italic type are terms which, for the purposes of the Code have been defined to ensure understanding of their intended meaning. Upon legal adoption of the Code such definitions are acceptable for legal use in any Court of Law having jurisdiction. The most important definitions are those relating to Building Types. It is most important that these definitions are clearly understood.

Part 2 - General Requirements

This Part contains the regulations pertaining to the efficient use and effective application of the Code, and defines powers, duties and responsibilities to that end.

It defines, among other things

a)   application of the code
b)   referenced documents
c)   Tests and construction review
d)   Equivalents in respect to materials, appliances, equipment or methods of design or construction not specifically authorized.
e)   requirements for plans, specifications and calculations.

Part 3 - Fire Protection, Occupant Safety and Accessibility

Define the conditions of use and occupancy of buildings which must be taken into consideration in the design of buildings. These conditions precede design and, therefore, emphasis shifts from construction to occupancy. The preamble to building regulations usually states - "to regulate the erection and provide for the safety of buildings" - not occupancies. The only way to relate the amount of building required for any use is to relate to rules which govern hazards of any declared intended occupancy of the building. A decision of the Supreme Court of Canada supports the view that one should only build that which is necessary to provide for the conditions and to counter the hazards of an intended occupancy.

Part 3 contains the conditions of occupancy upon which designs should be based and checked. For example, the health requirements for various uses and occupancies are to be found in Part 3, while structural live loads, though dependent upon use and occupancy, will be found in Part 4 - Structural Design.

Related to use and occupancy requirements are the Division of Space, Total Building Space, Floor Areas, Exits, Attic and Crawl Spaces, Interpretive Clauses as given in Section 3.1, Types of Construction, Fire Safety, Fire Separations, Health Requirements, Dead Ends, Life Safety in High Buildings, additional requirements for High Buildings and Requirements for Barrier-free design.

Part 4 - Structural Design

Three separate Sections comprise this Part of the Code which deals with loads to be used in design calculations and methods of design and construction. Sections are as follows:

Section 4.1: Structural Loads and Procedures

Outlines the requirements of design of all structural members and assemblies for the various buildings according to occupancies given in Part 3. These requirements are based on minimum safety and performance for specific uses and occupancy. The designer, however, has been given considerable choice of the basis of design within the stipulated requirements for safety and performance.

A dead load is defined as the weight of all permanent structural and non-structural components of a building. A live load is defined as loads other than dead loads, including loads resulting from snow, rain, wind and those due to occupancy.

The following loads and forces have to be considered in the design of any building, irrespective of its use and occupancy:

a)   dead loads
b)   live loads
c)   loads due to earthquakes
d)   loads due to wind
e)   loads due to earth

f) loads due to contraction or expansion from shrinkage, moisture changes and relaxation creep in component materials of a building

g) loads due to temperature changes

h) loads due to sway loads, impact and vibration forces

Other factors, such as variation in the height and shape of buildings must be taken into design consideration also.

Section 4.2: Foundations

This section is specifically concerned with those natural-in-place materials to be found on a building site. The foundation engineer must base his design on the values of the properties of these in-situ materials, such as their physical, chemical and engineering characteristics. It must be determined, how uniform or how variable these properties may be within any given building site. It must be determined at what depths significant stress changes may be expected to take place when subjected to the building loads being imposed on them. It must be determined how to utilize the bearing capacity of all in-situ materials.

Section 4.3: Design Requirements for Structural Materials

Part 4 applies to wood, masonry, concrete, steel, aluminum and air supported structures by reference to various published CSA and CAN standards.

Part 5: Environmental Separation

This part applies to the design of a building assembly such as a wall, floor, roof, floor-ceiling combination or roof-ceiling combination with respect to the control of ground water, condensation and the penetration of wind and rain.

Part 6: Heating, Ventilating, and Air-Conditioning

Design & Installation:
Heating, ventilating and air-conditioning systems shall be designed, constructed and installed to conform to good engineering practice, such as described in the ASHRAE handbooks, the HRA Digest, the Hydronics Institute Ventilation Manual published by the American Conference of Governmental Industrial Hygienists.

Application:
Sections of this part of the code apply to both residential buildings covered under Part 9 and to all other types of construction.

The main emphasis in this part of the code is fire safety, with clearances from combustible materials being a major component.

Part 7: Plumbing Services

Contains only the basic legal statements dealing with Scope, Application and Administration. All technical requirements are contained in the Canadian Plumbing Code.

Part 8: Safety Measures at Construction and Demolition Sites

This part deals with Public safety at construction sites, and will be included in a following Chapter - Construction Safety - being a subject worthy of separate treatment.

Part 9: Housing and Small Buildings

For those intending to engage in either the design or construction of residential buildings, this part of the Code is important. This part applies to buildings of three storeys or less in building height, with an area not exceeding 600 m², intended for Group C residential and Group D small business use and occupancy. Where such buildings are to accommodate barrier-free design, Section 3.7 of Part 3 shall apply. There are 35 Sections to this Part of the Code, together small buildings, reference should be made to Part I - Scope and Definitions, for the definition of Building, Apartment Building, Apartment House Dwelling Unit and House. All lumber grades, dimensions, span tables, etc., referred to in Section 9.23 - Wood Frame Construction - and elsewhere in Part 9, conform to the NLGA Standard Grading Rules for Canadian Lumber, which became effective July 1971. The sizes to which lumber is now being manufactured are specified in CSA 0141-1970, "Softwood Lumber" and descriptions of the new grades for lumber are contained in the National Lumber Grading Authority Standard Grading Rules.

12.5   ADOPTION OF THE NATIONAL BUILDING CODE

Throughout Canada there are statutory regulations of various descriptions related to the construction process. For quite some time individuals and construction organizations in Canada have campaigned not only for the adoption of the National Building Code by all municipalities, but have sought to bring about uniformity of all other regulations related to the construction process. It is the consensus of all concerned with construction directly that the adoption of the Code and subsequent uniformity of statutory regulations would mean a saving in cost as a result of uniform building standards and regulations. Early in 1968 it became evident that individual municipalities, left to their own devices, would probably never adopt the NBC and, even if they did, would in all probability change its provisions to the extent of defeating the objective of uniformity that the Code advocates.

The universal application of the National Building Code has been gradual. As of June 1997 the status of the National Building Code was as follows:

British Columbia - The next edition of the British Columbia Building Code was originally scheduled to be published in the Spring of 1998. This edition would have included any of the provisions of the 1995 NBC considered appropriate for British Columbia. However, the Building Standards Branch, responsible for establishing and maintaining provincial building and plumbing regulations, closed on January 31, 1997. As result, plans for the next BC Building Codes are on hold.

Alberta - The next edition of the Alberta Building Code, which will be based on the 1995 NBC, is scheduled for release in mid 1997.

Saskatchewan - Saskatchewan is expected to adopt the 1995 NBC early in 1997 with a few amendments.

Manitoba - Manitoba plans to adopt the 1995 NBC, with a few amendments in April, 1997.

Ontario - The next edition of the Ontario Building Code is scheduled for release in the Fall of 1997. This edition will include any of the provisions of the 1995 NBC considered appropriate for Ontario.

Quebec - The plain for adoption of the provisions of the 1995 NBC is still under review in Quebec. The most likely date for adoption is Fall 1997.

New Brunswick - New Brunswick is expected to adopt the 1995 NBC in Fall 1997.

Prince Edward Is. - At present there is no provincially mandated building code in PEI; however, the 1995 NBC has been adopted in the City of Charlottetown. The creation of province-wide regulations for buildings, based on the 1995 NBC, is under discussion.

Nova Scotia - Nova Scotia plans to adopt plans the 1995 NBC, with a few amendments, in April, 1997.

Newfoundland	-	At present there is no provincially mandated building code in Newfoundland; however, the NBC is referred to in provincial fire-safety and various other types of legislation, and the City of St. John's has adopted the 1995 NBC, is under active discussion, with the earliest date of adoption likely to be Fall 1997.
Northwest Territories	-	The 1995 NBC was adopted in the NWT on March 1, 1996.
Yukon	-	The Yukon began using the 1995 NBC once it was published.

12.6   ZONING BY-LAWS

Zoning By-Laws, like Building Codes, are predicated upon the interest of public health, safety and welfare. While Building Codes are enacted to govern the design and construction of buildings of all types, Zoning By-Laws are enacted to regulate the use of land with respect to the nature of use and occupancy, height of structures and building density. Because of the restrictive nature of Zoning By-Laws they are usually the most controversial pieces of municipal legislation in any municipality where such a by-law is in force.

The generally accepted basic principles of zoning are:

1. Zoning land use must serve a public purpose with respect to health, safety, morals, convenience and welfare.

2. The regulations a zoning by-law contains must be comprehensive and reasonable, not based upon mere opinion or prejudice.

3. Zoning by-laws should be enforceable.

4. Zoning, being predicated upon the interests of the whole community, should not convey vested interests to speculative property owners. That is to say, the Zoning By-Law should not legally establish any permanent right of tenure which cannot be changed for the benefit of the community at large.

5. Finally, to be most effective, Zoning By-Laws should be flexible enough to meet changing conditions of a community at any given time. Without this feature of flexibility, zoning becomes a block to progress and fails in the public interest.

A municipal zoning by-law is essentially a legislative method of putting into effect current features of a proposed Master Plan for the development of a municipality. A future Land-Use Plan, which is a basic part of any master plan, must not be confused with a current

Zoning Map, which is an immediate practical version of a Master Plan. A Zoning Use, to best serve the public interest, must be capable of revision in the direction of a future Land-Use Plan, as it deals with future land development involving either the original intent of land-use, or a change in land-use.

Zoning should not be considered as retroactive, and should not be used to require the removal of nonconforming uses and occupancies existing at the time of enactment of a zoning by-law. When, however, a nonconforming use is terminated, any re-use of the building should conform to the requirements of the zoning by-law.

A perusal of a City Zoning By-Law, will reveal that the City may have been divided into areas, which in turn may have been divided into zones. These zones have specific designations related to Use and Occupancy, such as:

P	-	Public Use
R1	-	Single Family Dwelling
R2	-	Single Family Dwelling
C1	-	Central Commercial
M3	-	Medium Industrial

These designations are usually defined on the basis of Use and Occupancy limitations within specific zones. It is this Use and Occupancy limitation which correlates the zoning by-law with the Municipal Building By-Law, which could be the National Building Code of Canada or a particular Provincial Building Code. The following of a municipal Zoning By-Law are correlated to the NBC and Provincial Building Codes.

1. Definitions
2. Conformity, restricting use of land, the erection, alteration and expansion of any structure in compliance with the requirements of the zoning by-law.
3. One dwelling per lot, describing the permitted area for residential buildings.
4. Street set back, designating the location of structures with respect to streets, roads and walks.
5. Corner lot sight lines, regulations for both vertical height and horizontal distance of obstructions to lot lines.
6. Permitted projections into yards, limiting the extent which carports, cornices, eaves, etc., may project into a yard. A yard is generally defined as an open space, or area, located between a main wall of a building and a lot line.
7. Location of accessory buildings and detached, subordinate buildings such as garages, etc.
8. Parking, defining the minimum space for a defined use and occupancy, thus limiting the horizontal area of a building in relation to the total lot area.
9. Loading, defining areas required for off-street loading for particular uses and occupancies.
10. Maximum building height, limiting the height of structures by zones.

The City of Vancouver Zoning By-Law is not only concerned with street setbacks, the horizontal distance a building must be set back from lot lines, but also horizontal setbacks of structures at various vertical heights. Structural setbacks exert considerable influence and control in respect of both the design and the construction of tall buildings.

12.7   ADMINISTRATION OF BUILDING BY-LAWS AND CODES

Building by-laws and codes, including the National Building Code of Canada, are somewhat similar in format as construction specifications in that they are divided into two distinct classifications:

1.   Non-technical parts, which are mainly administrative in nature for the purpose of enforcing the by-law or code.

2.   Technical and quasi-technical part which are the design criteria for all manners of buildings. Rarely does a building by-law or code, perse, embrace such Civil Engineering Works as Roads, Streets, Sewers, Water Systems, etc.

REFERENCES

National Building Code of Canada - National Research Council
National Research Council - History of the Code
Construction Economist June 1997- Canadian Institute of Quantity Surveyors

13

APPLICATION OF PART 3 OF THE
NATIONAL BUILDING CODE OF CANADA 1995

by William G. Nichols, Msc, PQS, GSC

Much of this information is taken from the Commentary on Part 3 issued by the Canadian Commission on Building and Fire Codes and the reader is encouraged to consult this document for a more comprehensive guide to application of the code.

13.1   INTRODUCTION

Part 3 is primarily concerned with safety from exposure to fire, the general health and physical safety of the building occupants, and the ability to access the building by persons with physical disabilities. To apply Part 3 it is necessary to understand the scope of Part 3 in relation to other parts of the Code and the relationship of Part 3 to the National Fire Code of Canada. The National Fire Code of Canada is a separate Code issued by the Canadian Commission on Building and Fire Codes.

13.2   APPLICATION OF PART 3

13.2.1 GENERAL

Part 3 regulates all buildings regardless of size, which contain assembly occupancies, or high hazard industrial occupancies. It also regulates buildings that exceed 600 square metres in area or three storeys in height which contain all other occupancies. Small buildings which contain major occupancies not referred to in the first sentence are covered by Part 9, Housing and Small Buildings.

If a building within the scope of Part 9 contains a room or space used for assembly occupancy, or for high hazard industrial occupancy , that room or space must conform to the applicable requirements of Part 3. Although there is no size limit placed upon the room or space, it is assumed that it would be of a subsidiary nature to the principal use of the building and would constitute only a small portion of the total building area.

Part 3 regulates only those aspects of the installation of building services and equipment that are relevant to its overall scope. Part 6 contains requirements for heating, ventilating and air-conditioning systems, while Part 7, through reference to the National Plumbing Code of Canada, specifies how plumbing facilities should be installed. Although Part 5 addresses the performance expectations for environmental separation barriers within and at the perimeter of a building, the fire safety aspects of those same barriers are addressed within Part 3.

13.2.2 RELATIONSHIP BETWEEN PART 3 AND THE NATIONAL FIRE CODE

There is a special relationship between Part 3 of the National Building Code of Canada and the National Fire code of Canada with respect to fire safety. The content of both Codes must be considered in building design, construction and maintenance. The role of each Code with respect to fire safety can be summarised as follows:

The National Building Code of Canada establishes the standard of fire safety for the construction of new buildings, for reconstruction of existing buildings, including alterations or extensions, and for buildings in which a change in occupancy occurs.

The National Fire Code of Canada establishes standards for fire prevention, fire fighting and fire safety in buildings in use, including standards for the conduct of activities having a fire hazard potential, for maintenance of fire safety equipment and egress facilities, and for portable fire extinguishers. It limits building contents and their arrangement and requires fire safety plans, which include the organization of supervisory staff for emergency purposes. In addition, the National Fire Code of Canada establishes standards for the prevention of fires outside buildings that could present a hazard to a community.

The two Codes have been developed as complimentary and coordinated documents, to reduce to a minimum any conflict in their content. To ensure their effective application, building owners and operators, designers, and building and fire officials must be fully conversant with the fire safety standards of both codes.

13.2.3 OBJECTIVE AND PRESCRIPTIVE REQUIREMENTS

Part 3 contains both objective and prescriptive requirements. Performance criteria are given for many requirements to help assure that an objective has been met. Provision is made in Part 2 to accept equivalent materials, assemblies or designs provided the authority having jurisdiction is satisfied that the overall performance of the building will not be diminished. Although the concept of equivalents is specially useful when objective requirements are being evaluated, it also applies to products for which the Code gives requirements in prescriptive form.

13.2.4 GENERAL PROVISIONS IN PART 3

Part 3 applies to a specific building under consideration and does not apply to adjacent buildings on neighbouring properties. The spatial separation requirements in the Code, for instance, use the distance from a building to a property line as a controlling dimension, rather than the distance to neighbouring building located on a different property. In this manner, each building is regulated independently of buildings on neighbouring properties, but each of the buildings on these neighbouring properties must conform to the requirements of the Code when construction is undertaken on them. If there is more than one building on a given property, a deemed property line between the buildings is established for the purposes of determining spacial separation requirements. This line is established in a location that assures that all buildings under consideration will comply with the intent of the Code.

The requirements of Part 3 are intended to be interpreted, applied, and enforced by reasonable and well informed persons using good judgement. This is especially important for users faces with situations which are not specifically covered in the Code, or in which alternative design solutions are proposed which were not envisaged by the Code committees. Sufficient factual knowledge to determine an absolute or relative level of safety of one set of design options and compare it with different design options is often lacking. In the design of any major complex or unusual building, situations arise in which judgement must be made, and it is assumed that persons with special expertise will be consulted. The Code can never cover all possible situations and designs; it is revised as experience is gained from its use and from additional knowledge obtained through research.

Part 3 requirements are predicated on an adequate supply of water being available for fire fighting. Deployment of fire fighting forces is assumed to take place in the event of a fire emergency. These forces may take the form of a paid or volunteer fire department or, in some cases, a private fire brigade. An appropriate water supply for each building must be determined through consultation between the designer, the building official and a fire department representative. If fire fighting facilities are not available, additional fire safety measures will be necessary and good judgement must be exercised in ensuring that the intent of the code is met.

13.2.5 OVERVIEW

The Arrangement of Part 3

Part 3 consists of eight major sections:

3.1	General
3.2	Building Fire Safety
3.3	Safety within Floor Areas
3.4	Exits
3.5	Vertical Transportation
3.6	Service Facilities
3.7	Health Requirements
3.8	Barrier Free Design

General-Section 3.1.

The requirements in Section 3.1. explain and develop concepts that are used throughout Part 3. This section can be viewed in part as an extension of the list of definitions in Article 1.1.3.2. Some concepts and defined terms are complex and interdependent, eg. grade, first storey, basement and building height.

Section 3.1 contains procedures for the classification of a building according to its use. Classification by occupancy is fundamental to the application of most requirements of Part 3. Section 3.1. has information on combustible construction, heavy timber construction, noncombustible construction, tents and air-supported structures, fire separations, protection of openings, fire walls, fire stops in concealed spaces, flame spread rating, interior finish, roof assemblies, roof covering and occupant load. It is from the foundation provided by this Section that many of the requirements of Part 3 are developed.

Building Fire Safety-Section 3.2.

Section 3.2. includes requirements that pertain to the building as a whole structure. Approximately two-thirds of the Section contains requirements relating to fire compartmentation of each storey and fire-resistance ratings for load bearing structural assemblies and members. These requirements vary in relation to the use of the building, its size, the number of streets it faces, and whether the building is sprinklered. Since many of the requirements in this Section depend on the size of the building, rules are provided on how building size is determined.

Section 3.2. has rules for determining the minimum distances between buildings that could affect one another in the event of a fire and sets limits on allowable openings and the construction of the building faces (spacial separation requirements). Spacial separation requirements, for the space of a building that could be exposed to fire or that might expose other buildings to fire, are expressed in terms of fire-resistance rating and combustibility, but should not be confused with the structural fire protection requirements for the load bearing structural assemblies mentioned in the preceding paragraph. Structural fire protection requirements ensure that a building will remain structurally intact for a given period of time after a fire breaks out within it, while exposing building face requirements ensure that a fire in one building compartment will not involve another building or another compartment in the same building for a specified period of time. Requirements are included for covered vehicular passageways and walkways between buildings.

Fire alarm and detection systems are regulated in relation to building size, use, and number of occupants. Requirements related to fire fighting include provisions for access, water supply, standpipe systems, and sprinkler systems. Other requirements cover emergency power and emergency lighting, and the lighting of exits and areas used by the public.

Section 3.2. includes additional requirements for high buildings. These include smoke control and venting, elevator control for emergency use, elevators for fire fighters, central alarm and control facilities, and voice communication systems.

Additional protection measures are incorporated in Section 3.2. for buildings with mezzanines or interconnected floor space that have openings through the floor assemblies that are not protected by closures or fire separations.

Safety within Floor Areas-Section 3.3.

Section 3.3 applies to safety within individual storeys (floor areas), including all rooms and spaces other than service rooms and service spaces covered by Section 3.6. This contrasts with Section 3.2., whose requirements affect the entire building. The requirements are grouped according to the occupancy of the floor area, room, or space. This occupancy is not necessarily the principal occupancy for which the remainder of the building or storey is classified.

For example, the principal occupancy of a building having most of its storeys used for offices would be classified as business and personal services. The provisions in Section 3.2. for structural fire protection and fire protection equipment for a business and personal services major occupancy building (Group D) would apply to the whole building. Within a specific storey, a room or a part of the floor area could be considered as a subsidiary occupancy to the office function and might be used for an assembly, institutional, residential, mercantile, or industrial function. In this case, the special rules of Section 3.3. apply to that room or space. A small boardroom used as an assembly room must therefore comply with the requirements for assembly occupancy in Section 3.3., even if it is contained in an office building, hospital, hotel, industrial building or any other building which would be classified as a major occupancy other than assembly (Group A).

However, a group of rooms used for meetings in a hotel would be considered as an assembly major occupancy, even though the principal use of the hotel would be considered as residential major occupancy.

In the Code, life safety for the occupants of any room, space or floor area depends on the use or occupancy of that space. The risk to these occupants occurs in the early stages of a fire. It is not the same for all occupancies, so each one must be regulated separately. Section 3.3. contains requirements for access to exit, both from open floor area and from floor areas divided into rooms and suites. Access to exit includes all portions of the floor area, up to the entry to the exit. This Section also regulates the size of access to exits, limits the travel distance to exits from within a floor area, and addresses the design of guards around openings and in stairways and the use of glass in doors or windows that may be mistaken for doors.

Exits-Section 3.4.

The requirements for exits are separate from the requirements of Section 3.2. that affect the building as a whole and from the requirements of Section 3.3. that affect the floor area. An exit that is that part o the evacuation route that leads from the floor area it serves to another building, a public thoroughfare, or a safe open space outside the building. In a typical building with exit stairs, it includes the stairway itself and the doors leading into and out of the stairway. Once in the exit system a person is considered to be in a relatively safe place, thus the exiting should be completed without re-entering another floor area in the same building. One exception involves the use of a lobby as a part of an exit facility. Some building designs provide for areas of refuge that act as intermediate holding areas between the occupied floor spaces and the exit facilities. Although these are intended for temporary use until an exit is available, they may be in use for extended periods of time where it is not practicable to evacuate the occupants directly from the floor areas in care or detention occupancies or in high buildings.

Section 3.4. defines what may be used as part of an exit system and the requirements for these facilities, their number and location, fire separation from the rest of the building, as well as exit signs and lighting.

Vertical Transportation-Section 3.5.

Section 3.5 contains requirements that apply to vertical transportation facilities. The principal item addresses elevator systems, however, reference is also made to dumbwaiters and escalators. Although the primary document to be used for the design of elevator systems is the Safety Code for Elevators published by the Canadian Standards Association, requirements for the fire safety of the system are contained in Section 3.5. Minimum dimensions are required for some elevator cars to assure that they can be used to evacuate persons from a building by means of stretcher beds in the extended position.

Service Facilities-Section 3.6.

Section 3.6. includes provisions applying to any space that accommodates building services, including mechanical and electrical equipment, chutes, ducts, pipes, or wiring. Requirements are also included that affect attics and crawl spaces, duct spaces, service shafts, service rooms, and concealed spaces that contain services in walls and floors. Requirements for these spaces are included in a separate Section because, unlike other parts of a floor area or exit system, they are not usually accessible either to the building occupants or the general public. They are not considered to have any appreciable occupant load and, in many cases are unoccupied except for occasional inspection or servicing.

Health Requirements-Section 3.7.

Section 3.7. includes requirements that affect the health of the building occupants. Health requirements in Part 3 are concerned with space dimensions as well as ventilation, illumination, sound control and medical gas piping systems. Some standards for space dimensions, for ventilation and illumination as well as sound control have changes from previous editions of the National Building Code and could vary substantially from local bylaws or regulations in effect at the time an existing building was constructed. In the case of medical gas piping systems, found in health care facilities and medical offices, the safety of any person receiving medical gas during treatment requires that there be no doubt concerning the integrity of the piping system and the quality of the gas. Thus there should be no compromise in ensuring that the complete medical gas system complies with the latest standards, even when minor changes are made to the system as part of an expansion or renovation project in the building.

Health requirements include the provision of sanitary facilities. Although the National Building Code prescribes certain numbers of lavatories and water closets for each occupancy based on the occupant load of the building, much of the design for a new building is hypothetical concerning the actual occupant load and the distribution of the sexes in the occupant load. Some slight redundancy of fixtures may be necessary to ensure that sufficient facilities are available as the occupant load of the building changes. The need for barrier-free units in the washrooms in accordance with Section 3.8 must be addressed at the time that the washroom is being designed.

Barrier-Free Design-Section 3.8.

The requirements of Section 3.8. affect the design of a building for accessibility to persons in wheelchairs. The primary areas are the approach to a building, entry to and movement within a building, parking, washroom and bathroom lad and design, and special elevator requirements. Many measures are included in other sections of Part 3 that address the special needs of persons with physical disabilities who are not restricted to a wheelchair.

13.2.6 CONCEPTS AND TERMINOLOGY

1.   **General**

Some terms and basic concepts that are defined in Article 1.1.3.2. are discussed in detail.

a)   **What is a Building?**

Many attempts have been made to define the word 'building' more precisely. Most have been relatively unsuccessful; the more precise the definition becomes, the more difficult it is to apply to innovative designs and unusual configurations. What suits one authority may not suit another. Some common sense, therefore, is necessary in applying the definition in the Code, which states that a building is "any structure used or intended for supporting or sheltering any use or occupancy". Occupancy is defined as "the use or intended use of a building or part thereof for the shelter or support of persons, animals, or property".

Many buildings do not fall precisely into the categories given in the Code and in these instances, the designer and the authority must agree on the most appropriate fit. This occurs most often in industrial uses, particularly in manufacturing facilities and in buildings that contain equipment that requires specialised design. For steel mills, aluminum plants, refineries, power generating stations and liquid storage facilities, it may be impracticable to follow the specific requirements in the Code. A water reservoir or an oil refinery, for example, has no floor area as defined in the Code, so requirements for exiting from a floor area would not apply. Requirements for structural fire protection in large steel mills, and pulp and paper mills, particularly in certain sections, may not be practicable in terms of the construction and materials normally used in these operations. In other portions of the same building, however, it is quite reasonable to require that the provisions of the Code be applied. This would include office area to which requirements for a business and personal services occupancy would be applied.

One problem with many building designs concerns what constitutes part of a building and what does not. A courtyard that is open to the sky but is surrounded by walls would normally be regulated by egress requirements, but would not normally be considered as a part of a building for many other requirements. If an unenclosed covered space is used for functions related to a building use, including parking of vehicles and storage, or utilisation of a roof deck by the building occupants, the space must be considered as part of the building. Numerous other examples could be cited on this subject, and each situation can present a different aspect of the problem. If there are walls surrounding the building, the limits of the building are obvious, however, if there are no external walls, as in an open parking structure, the perimeter of the floors or the downward projection of the roof would be an appropriate method to define the limits of the building. There are no simple answers to this complex problem; common sense and good judgement must be exercised in establishing the building limits before applying Code requirements.

b)   **Classification of a Building**

The classification of spaces within a building by occupancy is normally the starting point in establishing which Code requirements should apply to that building. Once each space in the building has been classified in terms of its occupancy, the broader concept of major occupancy is considered for each floor area. Major occupancy must not be confused with the term 'occupancy'. Major occupancy is defined as the principal occupancy for which a building or part thereof is used or intended to be used and includes the d=subsidiary occupancies which are an integral part of the principal occupancy.

In the case of a school, there are spaces that would be classified as assembly use and would include the classrooms, library, cafeteria, and gymnasium. Other spaces would have different occupancy classification and could include staff offices as business and personal services occupancy, and workshops, laboratories and storage areas as industrial occupancy. Washrooms and service rooms are not identified with any specific occupation category. The principal use of the building would be considered as educational and thus the building would be classified as an assembly major occupancy (Group A, Division 2). Assuming that the building contains a limited number of offices, laboratories, and workshops, these would be considered subsidiary occupancies. In situations in which a subsidiary function occupies an extensive portion of the building, it would be necessary to consider it as a second major occupancy within that portion of the building.

If a multi-storey building has more than one principal function, each storey must be classified for its major occupancy. For example, the entry storey could be used primarily for mercantile operations and upper storeys could contain offices. In this case the building as a whole would be classified for both types of occupancy and would be considered to have two major occupancies; business and personal services (Group D), and mercantile (Group E). Each major occupancy could include subsidiary occupancies.

If a hotel contained extensive meeting rooms on any floor, these would constitute an assembly major occupancy (Group A, Division 2). In some cases the same rooms would be available as suites for guests as well as being rented out for meeting functions. These rooms would be given two major occupancy classifications (Group C and Group A, Division 2) and requirements for both major occupancies would have to be considered and the more stringent applied.

Except in the case of high hazard industrial and medium hazard industrial major occupancies (Group F, Divisions 1 and 2), if the aggregate area of a major occupancy does not exceed ten percent of the floor area of the storey in which it is located, the storey does not have to be classified for that major occupancy for the purpose of determining structural fire protection. This does not exempt these major occupancies from the requirements in Section 3.1. that adjoining major occupancies must be separated from each other, even though they occupy less than ten percent of the floor area. This provision also does not exempt these small major occupancies from the requirements of Section 3.2, including spatial separation for the exposing building faces and fire alarm systems, nor for the requirements of Section 3.3. for specific occupancies.

c)   Prohibited combinations of major occupancies

A number of major occupancies are prohibited from being in the same building because of the perceived threat from one to another. High hazard industrial occupancies may not be located in the same building as an assembly occupancy, or a residential occupancy. Not more than one suite of a residential occupancy is permitted in a medium hazard industrial building.

d)   Separation of major occupancies

If there is more than one major occupancy in a building, it may be necessary to separate each major occupancy from adjoining ones, to protect a specific one from potential hazards occurring in the others. In the case of an assembly major occupancy, involving large numbers of persons, a care or detention major occupancy, involving persons under restraint or receiving special care or treatment, or a residential major occupancy, involving persons who may be sleeping, it is considered necessary to protect the major occupancy from a hazard created in an adjoining major occupancy. The Code therefore requires that each of these major occupancies be protected from other major occupancies by a fire separation, having a specified fire-resistance rating. This provides time to evacuate one major occupancy in case of fire in an adjoining one.

Business and personal services, mercantile, and medium and low hazard industrial occupancies do not present as serious a fire risk as a high hazard industrial occupancy. It is not necessary, therefore, to contain these occupancies in the same way. Life safety requirements are not as critical in these occupancies as they are in assembly occupancies, care or detention occupancies or residential occupancies. The occupants are awake and aware and there should be no unusual evacuation problems. Between these major occupancies, therefore, separation on the basis of major occupancy is not deemed necessary. There are, of course, requirements for separation other than those based solely on major occupancy. These separation requirements depend on the activities within a floor area and are not confined to a particular major occupancy.

13.2.7 CONSTRUCTION TYPES

1. General

The National Building Code deals with three principal types of construction: combustible, which has little inherent fire resistance unless protected; heavy timber construction, which, although combustible, has an inherent resistance to the effects of fire because of its substantial dimensions; and noncombustible construction; even noncombustible construction may require protection to prevent its collapse when exposed to fire because structural steel or reinforcing steel has its load carrying capacity reduced at elevated temperatures. The primary difference between combustible and noncombustible construction is that noncombustible materials do not burn and contribute fuel to a fire. Thus a basic noncombustible structural frame, if adequately protected from thermal effects of a fire, should remain in place throughout a fire and offer some degree of safety to occupants and fire fighters. However, the combustible components permitted in noncombustible construction do burn and contribute fuel to a fire.

Many requirements of Part 3 depend on whether the building is of combustible or noncombustible construction. Buildings greater than a specified height or area are required to be of noncombustible construction. The building area and building height limits which allow a building to be of combustible construction depend on the major occupancy classification, the number of streets the building faces, and whether or not the building is sprinklered. Since combustible construction is defined as construction that does not conform to the requirements for noncombustible construction, it is important to appreciate what is meant by noncombustible construction, and to differentiate this from the term 'noncombustible' as applied to a particular building material.

The term 'noncombustible' applied to a material, means that the material will pass the test for noncombustibility as defined in CAN4-S114-M, 'Standard Method of Test Determination of Non-Combustibility in Building Materials'. This standard constitutes a severe test, which a material either passes or fails, but is not the sole criterion for judging the acceptability of a building material. Other criteria include melting point temperature and the ability to remain in place when exposed to fire.

Since the term 'noncombustible' applies to a specific product or material, the concept of noncombustible construction is used in the Code. In this type of construction the loadbearing structural assemblies are required to be constructed of noncombustible materials, but certain combustible elements are permitted in the building, specifically those listed in Subsection 3.1.5. There are restrictions on the flame spread properties of many of the combustible materials that are permitted. Some materials used for interior finish have restrictions placed on their thickness. An assembly constructed essentially of noncombustible material, but containing combustible elements not specifically permitted in noncombustible construction, must be considered as combustible construction.

2. Combustible Construction

Combustible construction includes conventional wood frame as well as heavy timber construction. Conventional wood frame construction for residential buildings is described in detail in Part 9.

Combustible construction is permitted for most smaller buildings regulated by Part 3. In many cases combustible materials permitted by Part 9, and conforming to standards referenced in that Part, can be used without specific qualification in Part 3. These combustible buildings are typically wood frame using conventional construction techniques. If fire-resistance ratings are required, the wood studs and joists are covered with various panel membrane materials, the most commonly used being gypsum board. In smaller buildings of combustible construction the most important consideration is that the occupants can vacate the building safely by means of protected egress paths. Provided all the occupants are safe, the fire department may decide that control of the fire spread to other buildings is an adequate response and that it will not be practicable to save the property itself after the occupants have left.

By adding suitable protection to combustible framing, various levels of fire-resistance rating can be achieved. The Code recognises the use of protected wood framing having fire-resistance rating values of up to one hour. It may also be used for 1.5 hour fire separations required between a storage garage and the remainder of a wood framed building. Information on acceptable assemblies can be found in the Appendices to the Code as well as in commercial publications.

3. Heavy Timber Construction

Heavy timber construction is a special category of combustible construction and is acceptable where combustible construction would otherwise be required to have a 45 minute fire-resistance rating. This is achieved by specifying minimum sizes for columns and beams, as well as minimum values for the thickness of floor and roof components. These limits on dimensions, given that this type of construction does not normally contain concealed spaces, provide this construction with a substantial degree of fire safety. Heavy timber construction is relatively difficult to ignite and, once ignited or subjected to an exposing fire, resists collapse reasonably well. Under the standard fire test conditions, wood will char at an average rate about 0.64 mm per minute, so that after 40 minutes approximately 25 mm of the depth of the wood will have been burnt. Therefore, the larger the cross sectional area of the member, the longer the member will maintain its structural stability in a fire.

Heavy timber construction relies on the dimensions of the wood members to resist the effects of fire for close to 45 minutes. The actual period of time before collapse will depend on the fire load in the building and the size of the structural members. If the building is sprinklered, a fire of sufficient magnitude to threaten the structural integrity of the heavy timber members is unlikely to develop. This is recognised by permitting heavy timber roof assemblies in sprinklered buildings, even where noncombustible construction would otherwise be required. For additional confidence in the performance of the sprinkler system signals from the system are connected directly or indirectly to the responsible fire department.

4.   Noncombustible Construction

Noncombustible construction means that, except for combustible items specifically permitted, all components of the building regulated by the Code must be of noncombustible materials. The Code clearly indicates that in noncombustible construction most of the finishing materials and many other items not directly involved in the load carrying systems can be of combustible materials.

5.   Tents and Air-Supported Structures

Tents and air-supported structures are a special category of building construction that is regulated in Part 3. The shape of a tent is maintained by structural elements which may be in compression or tension. A fabric is draped over the structural supports to provide an enclosure that is often free form. In contrast, air-supported structures have shapes which are maintained through constant air pressure by a blower. Thus an air-supported structure has the potential for collapse if the air supply is interrupted.

These structures must conform to the spatial separations required for any other structure, subject to modifications that recognize the special features of the structure, and to the requirements for fire safety within floor areas in Section 3.3. and for exits in Section 3.4. While these structures do not have to conform to the combustibility and structural fire protection requirements of Section 3.2, since it would be impracticable for most of these structures, they have to be constructed of a material that will meet ULC-S109-M, 'Standard for Flame Tests of Flame-Resistant Fabrics and Films'. This concession is permitted on the basis that these structures do not contain interior walls, floors, mezzanines or similar construction and are not located higher than the first storey of a building.

13.2.8   FIRE SEPARATIONS

1.   Continuity of Fire Separations

The primary function of a fire separation is to act as a barrier to the spread of fire. Normally several fire separations are used in combination to surround a given space and contain fire within it, this space is termed a fire compartment. Except for openings in the outside face of a building, openings and gaps in the fire separations around a fire compartment are either provided with closures or are fire stopped. In a number of situations where it is impracticable to avoid openings, or the Code specifically permits the openings, special measures are taken to limit the spread of fire through these openings.

2.   Fire-Resistance Rating of Assemblies

Fire-resistance ratings of assemblies are established by tests or by information contained in Appendix D of the National Building Code of Canada. The test standards have changed little from those referenced in previous editions of the Code but there may be slight changes in how testing laboratories interpret the procedures. Many testing laboratories issue lists of assemblies that have been tested and shown to comply with the criteria in the test standards. Appendix D provides a method of determining a fire-resistance rating for an assembly that has not undergone formal testing.

A fire-resistance rating under the Code is based on Underwriters' Laboratories of Canada standard CAN/ULC-S101-M, 'Standard Method of Fire Endurance Tests of Building Construction and Materials'. In a wall or floor furnace, assemblies are subjected on one side to standard fire conditions intended to simulate a rapidly developing fire. Wall assemblies must be not less than 9.3 square metres in area and floor assemblies, not less than 16.7 square metres in area. The standard temperature in the furnace reaches 538C after 5 minutes, and increases to 704C after 10 minutes, 843C after 30 minutes, 927C after 2 hours, and 1093C at the end of 4 hours.

Floor/ceiling and roof/ceiling assemblies are rated for fire exposure from the underside of the assembly only. Interior walls and partitions are rated for fire exposure from each side. Exterior walls, in contrast, are rated for fire exposure only from within the building. Fire-resistance ratings are assigned to combustible as well as noncombustible assemblies; the ratings depend solely on the ability of the construction to meet the test criteria.

3.   Fire Separations and Fire-Resistance Ratings

It is important to understand the difference between the terms 'fire separation' and 'fire-resistance rating'. A fire separation is defined as a construction assembly that acts as a barrier against the spread of fire. If an assembly is required to act as a fire separation, then all openings through it must be protected. Not all fire separations are required to have a fire-resistance rating. A fire-resistance rating measures the length of time a representative portion of an assembly is able to withstand the conditions of the standard test. A column or beam may have a fire-resistance rating as a result of its ability to withstand the conditions of fire for a specified period of time, however, neither column nor beam would be able to control the spread of fire, and thus they would not act as fire separations.

In a number of situations, primarily in sprinklered buildings, a fire separation is required but no fire-resistance rating is specified. The intent is not that there be no resistance to the spread of fire at all, but rather that the fire separation prevents the spread of fire until the suppression system has actuated and controlled the fire within the fire compartment. In most buildings the normal construction of the partitions and other subdividing assemblies would result in fire-resistant ratings of 10 to 15 minutes. The automatic sprinkler system should respond to the heat of the fire within this period of time. *If the fire is smouldering and is not hot enough to actuate the sprinklers the fire-separation is expected to prevent the spread of smoke into neighbouring fire compartments.

4. Protection of Openings

A closure is defined as 'a device or assembly for closing an opening through a fire separation or an exterior wall, such as a door, a shutter, wired glass or glass block, and includes all components such as hardware, closing devices, frames and anchors'. Some closures are not required to have a fire-protection rating. The term 'fire-protection rating' is used instead of 'fire-resistance rating' because different criteria are used in determining the rating of a closure. Although the closure is subjected to the same exposure to heat as required in the standard wall and floor tests, the criteria for rating closures are less severe.

For example, closures generally do not have to meet the criterion of temperature rise on the unexposed face. Doors to exit shafts in buildings more than three storeys high, and doors opening onto a separated dead end corridor that provides the only access to exit, are exceptions to this rule. Temperature rise limits are imposed on these doors to ensure that the occupants of a building will be able to pass by the door without being unduly affected by the heat from a fire on the other side of the door. If an exit door is protected by an unoccupied vestibule or corridor, these limits are waived on the assumption that the potential for direct fire exposure is substantially reduced. Doors through fire walls have temperature rise limits because of the critical nature of this type of fire separation. Doors that are permitted to have a 20 minute fire-protection rating.

5.   Firewalls

Firewalls are special fire separations that subdivide a building into two or more entities which may be considered individual buildings for the purposes of fire protection. If a building extends across a property line and the portion on each side of the property line is under different ownership, a party wall on the property line must be constructed as a firewall. However, it is not intended that a building complex which is located on several different properties be internally subdivided by firewalls at the property lines, if the total complex has been designed to function as an integral unit. A firewall may be constructed within a building on one property and under one ownership for the purpose of applying less stringent structural fire protection requirements to each portion. The building area of each portion is less than that for the whole building, since by definition the building area can be bounded by a firewall. The firewall effectively divides the building into smaller buildings, and the structural fire safety requirements for the individual portions can be less than they would be for the building as a whole. If there are doorways or other large openings through a firewall an exception is made to this generalised permission to consider the portions independently because a fire alarm system must be designed as though the structure were one building.

A firewall is defined as having 'structural ability to remain intact under fire conditions for the required fire-rated time'. This means that if a portion of the building on either side of the firewall is exposed to a fire as intense as that simulated under standard fire test temperatures, a collapse of a portion of the building during that period would not cause the firewall to collapse. If a designer chooses to use two walls that together provide the required fire-resistance rating, the collapse of one of the walls must not damage the other wall and thereby reduce its ability to remain intact for the necessary period of time.

Firewalls must be constructed so that the required fire-resistance rating is provided by concrete or masonry. Any additional materials, including interior finish applied to the surface of the firewall, does not contribute to the required rating. If a firewall is supported on the structural frame of a building, the supporting frame must have at least the same fire-resistance rating as the firewall.

Since firewalls are intended to withstand a complete burnout of any portion of a divided building, the degree of fire resistance required for the firewall depends on the fire load of the adjacent occupancies. Mercantile occupancies, and high hazard or medium hazard industrial occupancies, have higher fire loads and the firewall is required to have a fire-resistance rating not less than four hours for these buildings. For other occupancies that have lesser fire loads, the fire-resistance rating has to be not less than two hours.

6. **Fire Stopping**

Fire stops are elements of building assemblies that are installed at strategic locations to resist the spread of fire from one space to another. Typically, fire stops perform two functions. One is to maintain the integrity of a fire separation, by filling gaps around pipe or duct penetrations. The second function is to limit the size and interconnection of concealed spaces within wall and floor assemblies, crawl spaces, attics, or ceiling spaces.

In typical wood frame construction, fire stopping of walls is normally provided by the top and bottom wall plates.

Large concealed spaces in ceiling or roof assemblies of combustible construction, including attic spaces, within which sprinklers are not installed must be fire stopped so that the area of individual compartments is not more than 300 square metres. The maximum permissible dimension in these spaces is 30 m for standard combustible construction with a flame spread rating of more than 25; if the flame spread rating of the materials exposed within the space is not more than 25, the area may be up to 600 square metres with a maximum dimension of 60 m.

A variety of materials can be used for fire stopping. The basic requirement for concealed spaces is that the material remain in place and prevent the passage of flames when it is installed in a typical assembly and subjected to the exposure conditions of Underwriters' Laboratories of Canada 'Standard Method of Fire Endurance Tests of Building Construction and Materials'. The duration of the test is 15 minutes. If a building is of noncombustible construction, the fire stopping must be noncombustible, unless it conforms to the performance requirements of the standard or consists of gypsum board or wood nailing elements used to attach finish materials. Fire stopping in combustible framed roofs on top of a building of noncombustible construction is permitted to be of combustible materials.

Typically in combustible construction, combustible materials are used. For fire stopping of small concealed spaces between nailing elements or floor sleepers, or at floor levels, 38 m thick lumber is commonly used, particularly with wood frame construction and for nailing elements used to attach interior finish to masonry exterior walls. In larger spaces, including attic spaces, crawl spaces, or spaces within gambrel or mansard roofs, plywood, strandboard, waferboard, gypsum board, or sheet materials are used.

7. **Fire Stopping of Service Penetrations**

The basic requirement for ensuring that service penetrations do not adversely affect the integrity of a fire separation is that the penetrating item be tightly fitted (eg. a pipe embedded in concrete or grouted into a concrete slab) or sealed with a fire stop system that prevents the passage of flame for the same time period expected of a closure in a fire separation. A specific ULC standard, CAN4-S115-M, is referenced for the performance evaluation of fire stop systems for service penetrations through fire separations and through membranes forming part of an assembly with a fire resistance rating, for example, a mezzanine floor assembly.

Unless otherwise permitted, all building services that penetrate a fire separation are required to be noncombustible. This requirement limits the combustible items that can be used for building services that will be incorporated within a fire separation or that pass through the separation. Products that are exempted from this requirement include optical fibre cables, electrical wires and cables and outlet boxes, and various types of piping.

8.   **Flame Spread Ratings**

Flame spread ratings are specified in various Articles in Part 3 to control the surface burning characteristics of building materials. The flame spread rating of a building material is determined by standard tests (CAN/ULC-S102-M and CAN/ULS S102.2-M) in which the specimen is mounted in a test chamber with a gas burner at one end directing a flame at the specimen; a draft is induced at the opposite end. For CAN/ULC-S102-M, the underside of the specimen is exposed to the flame. For materials intended to be installed horizontally with the top surface exposed to air (examples are carpets and attic insulation), materials that are not self supporting in the test apparatus (loose fill insulation), and materials that are thermoplastic, the top surface is exposed to the flame. Carper material intended for application on floors is tested to CAN/ULC-S102.2-M, whereas carpet material intended for application on walls is tested to CAN/ULC-S102-M. Testing agencies, manufacturers, and end users must ensure that the appropriate test procedure has been followed. This is particularly important when considering materials produced in other countries and tested to standards different from those referenced in the Code.

A flame-spread rating is calculated according to the speed at which flame travels along the test specimen or the maximum distance that flame travels in a given period of time. The rating system is complex, but essentially compares the rate of flame travel along the surface of a material against two standard materials: red oak is 100 and asbestos cement board is 0. For example, ordinary gypsum board on this scale would have a flame-spread rating of 10 to 30, and 19 mm thick untreated, unfinished softwood lumber would have a flame spread rating of 65 to 150, depending on the species of wood.

Flame spread requirements are employed in several areas of the Code. In noncombustible construction, for example, flame spread limits are specified for many of the combustible elements permitted in these buildings. A fire retardant treatment or some combustible materials used in noncombustible construction is required to penetrate the material, rather than a surface application, and in these cases the flame spread limit applies to 'any exposed surface or any surface that would be exposed by cutting through the material in any direction'. Fire retardant treated wood roof systems, which are permitted in lieu of unrated noncombustible construction, also have flame spread requirements to limit the tendency of the material to propagate flame. Fire retardant treatment processes do not significantly improve the fire-resistance rating of an assembly, nor do they reduce the fire load that is contributed by the combustible material. The treatment process primarily changes the surface burning characteristics of the material.

13.2.9 INTERIOR FINISH

1. Buildings which are Not High Buildings

In most buildings the property of the interior finish that is regulated is the flame-spread rating. Apart from the interior furnishings, the interior finish is the component that most enhances the spread of fire, particularly if it has a high flame-spread rating. It is important to reduce the rate at which fire spreads throughout an occupied area by controlling the characteristics of the finish materials, particularly on walls and ceilings. Except for some doors and bathroom finishes, which are permitted to have a flame-spread rating of up to 200, the maximum flame-spread rating of any interior finish is limited to 150. For areas in which large numbers of people gather, and for routes used during evacuation, the permissible values of flame-spread rating are much lower. Ratings are generally more restrictive for ceilings than for walls.

2. Variations for High Buildings

In high buildings, the smoke that is generated from a burning surface is an additional concern. Since evacuation of a high building takes considerable time to complete, the occupants must be protected from the effects of smoke until they have left the building or the fire has been extinguished and there is no further hazard. In high buildings the smoke emission characteristics of wall, ceiling and floor surfaces are regulated through the imposition of maximum smoke developed classifications. In these buildings, regulated by Subsection 3.2.6., there are additional restrictions on flame-spread rating of interior finish materials, in comparison to lower buildings. The additional restrictions apply primarily if the building is not sprinklered. If additional flame-spread rating requirements are specified for high buildings, restrictions on smoke developed classification are also specified. These additional limits on flame spread rating and smoke developed classification apply only to the more critical areas of these buildings, including public corridors, elevator and exit lobbies, and exit stairs and adjacent vestibules. The flame-spread rating for floor surfaces in these specific areas is also regulated.

13.2.10 OCCUPANT LOAD

Occupant load is the number of persons for which a building or part of a building is designed. The principal applications of occupant load are to determine the number and width of exit facilities that must be provided, the width of access routes leading to exits from within floor areas, the determination of the number of sanitary fixtures required in washrooms, whether a fire alarm system must be installed, and as one of the parameters used to establish whether a building is subject to the additional requirements for high buildings in Subsection 3.2.6.

Occupant load is determined on the basis of the total number of persons that the building or part of the building is expected to accommodate. Temporary occupants of service spaces, including furnace rooms and electrical equipment rooms, and transient occupants of access corridors and washrooms, would not normally be counted in determining the occupant load, since any occupants of these latter areas would have already been included in the occupant load in the regularly occupied parts of the building.

As a general rule the occupant load must be not less than that determined from table 3.1.16.1. This table shows the area assumed to be occupied per person, so that the total occupant load can be calculated. However, due to the large potential variation in population densities in most of the categories listed, it is very difficult to establish hard and fast rules for each category. For this reason, some deviation from these values may be justified if the area is to be occupied by fewer persons. In manufacturing and process rooms, for example, a value of 4.6 square metres per person is shown. Depending on the type of manufacturing operation and the degree of automation, this value can vary widely and could be excessively restrictive. In these situations, the occupant load estimates may be relaxed from those calculated from the Table, provided there is reasonable assurance that the occupant load will not be exceeded in the future. On the other hand, if the occupant load exceeds the values determined from the Table, the higher values must be used.

13.3   REQUIREMENTS FOR THE BUILDING AS A WHOLE

1.   General

This section applies to the requirements in Section 3.2. of the Code that are concerned with the building as a whole and include structural fire protection through fire compartmentation and fire-resistance rating of the structural members, spatial separation, fire alarm systems, fire suppression systems, additional requirements for high buildings, emergency equipment, and buildings with interconnected floor space.

2.   **Building Size Determination**

Throughout Part 3, many requirements depend on building height and building area.

Building area is the greatest horizontal area of a building above grade within the outside surface of exterior walls and the centre line of firewalls.

Building height is the number of storeys contained between the roof and the floor of the first storey. The first storey is the uppermost storey having its floor level not more than 2 metres above grade. Thus, a building with two storeys above the first storey is a three storey building.

Grade is defined as the lowest of the average levels of finished ground adjoining each exterior wall of a building.

4.   **Mezzanines-Effect on Determination of Building Height**

A mezzanine, by definition, is a floor assembly that lies between the floor and ceiling of a given storey, however, for many Code applications the mezzanine is treated as the space above the mezzanine floor assembly. Provided the area of this intermediate floor assembly does not exceed certain limits, it is not considered to add to the building height in storeys, even though the actual height of the storey in metres has been increased to make adequate headroom above and below the mezzanine. The area of a mezzanine is considered to be the sum of the areas of the individual portions of the mezzanine floor at approximately the same level. If a mezzanine is built as an open floor area and has no visual obstructions above or below it, except for items within 1070 mm of the floor, it need not be considered a storey.

If a mezzanine is enclosed or is visually obstructed and exceeds 10% of the floor area, it must be considered a storey for determining building height in storeys.

13.4   STRUCTURAL FIRE PROTECTION

1.   **General**

One of the main purposes of classifying the storeys of a building by major occupancy is to establish the structural fire protection requirements; the intent of these requirements is to ensure that the building as a whole will withstand collapse under fire exposure and provide floor to floor compartmentation to contain fires. The classification by major occupancy relates to the requirements to the potential fire load. To counteract the effects of this fire load, appropriate level of fire resistance is required for the load carrying members in the part of the building surrounding and including a specific major occupancy. In addition to the major occupancy classification, a number of factors are taken into account in arriving at the structural fire protection requirements. They include building height, building area, type of construction, the number of faces of the building to which fire fighting apparatus has access (based on the number of streets around the building) and whether it is sprinklered.

The Code assumes that the higher the building or the larger the building area, the greater will be the problems of evacuation and of fire fighting. On the other hand, the Code assumes that when a building faces several streets from which the fire can be fought, or when a building is sprinklered, a lower value for structural fire protection is sufficient. The number of streets that a building faces is only relevant for buildings that are not sprinklered and are not more than six storeys in building height. Most fire fighting equipment cannot reach the upper storeys of higher buildings.

2. Streets Faced

Code requirements based on the number of streets a building faces depend on the percentage of the building perimeter which is within 15 metres of a street. The Code considers fire department access routes to be equivalent to a street for the purpose of this calculation. Tunnels, bridges and similar structures from which fire fighting would be difficult are not considered access routes for the purpose of this calculation.

3. Rating of Roof Assemblies

In recognition of the fire suppression and cooling capabilities of automatic sprinklers, the Code permits roof assemblies of sprinklered buildings to be constructed without a fire-resistance rating. As required for all sprinkler systems, this sprinkler system would be electrically supervised and the fire department would receive notification if the sprinkler system were to be actuated. This contributes to the confidence that the sprinkler system will respond to a developing fire and keep its magnitude to a level that the roof assembly is not adversely affected.

4. Fire-Resistance Rating

In establishing the structural fire protection requirements for a building of a particular size and occupancy, a number of choices are usually available to the designer. In Subsection 3.2.2., which contains the structural fire protection requirements, a building containing several major occupancies may be regulated under several Articles. The owner is permitted to select the Articles that will provide the least restrictive requirements for the building.

If a building has different storeys containing different major occupancies, the entire building has to be considered for each of the major occupancies contained, except in circumstances in which the small areas (less than 10%) of a secondary major occupancy occur on the same storey as a more extensive major occupancy. If one major occupancy is located above another, then the structural fire protection requirements for the portion of the building containing each specific major occupancy are considered as if the entire building contained that major occupancy. For example, a building 1000 square metres in building area facing two streets could consist of six storeys, with the lowest two storeys used for mercantile occupancy, the next two and the top storey used for offices, and the fifth storey having a restaurant. In terms of structural fire protection, the restaurant portion would have to be designed as if it were the fifth story of a six storey building of assembly major occupancy (Group A, Division 2). The three storeys containing offices would be constructed as if they were three storeys of offices in a six storey building of business and personal services major occupancy (Group D). The first two storeys would be considered as the first and second storeys in a six storey building of mercantile major occupancy (Group E).

Although a building of Group D major occupancy of six storeys in building height does not require the installation of a sprinkler system, the presence of the restaurant on the fifth floor requires that an automatic sprinkler system be installed on that storey and on all lower storeys. The designer might choose to install the sprinkler system throughout the whole building by extending it to the sixth floor. This would increase the flexibility in designing the office portion and would permit future changes in occupancy for which the storey would have to be sprinklered. The installation of the sprinkler system on the sixth floor would also eliminate the need to provide a 1 hour fire-resistance rating for the roof assembly and the rating of the structural load bearing assemblies in that storey. Sprinkler installation is required in a mercantile building of six storeys, however, this would be automatically satisfied by satisfying the requirements for the fifth storey.

13.5   SPATIAL SEPARATION

1.   General

The concept of spacial separation ensures that buildings are spaced sufficiently apart that fire is unlikely to spread from one building to another by radiation. Part 3 assumes that, for a building that is not sprinklered throughout, fire fighting forces will respond to a call within 10 minutes of the outbreak of a fire and that these forces will apply hose streams to neighbouring buildings to keep them below the ignition temperature, in addition to fighting the original fire. The radiation levels will be reduced as the fire is suppressed. For buildings in remote locations where fire fighting is absent or will be delayed, increased spatial separation combined with other design options must be used to maintain an acceptable level of risk.

Subsection 3.2.3. contains tables that indicate the area of unprotected openings (windows, doors, etc) which can be permitted in an exposing building face. This is to inhibit ignition of an exposed surface of another building or of the interior of the other building by radiation through openings into the interior.

The Code addresses a given building on a specific property. The control of spatial separation is developed in terms of the boundaries of the property under consideration. If there is only one building on the property, then the distances are to the property lines. Building faces that front onto a street or lane are considered to have limiting distances measured to the centre of the street or lane, recognising that a building on the other side of the street or lane will be using the same reference line. If there is more than one building on a given property, the did=stances between the buildings can be considered in greater flexibility by assuming imaginary lines between the buildings located where the requirements for each building will be satisfied. If property lines are changed or the faces of a building are relocated during alteration, the effect on limiting distance must be examined and compensating measures used if the value is reduced so that the building face would no longer conform to the spatial separation requirements. These compensating measures could include the installation of an automatic sprinkler system or wired glass in fixed steel frames.

The intensity of the radiation depends upon the combustible contents of the occupancy. For this reason, the permitted area of openings for major occupancies which have higher combustible content is usually about half that permitted for occupancies with lower combustible content. Mercantile major occupancies (Group E), and high hazard and medium hazard industrial major occupancies (Group f, Division 1 and 2), have high combustible content.

2. Exposing Building Face

An exposing building face is an exterior wall of a building that could expose another building to thermal radiation and thereby cause fire to spread from one building to another. It is defined as 'that part of the exterior wall of a building which faces one direction and is located between ground level and the ceiling of its top storey'.

3. Unprotected Openings

An unprotected opening in an exposing building face is usually a window or door opening, although by definition it includes any part of a wall forming part of the exposing building face that has a fire-resistance rating less than that required for the exposing building face.

4. **Limiting distance**

Limiting distance is the distance from an exposing building face to a property line, the centre of a street or public thoroughfare, or an assumed line between two buildings or two fire compartments on the same property.

The spatial separation Tables in Subsection 3.2.3. list the maximum percentage of unprotected openings permitted in an exposing building face for a variety of limiting distances. Since the allowable unprotected openings are expressed as a percentage of the area of the exposing building face, this area is obviously important. The greater the percentage. the greater will be the total unprotected openings and the greater the thermal radiation.

5. **Exterior Wall Construction**

Except for exposing building faces in which 100% unprotected openings are permitted, and those portions of other walls that are considered unprotected openings, the exterior walls of each fire compartment are required to have a fire-resistance rating, which depends on the occupancy of the fire compartment and its limiting distance. The exterior walls may also be required to have noncombustible cladding or be of noncombustible construction, depending on the limiting distance of the exterior wall of each fire compartment.

For buildings up to three storeys in building height and for larger sprinklered buildings, it is permissible to use exterior walls that include combustible components even for a building that is required to be of noncombustible construction. These wall assemblies have to be tested in accordance with a specific standard and there are some limits based upon the permitted area of unprotected openings.

6. **Equivalent Openings**

The fire-resistance rating of an exterior wall is determined on the assumption that the wall is exposed to fire from the room side. One of the criteria for the failure of a wall assembly in the standard fire test is that the average temperature rise on the unexposed side must not be more than 140 C above ambient temperature during the rated time. The temperature rise limitation for an exterior wall ensures that any combustibles in contact with the unexposed side of the wall will not ignite. Accordingly the heat rise requirement is not considered to be necessary, provided allowance is made for the increased radiation from the surface of the wall in addition to the radiation from any openings. This additional contribution is calculated using a formula which determines an area of equivalent opening which is added to the actual openings. The result is an increase in the percentage of unprotected openings, with a concurrent increase in limiting distance, thus compensating for the increase in thermal radiation.

7.   **Fire Exposure between Fire Compartments**

If two exterior walls of separate fire compartments form an external angle of 135 Deg or less, fire could spread from one fire compartment to the other if the walls contain openings or do not have sufficient fire-resistance. To reduce this risk, each exterior wall must be constructed with limits on the amount of unprotected openings and with a fire-resistance rating not less than that of the fire-separation between the fire compartment and the rest of the building.

8.   **Protection of Exterior Exit Doors**

If the plane of a wall in which an exit door is located forms an angle of less than 135 Deg to a plane with an unprotected opening then openings that expose the doorway and are within 3 metres of the doorway must be protected.

9.   **Vertical Fire Spread**

Fire can spread up the face of a building and involve more than one floor. A special hazard can occur where the roof of part of a building is at a lower elevation than the remainder. If the lower portion of the building forms one or more separate fire compartments, then fire from a skylight opening in the lower portion could expose the face of the higher portion and simultaneously involve a number of floors in a fire. If there are windows in the wall of the upper compartment within three storeys of the lower compartment and within a horizontal distance of 5 metres from the lower roof, all skylights in the roof of the lower compartment must be at least 5 metres from the wall of the upper compartment to minimise the likelihood that fire will spread from these to the rest of the building. The restriction on the placement of skylight openings does not apply if the lower fire compartment is sprinkler

10.   **Fire Alarm Systems**

A fire alarm system is one of the major life safety systems that are installed in a building. At least one smoke alarm, interconnected with the other smoke alarms, is required on each storey of a dwelling unit. Although they are not complete fire alarm systems, smoke alarms installed in a dwelling unit are extremely important in alerting the occupants to the potential need to evacuate their unit.

Whether fire alarm systems are required depends upon a number of factors, mainly the major occupancy classification, the occupant load and the size of the building. If the building contains four or more storeys, including basement storeys, a fire alarm system must be provided regardless of the size, major occupancy classification or occupant load. Regardless of any other conditions, a fire alarm system is required in every building in which an automatic sprinkler system is installed.

Two different types of fire alarm system are specified in the Code to provide for a variety of different design conditions. The simplest is a single-stage system, in which manual pull stations or other devices send a signal to a control unit, sounding a general alarm throughout the building. The more complex system is a two-stage system, in which the actuating device sounds an alert signal to warn persons on duty that an emergency exists. This signal is followed by a general alarm initiated either by supervisory staff after verifying the emergency, or automatically within five minutes after the alert has sounded if supervisory personnel have not responded to the alert signal.

11.   Fire and Smoke Detection Systems

Typically, buildings which require a fire alarm system also require a means of automatic fire detection. A variety of devices are designed for detecting the presence of fire and smoke. The most common type of detector, which is part of a fire alarm system, is a heat detector designed to sense abnormally high temperatures or a rapid temperature rise. The disadvantage of heat detectors is that they will nit necessarily detect a fire in its early stages, when the fire is merely smouldering and the temperature is still low. A smouldering fire could produce enough smoke to cause a hazard to life before sufficient heat builds up to actuate the detector. On the other hand, these detectors need little or no maintenance and respond reliably to the temperature conditions for which they are designed.

Smoke detectors have the advantage of being able to detect the presence of fire at an earlier stage than heat detectors and thus can give the occupants of a building sufficient warning to ensure safe evacuation. Smoke detectors are of two types. A photoelectric detector measures light obscuration caused by the presence of smoke. The ionization type measures the presence of ionized particles or gases caused by a fire. Response and sensitivity of these two types differ and designers need to obtain advice from manufacturers to select the most appropriate type for a given set of criteria. Both types of detector require periodic maintenance for proper operation. Both heat and smoke detectors provide a signal to the building fire alarm system to indicate the presence of fire.

Smoke detectors of the single station type, called smoke alarms, are required to warn the occupants within a suite or dwelling unit of fire in time to safely evacuate the premises. Improvements in standards and design of these alarms, together with their relatively economical cost, make them attractive in contributing to fire safety. The Code recognises the value of these detectors and requires them in each dwelling unit and in every sleeping room not within a dwelling unit (except for care or detention occupancies that have a fire alarm system). Thus every sleeping room in hotels, motels, dormitories, and similar buildings must be equipped with a smoke alarm.

In buildings in which fire alarms are required, either heat or smoke detectors must generally be installed in the more hazardous portions, including storage rooms, service rooms, elevator and dumbwaiter hoist ways, janitors' rooms and any other room where hazardous substances are used or stored. This provided an early alarm to occupants in other areas who may be affected by a fire in these rooms. In a fully sprinklered building the release of water by a sprinkler and the subsequent operation of a waterflow detecting device gives a similar level of information compared to that provided by heat detectors. Thus heat detectors are not required in a fully sprinklered building. Smoke detectors are required in certain areas requiring a faster alarm, including egress corridors, exits, and sleeping rooms in care or detention occupancies.

Smoke detectors are required in certain air circulating systems. The prime function of these detectors is to shut down the equipment to prevent the contaminated air from being distributed throughout the building. These detectors are not intended to provide early warning, because the dilution of air from other parts of the building does not permit the system to act effectively in this manner. Any smoke detectors must be located in the fire compartment they serve.

To limit the potential for a central vacuum system to circulate smoke throughout a building, the vacuum cleaning system must shut down on actuation of the fire alarm system.

Fire alarm systems must be installed in conformance with CAN/ULC-S524-M, 'Standard for the Installation of Fire Alarm Systems'. This standard outlines the method of installing the various components of a fire alarm system. In order to ensure that the system has been installed correctly and will function in accordance with the design, it must be tested in accordance with CAN/ULC-S537-M, 'Standard for the Verification of Fire Alarm System Installations'.

12.   Annunciator and Zone Indication

An annunciator is an important part of any large fire alarm and detection system. It helps arriving fire fighters identify the location of a fire and go there directly, rather than spend time searching. The annunciator should be located close to the building entrance that would normally be used by fire fighters.

A building is zoned so that each floor can be identified, as well as other major fire compartments in the building. Some areas, including stair shafts, are identified individually so that caution can be exercised in using those facilities if they are involved in fire or have become contaminated with smoke.

13.   **Audibility of Alarm Systems**

The Code requires that fire alarm signals be clearly audible throughout the floor area in which they are installed. This includes alert signals, alarm signals and voice communication messages. Alert signals, which are intended to inform designated persons of a fire emergency, can be restricted to certain areas of the building where the designated persons are, but not necessarily on all floors, however, if there is no continuously staffed location, then the alert signal should sound throughout the building. The sound level should be sufficient to take into account any reduction in level as a result of the installation of partitions and furniture. In buildings where persons are unable to hear the signals due to high ambient noise levels, or where persons with hearing impairment are likely to be, the alarms should be supplemented by visual alarm signalling devices.

To ensure that the alarm signal is clearly distinguished from other sounds in the building, the Code requires that a specific pattern be used for the alarm signal. This pattern is a new requirement in the 1995 edition of the Code and will be available on all new fire alarm systems. If an existing system is being renovated or extended, the control unit devices that produce the sound pattern should be replaced to provide the new sound pattern.

14.   **Fire Department Access**

Two components of fire fighting access have to be considered in the design of a building. One is access to the building by fire department vehicles and personnel, and the other is access into and within the building itself.

Exterior accessibility deals with the design of streets and access routes and the location of hydrants and fire department connections.

The Code requires access openings in walls of all buildings in which an automatic sprinkler system is not installed and which are assumed to face a street. For fully sprinklered buildings, the requirement for access openings is waived, on the principle that the sprinklers will control the fire and eliminate the need to fight the fire from the exterior of the building.

Code requirements are based on the concept that easy access should be provided for the fire department to points where effective fire fighting operations can take place. Two types of fire department vehicles are involved and thus two sets of criteria for access routes are necessary.

Ladder and aerial trucks, ambulances, service vehicles, and similar emergency vehicles require direct access to the building face, so that rescue and fire fighting can be undertaken for upper levels. The fire department requires access routes up to the face of the building in which the principal entrance is located and also to every access opening in an exposing building face of a building or floor area that is not sprinklered.

The Code also provides details on access routes for a second type of fire department vehicle, the pumper. This vehicle is used to boost the available water supply by drawing from a water source, usually a hydrant, and pumping either directly through hose lines onto the fire or into a fire department connection, which in turn feeds standpipes or automatic sprinklers within the building. The pumper need not be located immediately next to the building to accomplish this task. However, it must be within 45 metres to reduce friction loss in hoses and to keep the travel distance for the fire fighter at an acceptable working limit.

Special requirements with respect to the location of the pumper vehicle depend on whether the building is equipped with a fire department connection. If the building is equipped with a fire department connection, the Code requires the connection to be within 45 metres of a hydrant.

The Code provides detailed requirements for access routes. Specific limits are set on the width, radius of curvature and overhead clearance of the access route, based on current vehicle sizes and past experience. A limit is also set on the change of gradient over short portions of the route, based on the angle of departure of the fire department vehicle. This angle of departure limit is intended to prevent a vehicle from dragging its back or centre sections as it negotiates a change in gradient. Load-carrying capabilities and surface compositions are controlled in terms of good engineering practice. Because of the difficulties in manuvering large fire department vehicles, turn-around facilities must be provided for dead-end portions of access routes longer that 90 metres.

15.   Fire Suppression Systems

A major concern in fighting a building fire is an adequate supply of water at the site. The water supply requirements for fire protection installations depend on the requirements of any sprinkler installations and also on the number of hose streams that may be needed at a fire, and the length of time the hose streams would be used. The quantity and pressure of water for the protection of both the interior and exterior must be ascertained before the water supply is decided upon. The selection of water supplies for each installation should be determined in co-operation with the authority having jurisdiction and the fire department. If water supplies are not available from a public waterworks system with sufficient pressure and discharge capacity, then the building owner would need to make other provisions, including automatic fire pumps, pressure tanks, gravity tanks or fire pumps operated by remote control at each hose station.

Fires in small buildings can be fought from hoses attached to external hydrants or pumper vehicles. If a building exceeds three storeys or 14 metres in height, an internal standpipe system is considered essential. For a building three storeys or less in building height that exceeds specified area limits (which depend on the major occupancy classification) the code requires a standpipe system unless the building is sprinklered.

If a building or part of a building is required to be sprinklered, the sprinkler system must be designed, constructed, installed, and tested in conformance with NFPA 13, 'Installation of Sprinkler Systems'. An exception to this is permitted if a total of fewer than nine sprinklers are required to give local protection to a specific area, in which case the sprinklers may be supplied from an adequate domestic water service. If the water supply piping for these sprinklers serves other equipment, separate shut-off valves are required. Typical areas for which limited local sprinkler installation would be required in a building that is not otherwise sprinklered include garbage and laundry chutes, common storage rooms in a residential occupancy, and some special service areas.

In addition to its acceptance through NFPA 13, the Code specifically permits combustible sprinkler piping in buildings. Some limits are placed on its use. It may be used only in a wet system and is restricted to floor areas, therefore it must not be installed in vertical service spaces. The combustible piping is restricted to residential and light hazard occupancies, however, the concept of light hazard occupancies in the NFPA standard includes a wide variety of uses including churches, nursing homes, offices, restaurant seating areas and theatre seating areas. A variety of protective membranes are available to protect the system piping from the sprinklered space and from other fire compartments.

Fast response sprinklers are required in residential occupancies and in care or detention occupancies. Fast response sprinklers respond to a rise of temperature much faster than standard sprinklers and so will provide an extra margin of safety in those occupancies in which the occupants may be asleep or restrained.

Waterflow signal devices are required to register a flow in the sprinkler system and transmit this information to the fire alarm system and through that system to a fire department either directly or indirectly. Electrical supervision of the sprinkler system is required to ensure that any interference with proper operation will be detected. Electrical supervision means that an electrical signal will be transmitted when a control valve is moved, a pressure loss develops, the electrical supply to the pumping system fails, the water supply becomes inadequate, or the temperature falls sufficiently to cause part of the water supply to freeze. To indicate a problem a signal is transmitted by means of the fire alarm system to the annunciator panel, at which it is registered as a visual or audible signal, and also to a remote monitoring centre which has connections to the fire department.

16.   High Buildings

A high building has a specific series of criteria that distinguish it from lower buildings. Although the criteria are predominantly established on the basis of height, the real concern is that the occupants may not have sufficient time to evacuate the building before smoke contamination in parts of the building, reaches lethal levels.

As a result of the automatic sprinkler requirements of Subsection 3.2.2. all new buildings designed under part 3 of the Code that are included in the category of high buildings will be equipped with an automatic sprinkler system.

The time required for complete evacuation of a high building can exceed the time that conditions in the building are likely to remain tenable. Studies of the stack effect in heated buildings in winter and of smoke movement in fires have shown that other measures in the Code may not prevent the movement of smoke through elevator, stair and other vertical shafts to the upper storeys of a high building. Occupants of a high building, particularly those on the upper storeys, may be faced with severe smoke conditions from a fire in storeys below them before their own evacuation is possible. Because of this and other considerations peculiar to high buildings, Subsection 3.2.6. provides additional safety features in these buildings.

The purpose of this Subsection is:

a)   To provide for the safety of the occupants of a building, either by maintaining the tenability of the occupied floor spaces during the period of a fire emergency, by providing a temporary accessible place of safety within the building, or by making it possible for all occupants to evacuate the building quickly;

b)   To maintain tenable conditions in exit stairs leading from floor spaces to the outdoors, through which occupants have to pass or in which occupants may remain.

c)   To maintain tenable conditions in elevators that can be used to transport fire fighters and their equipment from the street floor to the floor immediately below the fire floor and that can be used for the evacuation of injured persons or persons with disabilities.

It is assumed that fire fighters will use one of the protected stair shafts to walk up to the fire floor from the floor below.

13.6   LIGHTING AND EMERGENCY POWER

1.   Emergency Lighting

In order to provide a clear and recognisable path of travel for evacuation during emergency conditions, a minimum level of lighting must be maintained. Unless the power supply to the building is interrupted, it is assumed that the normal lighting in the building will be maintained. Some minimum lighting levels are specified for egress routes so that they will be easy to use. This is particularly important in buildings where the ambient lighting level is very low, as in theatres, certain restaurants and other places of entertainment. The power for emergency lighting can be supplied by a generator, however in many cases portable rechargeable battery units are used.

2.   Emergency Power Supply

For many buildings, including all high buildings, an emergency power supply will be required to operate emergency equipment and elevators. Although most power failures do not involve fire in the building, the emergency generator has to have sufficient capacity to power fire fighting equipment and devices including: fire pumps, elevators, venting devices, fire alarm systems, voice communication systems, and other ancillary devices.

3.   Interconnected Floor Space

Interior spaces that connect a number of floors in a building are commonly referred to as an atrium. For Code purposes the term 'interconnected floor space' is used and applies in a much wider sense than that of an atrium. An interconnected floor space is one in which two or more levels of a building are open to each other and the opening is not enclosed in the usual manner. Clearly then, interconnected floor space is also found in buildings whose floor areas are connected by open stairs and ramps, escalators and conveyors.

The Code normally requires all openings through fire separations to be protected by appropriate closures. The exceptions to this rule are found in Subsection 3.2.8. This Subsection starts with a general rule that any time a floor assembly does not terminate at an outside wall, a firewall or a vertical shaft, then that floor assembly must terminate at a vertical fire separation. The remainder of the Subsection deals with situations in which this vertical fire separation is not provided.

Interconnected floor space presents two major problems: the potential for rapid and progressive development of an uncontrolled fire between levels, and the lack of a barrier to prevent smoke from contaminating simultaneously all interconnected levels of the building.

A building that contains interconnected floor space must be of noncombustible construction or heavy timber construction.

Vestibules are necessary for exits opening into an interconnected floor space to provide protection for the exit. Vestibules are also required to protect elevator doors if the elevator serves floors above the interconnected floor space.

Sprinklers are required throughout a building containing an interconnected floor space. The Code, by reference to NFPA 13, requires that close-spaced sprinklers and baffles be provided around openings whose sides are closer that 6 metres or whose are is less than 93 square metres. The purpose of baffles is to restrain the products of combustion from spilling directly into the open space, and thereby provide a reservoir for these products below the ceiling level; the build up of heat ensures a faster operation of the sprinklers.

Fire alarm systems must be provided in all buildings which contain an interconnected floor space, and smoke detectors must be located around the opening in the baffled areas. The baffles help to ensure that any smoke will accumulate in the vicinity of a smoke detector.

To assist in clearing smoke from the open space, mechanical exhaust is required at the rate of four air changes per hour, based on the total volume of the interconnected space. This smoke removal system is controlled by a switch located near the street entrance. This is a manual system that would be operated by the fire fighters and not an automatic smoke control system, as is required for high buildings.

13.7   SAFETY WITHIN FLOOR AREAS

1.   General

The requirements of Section 3.3 apply to a specific occupancy within a floor area or part of a floor area, regardless of the major occupancy category of the floor area or the building. The hazards to which occupants are initially exposed are local and may have no immediate impact on persons on other storeys of the building. General items that apply in all categories of building are placed in the first Subsection, followed by other Subsections with requirements for specific occupancies.

Section 3.3. provides safety for occupants within floor areas. Even though the term 'floor area' is written in terms of the superficial area of a floor, the term 'floor area' in its broadest sense as used in Part 3 applies to all of the space on the storey, bounded by exterior walls and firewalls, from the top of the floor to the top of the floor of the next storey, but does nit include space occupied by exit stair shafts, elevator hoistways, or other vertical service spaces; it includes all the space within a storey, including that occupied by interior walls, less the area occupied by vertical shafts that extend through the storey. Although floor areas include service rooms, the requirements for these rooms are covered in Section 3.6. and not in Section 3.3. The hazard associated with a service room is specific to that space and does not relate to the occupancy of the remainder of the storey.

2.   Suites

Throughout Section 3.3. reference is made to the term 'suite'. A series of rooms that constitute a suite must be in reasonably close proximity to each other and have access to each other either directly by means of a common doorway or indirectly by an interior corridor within the suite, a vestibule, or other similar arrangement.

Tenancy in the context of the term 'suite' applies to both rental and ownership tenure. In a condominium, for example, dwelling units are considered separate suites, even though they are individually owned. The term 'suite' is not applied to service rooms, common laundry rooms and common recreational rooms that are not leased or under separate tenure. Similarly, the term 'suite' is not normally considered in the context of schools and hospitals, since the entire building is under a single tenure.

For certain requirements in the Code, the expression 'room or suite' is used (e.g. travel distance). In these cases the requirement applies within rooms of a suite as well as the suite itself and to rooms that may be located outside the suite. In other places the expression 'suite, and rooms not located within a suite' is used (e.g. installation of smoke and heat detectors). This expression means that the requirement applies to individual suites as defined, but not to each room within the suite. The rooms 'not located within a suite' include common laundry rooms, common recreational rooms and service rooms that are not usually tenant controlled space.

In general it is intended that suites be separated from one another by fire separations having an appropriate fire-resistance rating. The required fire separation will help to contain a fire to the suite of origin and prevent its spread to neighbouring suites. Suites of business and personal services occupancy, suites of mercantile occupancy, and food vending operations that do not provide customer seating, are permitted to be constructed side by side without fire separations between them provided they are located in a sprinklered building and the suites are served by a public corridor conforming to Sentence 3.3.1.4.(5).

3.   Access to Exit within a Floor Area

Access to exit in a building is a principal feature that ensures the safety of the occupants. Although commonly misunderstood to relate only to corridors, it is that part of a means of egress within a floor area that provides access to an exit serving the floor area. Means of egress is a continuous path of travel provided by a doorway, corridor, exterior passageway, balcony, lobby, stair, ramp, or other egress facility from any point in a building, floor area, or contained open space to an adjoining building, a public thoroughfare, or other safe open space.

Access to exit is the path taken from any point where a person might be when evacuation starts, to an exit facility. In most buildings the path is not a straight line but passes around furniture, fixtures, products and merchandise, and through internal corridors and doorways. Many of these obstructions to egress change periodically and there is no guarantee that the same access to exit will be available at all times. Persons who are familiar with the building normally follow the access to exit without difficulty, but those who are not regular users of the building will need help; this is usually provided by directional signs if an exit sign is not clearly visible.

Public corridors are corridors that provide access to exit from suites in a floor area that is divided into a number of suites. The term 'public corridor' does not refer to any specific category of persons who use the corridor. In comparison with corridors within suites, a higher standard of protection is expected of public corridors because of their importance in evacuating persons who may receive a delayed warning of danger arising from another suite.

Transparent doors and panels in and adjacent to means of egress within a floor area can cause injury to persons who may accidentally contact them. The primary safety measure is clear identification by decals, etching or other means, supplemented, if needed, by bars or barricades to keep persons away. Glazing in doors and side lights must be safety glass.

4.   **Egress Doorways**

A room or suite is required to have at least two egress doorways if the travel distance within the room or suite to a public corridor exceeds the area and travel distance limits of Table 3.3.1.5.A or 3.3.1.5.B. (depending on the presence or absence of an automatic sprinkler system in the floor area), the occupant load is more than 60, or the room or suite contains a high hazard industrial occupancy with an area more than 15 square metres. These doorways must be separated from each other to the extent that if one should become inaccessible, due to a fire in the room or suite, the other can be used. The same egress requirements apply to a platform, a terrace, a podium, or a contained open space, (e.g. an enclosed courtyard).

5.   **Corridors**

Corridors, other than those located within a suite, are subject to more restrictive requirements than are other parts of the floor area, since the occupant does not have direct control over that part of the escape route. These corridors are designed so that once the occupants of an adjacent space enter the corridor, they are in an area of relative safety, leading them to an exit facility.

Dead end corridors do not provide the degree of safety offered by those without dead ends. For this reason, their use is restricted in the code. The maximum length is 6 metres from the dead end to a point where it is possible to go in different directions to separate exits.

6. Capacity of Access to Exit

The capacity of an access to exit is based on its width and the number of persons that the access to exit serves. The method of determining adequacy of widths for access to exits and other exit facilities utilises a minimum width for each person, subject to minimum values when the occupant load is low.

7. Width Required for an Access to Exit

Although minimum widths are prescribed for an access to exit in terms of the space required to move occupants in an emergency, care must be taken that these routes are not blocked by items that intrude into the required width. A number of items, including handrails, are permitted to protrude into the width by up to 100 mm. Other obstructions which do not reduce the required width are allowed to protrude into corridors, but dimensional limits are imposed to ensure that these obstructions would not cause injury to a person with a visual disability who might be using the route.

When calculating the width of a corridor it is assumed that half the occupant load will use one exit and half of them the other exit, assuming each exit provides at least half of the required exit capacity. In a more complicated building, the flow patterns should assume that the majority of the occupants will move to the nearest exit.

8. Protection of an Access to Exit

If a number of suites share a floor area, the Code expects that the common route to the exit from the suites (which is termed a public corridor) should receive special protection to ensure that occupants of suites other than the one involved in fire can pass the fire suite safely while travelling towards the exit. To achieve this, the assemblies that separate the corridor from the remainder of the building are required to have a specified fire-resistance rating. If the floor area is sprinklered and the corridor does not serve a care or detention occupancy or a residential occupancy, the fire-resistance rating is waived, and, further, if the corridor is more than 5 metres in unobstructed width, the fire separation is waived entirely.

9. **Travel Distance to an Exit**

The travel distance to an exit governs the time necessary for a person to evacuate the space. If a room or suite adjoining a corridor is separated from the corridor by a fire separation with a fire-resistance rating of a least 45 minutes, the travel distance to the exit is measured from the doorway of the room or suite. The travel distance within the room or suite under these circumstances is based upon the requirements of Article 3.3.1.5. and the corridor has to be separated from the rest of the floor area by a fire separation conforming to the requirements for public corridors, whether or not the corridor is a public corridor. A similar relaxation in the measurement of travel distance is applied in a sprinklered building, provided there is a fire separation between the corridor and the rooms or suites, even though the fire separation is not required to have a fire-resistance rating.

10. **Doors in a Access to Exit**

All doors in an access to exit should swing on a vertical axis in the direction of travel, however, certain doors are permitted to open into a room away from the direction of travel towards an exit. These are usually small rooms with a low occupant load or doors entirely within a suite. Sliding doors are permitted where persons are under restraint and the doors will be released by security personnel. The hardware on other doors should permit persons who are not under restraint to readily open the door without keys or specialized knowledge and make their way to an exit. In rooms with a large occupant load, the hardware must release when pressure is applied and allow the door to swing open freely. Sliding doors are permitted in areas not under security control, but these doors must be able to swing freely in the direction of exit travel if they are pushed.

11. **Assembly Occupancies**

Special requirements apply to floor areas used for assembly occupancy, to provide for the large numbers of occupants using these buildings. Most requirements are concerned with seating and aisle arrangements, and with guards and railings to prevent falls. Relaxed provisions are allowed for outdoor places of assembly. These facilities are not enclosed and smoke is not likely to accumulate in occupied areas in the event of a fire because the smoke should be able to rise away from the seating areas into the open air.

12. **Tablet Arms**

The Code intends that where seat bottoms are fixed, a clear passage of 400 mm must be measured from the front edge of the seat bottom to the back of the seat in front. In some educational lecture rooms, the seats are equipped with tablets attached to the arms to allow the students to take notes. If the tablets are fixed in position, or require a complicated movement to retract them, the clear passage has to be measured from the front of the tablet. However, in the case of a tablet arm that will fall into its housing by gravity when raised to the vertical position, the Code will permit the distance between the rows of seats to be measured with the tablets in the retracted position.

13.   Theatre Stage Protection

Although the Code requires in Section 3.3. that stages used for theatrical performances be sprinklered, together with the ancillary spaces that serve the stage area, this should be automatically satisfied because a Group A, Division 1 building always has to be fully sprinklered. The stage area is required to be separated from the ancillary areas by a fire separation with a one hour fire-resistance rating and all of these facilities must be separated from the seating area by a fire separation with a one hour fire-resistance rating. However, recognizing the need to have an opening between the stage and the audience, the Code permits the proscenium opening to be equipped with a fire curtain to act as a closure in the opening. Traditionally these fire curtains were fabricated with asbestos fibres, but it is almost impossible now to find appropriate materials. The Code permits the omission of the fire curtain if a sprinkler deluge system is used to protect the opening.

14.   Care or Detention Occupancies

Care or detention occupancies are those in which the majority of occupants are unable to evacuate the building by themselves because of physical restraints due to age or illness or because they are under security control and require other persons to release locking devices that restrict their egress. Code requirements for care or detention occupancies primarily involve additional fire safety measures to compensate for the inability of the occupants to take effective action in the event of an emergency. A basic assumption is made that persons under security control will be able to evacuate without difficulty when the locking devices have been released; persons with physical constraints must remain in place until another person helps them reach a place of safety.

In hospitals and nursing homes, fire separations are required to separate sleeping rooms from each other except when two or more intercommunicating rooms have an occupant load of not more than five, in which case the walls between the rooms need not be fire separations. In a fully sprinklered building, the fire separations between sleeping rooms are not required to have a fire-resistance rating. In addition, the Code requires corridors to be separated from adjacent rooms, but exempts doors serving patient's rooms from the requirements for positive latching devices if the doors are equipped with roller latches. Further, the code waives the requirement for self closing devices on doors between patients' rooms and corridors on the assumption that there will be sufficient trained staff of duty at all times who will respond in an emergency by closing all patients' room doors, if deemed necessary.

To permit the horizontal movement of patients to a relatively safe location, floor areas containing patients' sleeping rooms in hospitals and nursing homes must be divided into two or more zones, separated from each other by fire separations. These zones must be large enough to contain both their own occupants and the occupants of the largest adjacent zone; the travel distance to a zone door must not exceed 45 metres in a sprinklered building. These zones permit patients to be moved horizontally away from a fire, thus avoiding the difficulty of moving them down stairs.

15.   Residential Occupancies

Subsection 3.3.4. is concerned with fire separations around residential suites and with egress from suites and dwelling units in residential occupancies. There must be no confusion between egress doors from dwelling units and exit doors from dwelling units. An egress door leads into a corridor or another shared facility that leads to an exit, whereas the exit door leads into an exit enclosure or directly to the outside. A single exit from a dwelling unit is permitted if the exit is an exterior door within 1.5 metres of ground level, and the travel within the dwelling unit is limited to one storey above or below the exit storey, except when the highest floor level of the dwelling unit is served by a balcony within 6 metres of ground level.

A multi-storey dwelling unit in an apartment building is required to have an exit or egress door located at the upper and lower floor levels. An exception to this rule occurs when the upper and lower floor levels in a dwelling unit are provided with an egress door within 1.5 metres of both the upper and lower floors.

16.   Sound Transmission

To ensure a reasonable reduction of unwanted d=sound from other areas of the building, the construction assemblies separating dwelling units from other areas are required to have a sound transmission class rating of not less than 50, except in the case of assemblies separating dwelling units from elevator hoist ways and refuse chutes; there the value is 55.

17.   Industrial Occupancies

Additional restrictions are placed on industrial occupancies, depending on the degree of hazard that occurs as a result of the production, storage or use of products. These restrictions relate to fire separations, fire protection systems and protection of hazardous equipment or processes. The National Fire Code of Canada includes requirements relating to different classes of products used, manufactured or stored in industrial buildings and provides rules for the incorporation of fire safety measures that are not included in the National Building Code of Canada. The intent of the National Building Code of Canada is that a designer should consult the National Fire Code of Canada for specific requirements whenever an industrial building is being designed or altered.

Repair and storage garages are classed as industrial occupancies. They require separation from all other parts of the building in which they are located to minimize the risk to occupants from fire or explosion from volatile fuels and also from the health hazards caused by products in vehicle exhausts. A repair garage is any space within a building in which repairs or maintenance of vehicles takes place. A 2 hour fire-resistance rating is required for the fire separation between a repair garage and any other occupancy.

A storage garage is any space within a building where vehicles are parked for various periods of time, and includes unloading docks and ambulance entrances at hospitals. Many apartment buildings include first floor storage for vehicles, in which the floors cantilever over the space where the vehicles are parked. This area is a storage garage and should be separated from the remainder of the building by a fire separation with a 1.5 hour fire-resistance rating.

Buildings in which one or more bays or rooms are individually rented to persons to store personal property are considered as industrial buildings. Because the contents can be varied and there is little control over the method of storing, these buildings should be classified as medium hazard industrial occupancies. If an automatic sprinkler system is not installed throughout the building, the Code requires that each individual rented area be separated from its neighbours by fire separations having at least a 45 minute fire-resistance rating.

13.8   EXITS

1.   General

Egress from a building is divided into two components; the path of travel to reach an exit (access to exit), and the path of travel within the exit. In the previous section, the components involved in travelling to an exit were discussed, this section considers the design of the exit itself.

An exit is defined as that part of a means of egress that leads from the floor area it serves to a safe location. A door opening directly to the outside at ground level fulfils this requirement. The Code recognises a number of other exit facilities; interior and exterior passageways and ramps, fire escapes and horizontal exits.

The portion of a means of egress that is designated as the exit starts at the boundary of a floor area and is expected to provide a substantial protection from exposure to a fire within the floor area and from lower floor areas that would have to be passed while using the exit stair. In the case of a single storey building the exit is usually an exterior door leading directly to the outside. In the case of multi-storey buildings the exits from the upper floors usually consist of interior stairs that are enclosed within protective shafts. Although not frequently used on buildings more than three storeys in building height, the exit stairs from upper floors can be outside the building and unenclosed, subject to protection from fire in the building.

The difference between an interior exit passageway and public corridor is often questioned. An exit passageway must be designed as an exit for occupant flow in one direction. This applies to both interior and exterior passageways. The fire separation between a passageway and a floor area must be rated as an exit fire separation. There can be no openings in this fire separation except for exit doors, and openings for standpipes, sprinkler system piping, and smoke control system ducts serving the exit. Certain rooms are not permitted to open directly into an exit. Doors opening into an exit passageway must open in the direction of the passageway and thus, for the most part, be recessed to avoid obstructing the exit. An exit passageway is subject to substantially more restrictive requirements than a public corridor, due to its role as an exit. An exit passageway would normally be designed for unidirectional flow of the occupants, whereas most public corridors must allow for movement in two directions to two different exits. An exit passageway may not contain an occupancy, whereas a public corridor may contain an occupancy. Flame-spread ratings are more restrictive for exit passageways than for public corridors. A public corridor is part of the floor area, whereas an interior exit passageway is located outside the floor area.

The Code limits the use of transparent panels and mirrors in or adjacent to exits. The restriction on transparent panels is intended to reduce the possibility of injuries arising from breakage of the panels during crowding in an emergency and the confusion that can arise if the presence of the panel is not obvious and intervenes between the person and the exit. Mirrors are restricted to reduce the possibility that the real exit location is reflected in the mirror and could cause evacuating persons to collide with the mirror or head in the wrong direction.

In most buildings at least two separate exits are required. This provides a degree of redundancy in case one exit were to be blocked and provides a route for fire fighters to reach a fire floor while allowing one exit to be used for the continuing evacuation of occupants. If more than two exits are provided from a floor area, the Code permits convergence of some of the exit routes, provided not more than 50% of the required egress capacity of the building is provided by any one converged exit facility.

---

2. **Width of Exits**

The primary factor used to determine the width of exits is the occupant load of the floor area. This concept was discussed earlier.

The width of exits is calculated by multiplying the occupant load for the floor area by the stated number of millimetres for each person. In a symmetrical plan it would be assumed that half the occupants travel to each exit. In a stairway the required widths of exit are not cumulative from floor to floor (i.e. the width of stairway does not increase as one proceeds down the stair from upper to lower storeys). Exceptions to this general rule apply in situations in which exits from more than one floor converge, or to exits that serve an interconnected floor space.

Exits are subject to minimum widths, but are allowed to have encroachments for handrails, stair stringers, door hardware and door leaves. Although the Code permits obstructions in corridors within a floor area, subject to limits to minimise hazards in the path of persons with visual disabilities, these obstructions are not permitted in exit facilities.

3. **Clear Height within an Exit**

The minimum headroom clearance in an exit facility is 2100 mm. In the case of stairways, doorways and beneath door closers slightly less headroom clearance is permitted.

4. **Number of Exits and Travel Distance to Them**

With few exceptions, every floor area must be served by at least two exits. One exception allows single exits for small suites in one and two storey buildings in which the occupant load does not exceed 60 persons, the travel distance is minimal and the floor area does not contain a high hazard industrial occupancy. Dwelling units are the other major exception.

It is recognised that the presence of an automatic fire suppression system will reduce the threat to the occupants of the building from a fire and thereby allow an extra length of time for the evacuation to take place. In a sprinklered building the permitted travel distance is usually greater than in a building that does not have an automatic sprinkler system.

Travel distance is defined as the distance from any point in a floor area to an exit measured along the path of travel to the exit. Many buildings do not have developed interiors when they are initially constructed and approximate travel distances are used based upon experience of similar existing buildings. During the occupancy of the building, walls and partitions will be installed or relocated and can easily produce extended travel distances that greatly exceed the permitted values.

The Code permits variations in the method of measuring travel distance in large shopping complexes, in sprinklered floor areas and in open air parking structures.

One of the criteria in determining the number of exits is the travel distance to an exit. Limits on the travel distance to the nearest exit are governed by occupancy The maximum travel distances permitted by the Code are:

a)   25 metres within a high hazard industrial occupancy,

b)   40 metres within a business and personal services occupancy,

c)   45 metres within a sprinklered floor area, other than one used for a high hazard industrial occupancy,

d)   60 metres within an open air storage garage complying with Article 3.2.2.83.,

e)   105 metres within a floor area served by a public corridor complying with Clause 3.4.2.5. (1) (d),

f)   30 metres for any other application.

Limiting travel distance to an exit is one way to reduce the hazard to the occupant. The measurement of travel distance is, therefore, important in the Code context. For an open floor area that serves a single tenant, the travel distance is measured from any point on the floor area to the nearest exit door. If however, the room or suite is separated from the remainder of the floor area by 45 minute fire separations or is located in a sprinklered floor area and surrounded by fire separations that are not required to have a fire-resistance rating, the travel distance can be measured from the suite door to the exit.

5.   Distance between Exits

The Code assigns a minimum distance between exits of half the diagonal dimension of an open floor area or 9 metres in floor areas served by a public corridor. If a floor area is divided by a fire separation, with not less than one third of the floor area on one side of the fire separation, and occupants must pass through the fire separation to travel from one exit to the other, then the minimum distance does not apply.

6.   Doorways

Exit doorways must have a headroom clearance not less than 2030 mm (this can be reduced to 1980 mm to allow for closers) and a clear width not less than 790 mm, except that this clear width must be 1050 mm if the doorway serves patients' sleeping rooms.

A door serving an exit facility is normally required to swing on a vertical axis in the direction of travel to the exit. This ensures that the door will not be blocked from opening if a person collapses against it. Sliding doors are acceptable for exits leading directly outdoors at ground level, provided they can swing on a vertical axis when pressure is applied in the direction of exit travel.

Doors that revolve around a central axis are permitted to form part of an exit route. The Code recognises two main types. One type is relatively small in diameter and forms a constriction on the movement of persons through the doorway. This type of door is not credited with an egress capacity of more than 45 persons per door and in addition requires swinging doors with equivalent capacity to be located alongside the revolving doors.

A different type of revolving door is one that has a diameter usually 3 metres or more and has special door leaves that can collapse in an emergency and remain in a position that does not obstruct passage through the doorway. Full exit capacity is credited based on the clear width when the door leaves are in the parked position and no swinging doors are required. These doors provide sufficient capacity that they can be used in a barrier-free path of travel. For movement of a wheelchair through these doors a button is included that temporarily slows the rotation of the door to a speed compatible with that of a wheelchair.

To ensure that a person standing or moving on a flight of stairs is not injured by an opening door, it is required that the edge of the door must be at least 300 mm away from the closest riser. Exit doors cannot reduce the required exit width by more than 50 mm for each door leaf. This 50 mm allowance gives some latitude for door hardware and the obstruction of the door in the open position.

7.   **Door Release Hardware**

Except for doors that are under security control, exit doors and doors from dwelling units must be operable from the inside without the use of keys, special devices or specialised knowledge of door-opening devices. The intent is to permit a person to leave the space in an emergency even if they do not have a key or are unaware of specific operations needed to release the door. Exit doors as well as principal entrance doors are not permitted to have hardware that requires more than one releasing operation.

The Code recognises that there are circumstances in which an owner wishes to control egress during normal use of the building. Thus, doors equipped with magnetic locking devices are permitted at exit locations, except for high hazard industrial occupancies, provided the devices release immediately in an emergency. It is also necessary that the device release within 15 seconds of a person applying pressure to the opening hardware.

Banks and retail stores warrant additional security to reduce the potential for theft and other criminal activity. This need is recognised by the Code by permitting locking devices, that cannot be released from inside the building, on exit doors. However, there are several conditions imposed if this option is used. An automatic sprinkler system must be installed throughout the building, lighting, both normal and emergency, must be maintained in operation while the doors are locked, a telephone must be available, and several requirements apply to the exits to ensure that there are always sufficient openable exit doors at any time that persons are known to be in the building.

In exit stairways in buildings more than six storeys in building height, doors must be openable from the stairway side so that a person does not have to travel up or down more than two storeys to reach an unlocked door to permit the person to re-enter a floor area to reach another exit should the first stair shaft become contaminated by smoke.

8.   Separation of Exits

The walls of an exit shaft must have the same fire-resistance rating as required for the floor through which it passes, with a minimum rating of 45 minutes. Exit doorways, openings for standpipe and sprinkler piping, electrical wiring, noncombustible conduit and piping that serve the exit, and openings for smoke control are the only openings permitted in exit separations.

Exit doors other than exterior doors are closures in a fire-separation. They must have the prescribed fire-protection rating and be equipped with rated hardware and latches. As previously discussed, some exit doors must also provide protection against temperature rise on the unexposed face for specified time periods.

9.   Lobby

The only exception to the continuous fire separation for exits is for a protected lobby. For some buildings it is desirable to have surveillance of persons who are leaving the building by means of the exit stairs. A typical solutio is to include a lobby at the foot of the stairs and have security personnel monitor the movement of persons through the lobby.

Lobby designs conforming to the intent of the Code should not create a hazardous condition. The Code permits occupants to leave exits and pass through the lobby to the continuation of the exit, provided certain criteria are met. These criteria include the establishment of a maximum 15 metre path of travel through the lobby, limits on the adjacent occupancies, and fire separations between the lobby and adjacent spaces.

The doors to elevator hoist ways are not permitted to open onto an exit, and similarly, an elevator hoist way entrance is not permitted to open onto a lobby that forms part of an exit route.

10.   Flame Spread in Exits

Since fire fighters often use exit stair shafts to reach the fire long after the occupants have evacuated, flame-spread rating of the surfaces within the exit shaft is restricted. Only 10% of wall and ceiling finishes in exits can have flame-spread ratings of up to 150; the remainder of the finish materials are required to maintain a rating of 25. This permits some use of combustibles for finishes, including wood handrails and trim.

11.   Interior Exits

Interior exits consist primarily of stairways and passageways, however in some situations ramps may also be used. The doorway by which the exit is entered is also considered to be part of the exit. In cases where there are two buildings side by side or a building is internally divided by a firewall, horizontal exits will be encountered. These are exits that lead into another building instead of leading to the exterior.

In the case of exit doors leading directly to the exterior, a fire-protection rating is not normally required, however, in the case of a horizontal exit the door is required to have a fire-protection rating that will depend on its precise location and the fire-resistance rating of the wall in which it occurs.

12.   Exterior Exits

The exterior part of an exit system can include passageways, ramps and stairs. The Code intends that an exit leads to an open public thoroughfare or an exterior space protected from fire exposure from the building and having access to an open public thoroughfare. Unless a building is surrounded by a large open space at a sufficient distance from the building that the occupants from the building would not be exposed to the building fire the normal exit route terminates at the boundary between the property on which the building is located and a public street or thoroughfare. Thus steps, ramps and sidewalks between the building and the street are included as part of the exit and are regulated by the Code. For most buildings this part of the access system to the building is part of a barrier free path of travel and will have to meet appropriate requirements.

13.   Stairs

Stairs are an important part of a means of egress in an emergency, they are also used on a daily basis for circulation within the building. As a result of this frequent use, any anomaly or problem will exacerbate the number of falls and consequential injuries. During daily use of stairs, the building occupants may be carrying items in their arms and be unable to make full use of handrails and other safety devices and for this reason it is important to avoid or remedy designs that may lead to injuries. The dimensions required by Part 3 of the Code should control the number and severity of falls on stairs in complying buildings.

14. Handrails

The function of handrails on a stair is to provide an object that can be gripped and lessen the effect of a fall as well as being a guidance device to persons who have difficulty in negotiating the stairs by reason of physical or visual disability. Handrails must be easily graspable and should have sufficient clearance that a person's hands cannot be trapped between the handrail and the wall to which it is attached. A 300 mm horizontal extension parallel to the landing is required at the top and bottom of handrails to provide a cue to persons with impaired vision and as an assistance to persons who have difficulty in negotiating stairs. The height of this extension above the landing should be the same as its height above the nose of the stairs.

15. Guards

A guard is intended to prevent a person from falling from one level to a lower level. In addition to the height of the top of the guard, the presence of openings through the guard is critical. The top of a guard should be set above the centre of gravity of most persons coming into contact with it, accidentally or deliberately. With a tendency to an increase in height for the population of Canada there has been an increase in the height of guards during the time the Code has been published. The current height of 1070 mm should prevent the majority of falls, but cannot prevent falls that occur from persons who climb onto the guards or who engage in hazardous activities.

The size of the openings is clearly stated in the Code. An opening of not more than 100 mm is permitted, however, the Code allows the use of larger openings provided it can be shown that these larger openings do not present a hazard. The 100 mm value is based on the physical dimensions of young children and is intended to prevent them forcing their bodies or heads through a gap in the guard and then falling through or becoming asphyxiated or otherwise injured.

16. Horizontal Exits

A horizontal exit is one that permits occupants to move from a floor area in one building to a floor area of an adjacent building, either via a passageway or through a firewall. The Code requires that the floor area on either side of a horizontal exit be large enough to accommodate the occupant load of both sides.

Doors in a horizontal exit must be designed to swing in both directions, or paired doors must be provided, one opening in each direction.

17.   **Signs indicating Presence of Exits and their Location**

The purpose of exit signs is to direct occupants of a building to facilities that will enable them to evacuate the building in safety.

In large buildings there is a need to classify which of the many doors and corridors lead to places of safety. This is accomplished by placing signs above or adjacent to the exits from each floor area as well as placing directional signs, pointing in the direction of the exits, in locations within the floor area from which the principal exit signs cannot be seen.

The Code provides two choices for exit signs. One is to use an internally illuminated sign, the other is to use a sign that is externally illuminated.

All exits require illumination to enable a person to use that exit safely.

18.   **Fire Escapes**

Fire escapes are not permitted on new buildings. In the case of existing buildings it is recognised that it may not be possible or practicable to modify existing exit facilities to allow for changes in the use of a building and an increase in the number of occupants who might have to use the exits. A fire escape is essentially an exterior stairway that is built to less stringent standards than would apply to an exterior exit stairway. Even though the Code accepts the use of fire escapes to improve exiting from an existing building, it limits their use to the first two storeys above ground level for care or detention occupancy buildings and the first five storeys above ground level for other buildings.

13.9   SERVICE FACILITIES AND VERTICAL TRANSPORTATION

1.   Service Facilities

The service facilities in a building that are covered by the Code are those facilities that are installed in the building to provide control of the building environment, to provide lighting and other electrical services including telephone and communication circuits, to supply water and remove sanitary wastes and rainwater, to provide fire fighting water supply as well as fire detection and alarm systems, to provide for the vertical movement of supplies and waste materials within chutes and dumbwaiter systems, and to provide for transportation of the occupants and their property between levels.   Processing equipment in industrial occupancies, medical care equipment, other than medical gas systems, in care or detention occupancies, and furnishings and domestic appliances in residential occupancies are examples of items that are not considered service equipment for purposes of the Code.   Most service facilities can be considered in the two broad categories of equipment and of interconnecting piping and wiring.   The equipment is normally located in a service room whereas the linking elements are normally found in service spaces.

Section 3.6. contains specific requirements for service facilities.   These include service rooms, containing equipment serving the building, and horizontal and vertical service spaces, which are used to install wiring and piping from service rooms to the spaces served and also from room to room.   Elevator systems are included in Section 3.5., which also includes requirements for escalators and dumbwaiters.

Many of the requirements of this Section relate to fire separations or other fire protection equipment needed to protect the service facilities.   Equipment in service rooms, especially fuel-fired equipment, has the potential to start fires, so the service rooms are isolated from the remainder of the building by fire separations.   Service spaces contain wiring and piping that form part of the emergency systems of the building and these must be separated from other parts of the building in which a fire could occur.   The separations around service spaces also protect the remainder of the building from a fire that might start or travel through a service space.

2.   Service Rooms

The function of a service room is to contain service equipment.   An appropriate fire-resistance rating should be provided and openings between the service room and the remainder of the building must be properly fire stopped or equipped with closures.

Some types of equipment are subject to explosions and service rooms containing this type of equipment (some boilers, transformers and refrigeration plants) must not be placed under exits.

3.   **Service Spaces**

Service spaces are included in a building to contain building services. The services include piping, wiring, ducts and other distribution and control facilities. It is not intended that fuel-fired equipment or other equipment with a potential to start a fire be included in a service space.

Service spaces are normally concealed behind building finishes and occur in shafts, walls, floors, ceiling spaces and roof spaces. A major concern involves the interconnection of these spaces. A fire that breaks into a service space or that starts in a service space can easily spread through a building if the service spaces are interconnected. Because these spaces are hidden within the building structure it is difficult to detect a fire in these spaces and difficult for fire fighters to ensure that a fire has been fully extinguished. The Code requires that the intersections of different service spaces be blocked with fire stopping.

a)   **Vertical Service Spaces**

Vertical service spaces are shafts that penetrate storeys of a building and have building services installed in them including heating and ventilating ducts, plumbing pipes, or electrical cables. Vertical service spaces may also be used as smoke shafts for the removal of smoke in a high building. Vertical service spaces also include linen and garbage chutes. Vertical service spaces do not include shafts for exits.

In order for these vertical service spaces to function effectively it is necessary to have openings leading from them into the storeys. These openings must be effectively fire stopped and in the case of ducts there should be functional fire dampers at locations where they penetrate rated fire separations.

Sprinklers are required in refuse and linen chutes and in the room into which the chute discharges. These sprinklers, intended to control any fire which originates in the chute, are required at the top and at each alternate floor level.

b)   **Horizontal Service Spaces**

Horizontal service spaces primarily occur as crawl spaces within floor ceiling assemblies and spaces within roof systems. The Code intends that these spaces have limits on their size to control the potential spread of fire.

If the concealed space above the ceiling is to be used as a plenum for heating, ventilating or air conditioning systems, then the types of material that can be located in the space are restricted. The intent is to reduce the possibility of fire spreading in the space and producing smoke, which could be spread through the air handling system, either by fans or by the normal stack effect in the building.

c)   **Interstitial Service Space**

In some large buildings, particularly in health care facilities, in which specialised functions are undertaken, the space above the ceiling is increased in height to permit service personnel to enter the space and undertake maintenance or renovation activities without disturbing the space below. In the majority of these spaces catwalks or a solid deck are installed to provide a suitable surface for the workers to use. This surface may also be used to support portions of the building services located within the space.

As a result of the potential to start fires in those spaces, several requirements address the particular concern of safety, not only for the occupants of the storey immediately below the service space but also for persons who could be working within the space. An initial concern is that materials for maintenance could be stored within the space, and packing materials could be highly combustible and far exceed the characteristics of normal building materials. A second concern is that building occupants could be attracted to the large open space and start using it for storage of supplies for the building. This would be difficult to control and would require frequent inspection to verify the absence of combustible material.

To minimise spread of fire, the Code intends that horizontal service spaces and vertical service spaces should not be interconnected, and that vertical service spaces should be separated from these horizontal spaces by fire separations with fire-resistance ratings based upon those of the walls of the vertical service space.

There is a potential for these spaces to be used for returning air to a central conditioning unit and if this is done the service space must also conform to the requirements for plenums.

4.   **Air Duct and Plenum Systems**

Part 6 of the Code includes requirements pertaining to heating, ventilating and air-conditioning equipment and its operation. Items that were formerly in Part 6 for the purpose of controlling flammability of ducts and other items in service spaces have been relocated into Part 3. Selection of equipment and other items to ensure satisfactory performance in controlling the indoor environment are still in Part 6.

Requirements are included to address the clearance that is required between a duct carrying heated air and combustible material. In many cases the nearby combustible material consists of the wood frame construction of the building.

5. Vertical Transportation

A number of different devices are used in a building to provide vertical transportation between different floor levels for persons, goods and other items. Two devices predominate in this function; elevators and escalators. The design, construction, installation and maintenance of elevating devices are fully covered in the Safety Code for Elevators, CAN/CSA-B44.

In addition to their role in moving persons during normal use of the building, elevators are also used by fire fighters and other emergency personnel. In a fully sprinklered building the elevators continue to operate during an emergency, unless they are manually recalled to a specific level by persons in authority. To improve the tenability of elevator systems in an emergency a number of requirements are included in the code.

An elevator hoist way has to be separated from the remainder of the storey it serves, or through which it passes, by a fire separation that has the same fire-resistance rating as would be required for an exit stair shaft. Considering that the elevator machine room cannot easily be separated from the hoist way it serves, the Code permits the omission of the fire separation that would otherwise be required between the elevator machine room and the hoist way provided the machine room and hoist way are separated from the remainder of the building by the same level of fire separation as would be required for the hoist way.

a) Wheeled Stretchers

Part 3 includes requirements that affect the design and installation of elevators to ensure that at least one will have sufficient size and accessibility for ambulance and paramedic personnel responding to a person with a medical emergency. The size is based on a wheeled stretcher unit used in the extended position. It is intended that the stretcher and two attendants should be able to enter and use the elevator and continue initial treatment of a person with a major injury or other medical trauma and expedite their transfer to hospital facilities.

13. 10 HEALTH REQUIREMENTS

1. General Health Requirements

Health requirements included in Part 3 are primarily concerned with those aspects of the building that could result in sickness or discomfort for the occupants. Part 3 does not regulate health and safety matters that are under the jurisdiction of other authorities including those responsible for the health and safety of workers, swimming pools, and the preparation and storage of food.

2. Height and Area of Rooms

Part 3 contains a basic statement that the height of any room or space should be sufficient to ensure that adequate light and air can be provided for the occupancy and that there are no obstructions below the ceiling level which would contact a person using the space. Lighting can be provided through the use of windows supplemented by artificial lighting, or can be provided without the use of windows. The height within any space is related to the activities occurring in the space. The minimum value of 2100 mm will be substantially increased in recreational facilities and industrial occupancies, however, there is no specific value given in the Code other than the minimum.

In new construction unobstructed height in dwelling units is required to conform to Part 9. Most existing dwelling units more than meet the minimum height given in Part 9.

3. Windows

Although the requirements for windows in Section 3.7. are intended to provide a reasonable quantity of daylight into rooms in dwelling units, these windows may also provide natural ventilation, venting of a fire in the dwelling unit, and access to the dwelling unit from the exterior for fire fighters, if the window is within reach of ladders. The area of windows is required to conform to Subsection 9.7.1.

4. Ventilation

Part 3 makes reference to ventilation to ensure that designers are aware of the need to provide ventilation in Part 3 buildings.

5.   **Plumbing Facilities**

Although the National Plumbing Code, or any municipal, provincial or territorial plumbing regulation, governs the installation of a plumbing system, it does not stipulate the types or numbers of sanitary facilities that are required in a building. These requirements are contained in the Code. Part 3 requires any building situated on a property that abuts a street having a water main have a plumbing system that includes a potable water supply, a sanitary drainage system and toilet fixtures. In the absence of a water main other means for the disposal of human waste are required.

Section 3.7. includes rules concerning the number of water closets, urinals, and lavatories that are required in a new building based upon the expected occupant load and the proportion of males and females in the occupant load.

13.11   BARRIER FREE DESIGN

1.   **General**

Requirements for barrier-free design are intended to address the specific needs of persons who have physical disabilities. Although most categories of disability have been considered by committees developing the Code, there can be specific combinations of disabilities that may impact the ability of a person to use a building. Many municipalities, provinces and territories have regulations that vary from or are more stringent than Section 3.8. It is necessary for a designer to consult with local authorities to ensure that all variations are accounted for and have been satisfied in the building design.

Although Section 3.8. is contained within Part 3, it is also referenced by Part 9. Thus many buildings that are within the scope of Part 9 also have to be designed to satisfy the requirements of Section 3.8.

Section 3.8. is predominantly concerned with providing barrier-free paths of travel for persons in wheelchairs. Although there is some coverage in the Section of requirements for persons with hearing disabilities, many requirements for persons whose disability does not require the use of a wheelchair are included in other Sections of Part 3. Unless these other Sections are referenced by Part 9, they would not apply to a Part 9 building. Examples of requirements not contained within Section 3.8. include provision of visual alarm devices to warn persons with hearing disabilities of the possible need for evacuation, as well as stair marking and handrail extensions to assist persons with visual disabilities in the use of ramps and stairs. Many other requirements in Part 3 have been modified or developed in response to requests by individuals and groups representing those persons with physical disabilities. An example is the requirement to address egress in buildings with barrier-free paths of entry. The means to address this include balconies or fire compartments that can provide an area of refuge or elevators that will function in an emergency and provide an alternative means of egress to stairs.

2.   Path of Travel

The path of travel that is considered by Section 3.8. starts outside the building and ends at each location that there is a feature or service that is to be used by the person with a physical disability.

In some buildings suites are located on the main level of the building near ground level and each suite is completely separated from the rest of the building. If the building is within the scope of Section 3.8., each suite that is used for assembly occupancy, for business and personal services occupancy, or for mercantile occupancy is required to be provided with an entrance that is barrier-free. Unless the individual suite is less than 500 square metres in area, the door at the barrier-free entrance is required to be equipped with a power operator.

In addition to any entrances to suites that are referred to in the previous paragraph, not less than 50% of the pedestrian entrances to a building are required to be barrier-free. Thus a building with three entrances would need to have at least two of the entrances barrier free.

From the entrance it is expected that a person can move to any part of the building in which there is a facility to be used or a service that is being provided. However, the Code recognises that it is not possible to provide barrier-free access to upper storeys of a building in which vertical transportation is not provided by means of elevators.

If escalators are used to provide access to storeys above or below the entrance storey, the Code requires that a barrier-free path of travel be provided to those storeys. The Code does not address the use of inclined moving walks, the ability to use those walks by wheelchairs falls under the jurisdiction of the authorities responsible for the licensing of those facilities.

3.   Signs

The Code intends that persons requiring a barrier-free path of travel will be able to identify the path as well as knowing that facilities they encounter in the building will be barrier-free. Standard signs using the stylised wheelchair symbol are widely used, however additional or varied signs are required to indicate facilities for other persons, especially those with a hearing disability. If all washrooms are designed for barrier-free access, the need for specific signs is reduced, however, signs should be installed to assure those who have a need of them that the facilities can be used.

4.   Doors

Although doors are used to provide privacy, security and control of the indoor environment, the main concern of Part 3 relates to their use in fire separations to control spread of fire and the products of a fire. Thus doors in fire separations are equipped with closing devices and latches and these render passage through the door more difficult for persons with physical disabilities. The Code specifies the maximum force that is required to open a door in a barrier-free path of travel.

Door widths in a means of egress are specified in other Sections of Part 3. In most cases, doors in public areas will be sufficiently wide to permit barrier-free movement, however, door width within individual suites other than residential suites, may be governed by the requirements of Section 3.8. Even if a suite of residential occupancy is not required by an authority having jurisdiction to be barrier-free, the Code intends that the entry door be barrier-free if the suite is on a barrier-free storey and further that the doorway into at least one bathroom be at least 760 mm wide.

5.   Vertical Transportation

The vertical transportation for wheelchairs is usually accomplished through the use of elevators, however, the Code does not prohibit the use of other passenger elevating devices.

6.   Toilet Facilities

Although Section 3.7. is used to determine the number of water closets and lavatories that should be installed in a building, it is Section 3.8. that addresses the specifics that address the need for barrier-free use. Section 3.8. also considers special washrooms that can be used by persons having disabilities and their helpers as well as shower facilities in assembly buildings.

Although Section 3.8. implies that a special washroom can provide facilities in lieu of their location in a washroom used by the general public, these rooms are increasingly being used to supplement barrier-free facilities installed elsewhere. They are used by persons with a physical disability whose helper or partner is not of the same sex and thus would be discouraged from entering a washroom posted for use by a single sex. In some areas r-these are referred to as family rooms and allow a parent to take children of either sex into that washroom without leaving their children exposed to hazards that could occur when entering a public washroom by themselves. Section 3.7. permits a reduction in occupant load to be used in determining overall water closet requirements in the building if the special washroom is not the only facility available to persons with physical disabilities.

In a building that has a number of storeys but in which elevators are not installed, the Code intends that a barrier-free washroom be provided on the entrance storey. This is required even if the building design would not otherwise provide a washroom on that storey. In these circumstances a special washroom, usable by either sex, would be appropriate. In shopping centres, airline terminals and other buildings that have very large floor areas, the Code does not require that all washrooms have barrier-free facilities, but does require that the travel distance to a barrier-free facility from any other facility not exceed 45 metres and that signs be posted to indicate the location of the barrier-free facility.

If showers are installed in an assembly occupancy, at least one shower stall is required to be barrier-free. In most circumstances this means one shower for each sex in an appropriate location, however, there could be valid reasons for having a separate shower room for use by a person with a helper who might be of the opposite sex. The features to be included in the shower stall are clearly stated in Section 3.8.

7. Work Spaces and Counters

Although it is expected that Work spaces for persons with disabilities should be provided, the Code only specifically mentions counters which are used to serve the public. In these cases it is assumed that the person being served is in a wheelchair, however, this same counter position could also be used by an employee who uses a wheelchair. Although the Code requires a section of the counter to be barrier-free, the precise dimensions are not given. It is assumed that the dimensions will vary with the specific needs of the operations being carried out or the service rendered.

13.12 SUMMATION-CHAPTERS 12 AND 13

Building Codes are essentially for the protection of public health, safety and welfare, and they provide the minimum design and construction requirements for this express purpose.

Although the ownership of property is exclusive, it is not absolute. The use of land and the buildings placed upon it are limited by Zoning By-Laws, and the erection of buildings is governed by Building Codes.

Building Codes establish the design criteria of all buildings according to the intended use and occupancy of them. The use and occupancy of the building and spaces within the building are determining factors in respect of design as to the stability of the buildings and life safety as related to fire spread in the building.

Building Codes are administered by some **authority having jurisdiction**. This authority will be defined, among other things, in that section of the Code relating to the administration of it.

In construction contracts, contractors are usually admonished that their performance of the contracted work must comply with the local Code. For this reason alone, anyone associated with construction, no matter how remotely, should be conversant with the Code of the place in which the work is being performed.

14

CONSTRUCTION SAFETY

by Evan B. Stregger, PQS(F), AScT, C.Arb., GSC

"Daily we read in our newspapers reports of construction accidents, many of which are fatal. Rarely, are such accidents acts of God, but, rather acts of man himself, who, most generally, is his own worst enemy. To protect man in spite of himself, laws and regulations are enacted to ensure safety during the process of construction."

Anon.

14.1   INTRODUCTION

Our previous discussions, concerning Building By-Laws and Codes were related to the safety, or stability, of buildings, and the safety of building occupants once a completed building is put into use.

Our present concern is safety during the process of actual construction, particularly of persons employed on a construction site and the safety of the public with respect to construction.

Far too many persons employed in the Construction Industry are not too greatly concerned about construction safety. Unsafe people abound at all levels, from the rawest apprentice to the top executive of a construction firm. No one deliberately commits unsafe acts. There are, however, omissions in respect of safety resulting from carelessness and thoughtlessness to downright negligence. Perhaps the most serious omission in this regard is the neglect of not only, instituting an accident prevention program, but not carrying out one that may have been instituted. It is a fact of life that every one loses when an accident occurs.

Safety in construction has always been a much discussed subject. It must be recognized however that, regardless of the various statutes, regulations, by-laws and codes enacted in the interest of construction safety, in the final analysis, safety cannot be legislated for entirely. Safety begins with training, education, the understanding and appreciation of the problems involved and the primary purposes of legislation related to construction safety.

14.2   LEGISLATION AND STATUTORY REGULATIONS

All who are associated with construction, should be familiar with the enforceable safety regulations of the place of a construction project. A municipal by-law may not be the only regulatory authority. It has become necessary that all levels of government enact laws and regulations to ensure construction safety, primarily to protect both workmen and the public from the hazards of construction.

Part 8 of the National Building Code addresses a wide range of safety issues including:

Section 8.2. Protection of the Public and Fire Safety
8.2.1. Fencing and Barricades
8.2.2. Fire Safety at Demolition Sites
8.2.3. Fire Safety at Construction Sites
8.2.4. Excavation
8.2.5. Use of Streets or Public Property
8.2.6. Direction of Vehicular Traffic
8.2.7. Waste Material

Some Provinces have enacted legislation solely for construction other Provinces legislate for construction safety in various acts related to the problems of industrial safety.

The Industrial and Commercial Establishment Act of the Province of Quebec has been in force many years, and is administered by the Quebec Department of Labour. Construction safety is dealt with in various parts of the Act and its Regulations, as do certain Articles of the Quebec Civil Code.

Most of the Canadian legislation related to construction safety is the result of investigation by Worker's Compensation Boards into the cause of accidents and determining the means of preventing re-occurrence of similar types of accidents.

Unfortunatly the regulations adopted by goverments are usually the result of serious accidents, and fatalities, arising out of construction work. The Heron Road Bridge collapse in Ottawa in 1966 caused Regulation 42/67 of the Ontario Construction Safety Act to be enacted. This amending regulation placed the responsibility for the design and construction of multi-tiered and other complex falsework, in particular the structural members and bracing of concrete forms, upon a professional engineer. It would appear that death was necessary to ensure safety.

14.3   WORKER'S COMPENSATION

Except by "disobedience to an express order or a deliberate breach of law or rule, well known to the worker and designed for safety", an injured worker has the right to claim for and receive compensation for an injury arising out of and in the course of employment.

There was a time when a worker could not obtain compensation for personal injuries sustained during the course of his employment, and in the event of his death his dependants were without the right in law to any financial relief or assistance from the worker's employer. Over the years, as social and industrial conditions improved, the justice to which a worker and his dependants are entitled has become firmly established.

In the early 1900's the various Provinces of Canada adopted a system of Worker's Compensation, which has not changed greatly since its inception, which provides a simple and speedy relief for workers who become disabled to any degree by reason of accidental injury arising out of and in the course of their employment. The system also makes provision, both directly and indirectly, for the dependants of injured workers. It provides workers freedom from the costs of litigation, compensation for the loss of the capacity to earn owing to disability arising from accidental injury sustained while working, and, in the event of a death from such a cause, provides sustenance for the dependants.

The worker's compensation system frees the employer from legal action which might be otherwise brought by the employees and places compensation benefits under such control as to ensure fair and proper use as intended by the Acts.

The various Provincial Worker's Compensation Acts limit the application of the provisions of the Acts to certain categories of workers. For our purpose, each Provincial Act does make provision to compensate workers injured while actively employed on construction works.

Although a worker does not receive compensation equivalent to earnings at the time of incapacity by accidental injury, the worker does receive a percentage of wages, plus free medical attention and hospital care as may be necessary. Such costs are borne indirectly by the Contractor, who in turn, by the current bidding procedures, passes them on to the purchasers of construction. To pay compensation to workers the Compensation Boards derive the necessary revenue by levying upon an employer a percentage rate of wages paid. This levy fluctuates according to the safety record of individual employer. A contractor with a good safety record will have a lower levy rate than one with a poor safety record.

Although workers and their dependants are protected by the Compensation Acts, such protection is only partial. Since the disabled worker receives but a portion of the wages being earned at the time of his disability, a reduction in purchasing capacity is experienced. Granted the worker receives medical attention and hospital care at no expense. Nevertheless, financially incapacitated to a degree while receiving compensation.

As a rule, permanent disability pensions are based on the degree of disability and the construction worker's earnings prior to the accident. Death benefits are usually payable to the dependants of a permanently totally disabled construction worker where death occurs from any cause.

The worker's Compensation Acts are good social legislation. But the cost of fatalities and injuries are reaching astronomical proportions, quite apart from loss of life and permanent disablity. All employers, large and small, are vitally affected.

GC 10.4 - Workers' Compensation in CCDC2 - 1994 ensures that contractors comply with the contribution requirements for Worker's Compensation as follows:

"10.4.1   Prior to commencing the Work, Substantial Performanc eof the Work, and issuance of the final certificate for payment, the Contractor shall provide evidence of compliance with the workers' copensation legilation at the Place of the Work, including payments due thereunder".

"10.4.2   At anytime during the term of Contract, when requested by the Owner, the Contractor shall provide such evidence of compliance by the Contractor and Subcontractors."

14.4   PUBLIC SAFETY AT CONSTRUCTION SITES

It is not unusual to find in the General Conditions of contract the following requirement:

"The Contractor shall protect himself and indemnify and save the Owner harmless from any and all claims which may arise from the Contractor's operations under the Contract where bodily injury, death or property damage is caused...".

Such a requirement, by implication, places the onus on the Contractor to ensure that the general public generally is protected during construction.

14.4.1 PUBLIC WAY PROTECTION

Most Canadian Construction Safety Regulations require that where a building or other structure is being constructed, altered, repaired, dismantled or demolished is located within 2 m. of a public way, work is prohibited unless a covered way is provided over that part of the public way immediately adjacent to the work.

The National Building Code (1995) sets out the requirements for this cover as:

8.2.1.2.Covered Way Construction
1) A covered way shall
    a)   have a clear height of not less than 2.5 m,
    b)   have a clear width of not less than 1.5 m or the width of the public way, whichever is the lesser,
    c)   be designed and constructed to support safely all loads that may be reasonably expected to be applied to it, but in no case less than 2.4 kPa on the roof,

d)   have a weathertight roof sloped towards the site or, if flat, be equipped with a splash board not less than 300 mm high on the street side,

e)   be totally enclosed on the site side with a structure having a reasonably smooth surface facing the public way,

f)   have a railing 1 070 mm high on the street side where the covered way is supported by posts on the street side, and

g)   be adequately lighted when the public way is lighted.

It is usual to specify in requirements for covered ways minimum requirements as to lighting, fences, barricades, and watchmen where a special hazard exists from which it is not possible to protect the public by other means.

14.4.2 FIRE EXTINGUISHING EQUIPMENT

It is not unusual for Canadian Construction Safety Regulations to stipulate what fire extinguishing equipment is required, where it is to be located, and when it is to be inspected, and the access to such equipment by the local fire department, all in the interest of safety to the public.

The National Building Code (1995) sets out differnent requirements for fire safety equipment for the following conditions:

    8.2.2.   Fire Safety at Demolition Sites
    8.2.3.   Fire Safety at Construction Sites
    8.2.4.   Excavation

14.4.3 EXCAVATIONS

Most Canadian Construction Safety Regulations require the shutting off all existing gas, electrical, water (excepting for fire fighting), steam and other services, the capping of such all before excavation begins, again in the interest of public safety. Regulations related to excavations may make stipulations as to dry excavations and the stability of adjoining buildings during excavation, work, and the erection of barricades. Such regulations may require that, except where a professional engineer has certified in writing that the stability of walls is such that no danger is presented to anyone, the walls of an excavation be supported by adequate shoring and bracing at all times to prevent their collapse.

14.4.4 USE OF STREETS

It is unusual for Construction Safety Regulations to deal with the use of streets as to safe passage for pedestrians and vehicles, the closing of streets for short periods, the protection of the public from hazards related to excavations in streets or public property, and the repair of damaged public property and the provision of warning lights. Such Regulations are important insofar as safety to the public is concerned. Unfortunately, regulations related to the control of vehicular traffic where hazards are created by construction, are not always acted upon nor adequately enforced to ensure positive safety for the public. Usually such Regulations state the necessary safeguards for vehicular traffic on a public way, the composition of the flagman's flag and sign, what the flagman must be instructed to do and how the flagman should be dressed.

Again these requirments are set out in Part 8 of the National Builidng Code (1995).

14.4.5 DEMOLITIONS

Construction Safety regulations usually stipulate that in addition to taking adequate precautions to prevent the public from entering into an area affected by demolition work, and ensuring that no part of a demolished structure or building is left in a condition as to be hazardous to the public, swinging weights used for demolition must be approved by the authority having, jurisdiction.

14.4.6 CONTRACTOR RESPONSIBILITY

Most Construction Safety Regulations require the Contractor, or Constructor to ensure that the requirements of the Safety Regulations of the place of the work are complied with and do not relieve subcontractors of their respective responsibilities. Like the Constructor every sub-contractor is required to ensure that all equipment, the materials provide and the safeguards use are used as prescribed and are maintained in a safe condition. Individually, each worker is required to conduct himself in such a manner as not to endanger the safety of other persons, the public included.

14.5 CONSTRUCTION SAFETY MEASURES GENERALLY

The administration of Construction Safety Measures will be according to the municipal by-law, or the provincial acts and regulations applicable to the place of the work. In many juridictions the Provincial Acts and their regulations in respect of Construction Safety take precedent over municipal by-laws, although the enforcement of Provincial requirements is delegated to the municipal authority having jurisdiction.

Construction Safety Measures not only set out special provisions for the protection of the public, but usually require the employer to supply safety clothing to his workmen. Fencing and barricades are required under specific conditions. The use of streets or public property is limited and these must be kept free of obstructions at all times, requirements as to warning lights for the safety of the public must be obeyed. Unoccupied or incomplete construction must be made safe and means to prevent access by the public must be effected.

14.6 HOUSEKEEPING

As stated previously, a clean construction site is to everyone's benefit. Not only is a clean construction site safer to work on but it contributes greatly to the efficiency of the performance of the work. Yet, it is surprising how much resistance is experienced whenever attempts are made to enforce compliance with the "housekeeping" provisions of a construction contract.

Certain "housekeeping" chores are legal requirements and, owing to the provisions of municipal by-laws, provincial acts and their regulations, it becomes an Owner's responsibility to ensure that the contractor is complying with the law.

Most statutory regulations set out "housekeeping" requirements as:

1. Prohibition of accumulation of waste materials and how such are to be disposed of.
2. Necessary removal of protruding nails in lumber.
3. Collection and storage of small tools.
4. Necessity to maintain clear passage on scaffolds, runways, stairs and passageways.
5. Removal of ice and snow from scaffolds, etc.
6. Stacking and storing of materials.
7. Security of temporary enclosures.
8. Posting of danger signs.
9. Maintaining clear passage in lanes of travel, walks or other paths on the site of the work.

In spite of these requirements, it is not unusual to find broken stone, concrete block, bricks, paper of all kinds, pieces of lumber with protruding nails and broken glass of every description lying scattered about a construction site. Obstructed passageways preventing easy access for pedestrian traffic are common. The tragedy about accidents is that many can be prevented, yet it seems far too few to give a damn.

14.7   HANDLING AND STORING OF MATERIALS

Generally a contractor and his sub-contractors, will take precautions to prevent loss or damage to materials they have stored on a site. Such precautions are usually predicated upon replacement costs in terms of unrecoverable expense, rather than upon safety of persons employed on a construction site. There are statutory regulations concerning the manner in which materials are to be handled and stored. Such regulations are not precautionary measures to prevent financial loss, but are to protect persons by prevention of accidents arising out of unsafe handling and storage of materials. Such regulations cover the supervision of storage; superimposed loads on floors or temporary storage; proper stacking of lumber and masonry units; reinforcing steel and pipe; and such bagged materials as cement, lime,etc. A tour of construction sites will indicate that far too many of them show a lack of planning for such details as proper storage, even though such storage is a statutory requirement.

14.8   SANITATION

There are statutory regulations related to toilet facilities, the lighting of them and their cleanliness; the supply of drinking water with individual cups and washing facilities. Of these requirements, about the only one usually complied with is the toilet facility, the rented toilet facility commonly known as the "Jiffy Biffy", Johnny-on-the-Spot, etc. There may be drinking water available, but individual drinking cups are rarely seen. As for washing facilities, whoever heard of such a luxury? In the case of washing facilities, these are particularly specified in most statutory regulations.

Recent changes in some juridictions and under some union contracts require flush toilets to be supplied and in these instances the washing facilities are available.

14.9   FIRE PROTECTION

By close study of the various statutory regulations concerning construction safety it will be noted that fire extinguishers are required, but as construction progresses and where there is a water supply available that is not less than 70/gal/min. at not less than 20 p.s.i., such water supply must be made progressively available for fire protection. This requirement includes the temporary use of stand pipes for fire hose cabinets, and the availability of sprinkler systems. Such temporary fire fighting equipment facilities must be able to fit the fire fighting equipment of the local Fire Department. Access to all fire fighting equipment, such as hoses, hydrants, extinguishers, stand pipe and sprinkler connections must be maintained at all times.

These are difficult regulations to enforce. First, it is difficult to overcome the inherent resistance of the General Contractor and his Sub-contractors to make these provisions mechanically. Secondly, the matter of access from area to area and from level to level is not always easy as passageways and stairs are frequently blocked with scaffolding and cluttered with the litter of all sorts of construction debris. Frequently access to the construction site is difficult owing to poor planning of yard layout and the lack of general cleanliness.

The best fire protection is a clean project.

14.10   ELECTRICAL SERVICES

It is usually required that both permanent and temporary electrical services conform to Provincial Codes or, in the absence of such, to the Canadian Electrical Code, C.S.A. Standard C22.1. Generally the main service switch of any temporary electrical service is inspected by the authority having jurisdiction before being energized. It is usually required that inspection take place the main service switch and panel, together with other secondary service panels, which are usually required to be placed as to be readily accessible, with no obstructions of any kind within one (1) metre of them. It is a requirement that these panels and other electrical equipment being used on the site of a work are inspected frequently. This inspection, unfortunately, does not occur with the frequency intended. As a result dangerous infractions are allowed to occur. It is most providential that more construction workers are not injured as a result of hazardous electrical installations than are reported.

It is usually required that adequate lighting be provided throughout a building, and that all electrical lamps used for temporary lighting have wire guards to prevent breakage of lamps and subsequent injury to workers. Temporary lighting is not only too frequently inadequate, but seldom are the lamps of temporary services properly protected by wire guards.

14.11   TEMPORARY HEATING

In providing temporary heating for a building, only steam heaters, approved electrical heaters or approved gas and oil heaters should used and these should be installed according to the appropriate installation codes. Improvised salamanders or other makeshift heaters are usually prohibited.

Solid fuel heaters or salamanders should only be used where other heaters are not practicable.

All heaters should be located so that specified clearances from combustible construction or other combustible materials are maintained. Solid fuel heaters should be provided with covered metal receptacles for the disposal of ashes.

Owing to the carbon dioxide content of the fumes they release, salamanders should not be used in the following areas:

1.   Newly placed concrete, less than 28 days.
2.   Exposed surfaces to be painted eventually.

14.12   EXCAVATION

Perhaps one of the most hazardous operations in construction is excavation. This is mainly because the proper precautions are not taken during the work, particularly in respect of the stability of banks or sides of excavations.

One Canadian city By-Law requires the following in respect of excavations:

1.   Prior to excavation, drawings prepared by an Engineer showing the method of supporting the walls of all excavations in excess of four (4'-0") feet, must be approved.

2.   Give at least 24 hours prior notice of the start of any excavation.

3.   Protect any building, party wall, foundation, structure of which the safety may be endangered by an excavation.

Other statutory regulations governing excavation are:-

1.   Disconnect and cap existing services before start of excavation.

2.   Protect the stability of adjoining property.

3.   Boulders and other surface objects are to be located so they do not create a hazard during the work.

4.   Barricades to be erected and warning lights set out at all excavations.

5.   The stability of banks is to be accomplished by trimming to a stable slope, or by by other retention methods all of which should properly be designed by and installed under supervision of a Geotechnical engineer.

6.   Staging and escape ladders are required in all trenches where excavations exceed four (4'-0") feet. This is a mandatory requirement in most provinces. Excavations of considerable depth may require special staging to the approval of the authority having jurisdiction.

7.   The removal of water from excavations is usually mandatory. Dewatering is necessary to ensure the safety of workers, apart from what may be considered necessary to construct work at the bottom of excavations.

8.   Work related to caissons, piers and tunnels may be regulated by statute othe rthan the building code.

9.   Explosives must be handled, and records of explosives used, both in conformity with both Federal and Provincial regulations.

10.   Most statutory regulations require that all deep excavations be ventilated.

14.13   CONSTRUCTION EQUIPMENT

There are statutory regulations governing the use of trucks; wheel-barrows; lifting jacks; power-driven cranes, shovels, etc.; pile driving equipment; derricks; welding and cutting equipment; and wood-working equipment such as bench saws, etc. All welding, arc, gas and cutting by gas torches, must be according to the appropriate provincial statutes and applicable Canadian Standards Association Standards:

Most provincial regulations require the inspection of hoists and elevators intended for use in construction work to be made whenever this equipment is erected at the site of a work, regardless of whether it had been inspected previously at some other location. To begin using this equipment before proper inspection is to do so at considerable risk.

The hoisting platform must be so constructed as to ensure the safety of workers using the hoist for vertical transportation from floor to floor. The hoist platform must be so constructed as to ensure that materials and equipment being hoisted or lowered will not be able to fall from the platform. The hoist must be equipped with all safety devices prescribed for freight and passenger elevators, and be operated by qualified personnel only.

14.14   SAFETY AND SCAFFOLDS

Most construction safety regulations either state or imply:-

"Where work cannot be safely done on or from the ground or from a building or other permanent structure, a scaffold or other safe means of support for workers shall be provided".

Such regulations may also stipulate:

1. An employer shall designate an experienced person, who may be himself, to supervise the installation, use or removal of a scaffold.

2. Each worker on a suspended scaffold shall, where practicable, use a safety belt attached in a satisfactory manner to a vertical lifeline of five-eighths of an inch or larger manila rope securely attached overhead to the project.

3. A boatswain's chair shall be provided with the means of preventing the supporting rope from being chafed.

In nearly every case where scaffold accidents have occurred, it has been found that the scaffold had not been properly constructed or erected; materials used did not conform to the minimum standards described in the regulations; ropes were worn and unsafe; scaffolds were overloaded at the time the accident occurred; or there were too many workers working off the scaffold.

The danger spots in scaffold construction are:

1. <u>Bracing</u> - To prevent scissoring, crossbracing should be secured to uprights and should be tied into the building under construction at intervals of not more than 5 metres.

2. <u>Footings</u> - On uneven ground, part of the scaffold will take the full weight of the load, with the possible result of collapsing the scaffold. To prevent settling and possible collapse, install load spreading planks at least 300 mm square under scaffold poles.

3. <u>Posts,</u> - When vertical posts are spliced, joints should be square, spliced with (25 mm) inch. Materials in 750 mm lengths. Adjacent poles should not be spliced at the same level.

4. <u>Planks</u> - Good lumber of uniform size is essential and should be spaced no more than 50 mm apart to prevent falls. Planks should be securely nailed to bearers. All staging should be not less than 450 mm wide, and planks should not extend more than 150 mm beyond bearers.

   "The best scaffold in existence today is no safer than the weakest scaffold plank that forms the working deck. A knot in a plank can mean a knock on the head".
   W.G. Bryson, Tidewater Construction Corporation.

5. <u>Railings</u> - Although guard rails are essential for safe scaffolds accident investigations have shown that the false security of a weak guard rail is WORSE

than no rail at all. Sturdy rails, properly secured and braced should enclose all work areas and walk-ways.

6   <u>Safe Access</u> - Far too frequently safe access to scaffold platforms is overlooked.

14.15   LADDERS

The construction and installation of ladders to be used when neither permanent stairs, runways or ramps are available to provide floor to floor access during the construction of a building and access to platforms and scaffolds above ground level, need to be considered seriously.

Most Worker's Compensation Board regulations regulate materials for ladder construction; the inspection of ladder installations and the maintenance of them; how and where ladders are to be installed; the height limits of single and cleated ladders, and extension ladders; how ladders are to be constructed for various installations, prohibiting the splicing of ladders; and that special reinforcement of ladders be such that no hazard is created.

The construction of ladders and their installation as required by statutory regulations is no great hardship for any contractor. However, far too frequently, poorly constructed and poorly maintained ladders are found on a construction site, many of which in no way conform to statutory regulations. <u>Unsafe ladders are a real peril to the safety of workers.</u>

Also, it often happens that there are insufficient ladders of any kind to perform the work properly. Easy access to and from ladders is frequently lacking also, thereby creating a further hazard.

<u>No ladder is better than one that is unsafe.</u>

14.16   TEMPORARY FLOORING

The requirements set out in statutory regulations governing temporary flooring in buildings are most stringent and are based upon the need for the safety of those required to work on them and those required to work under them. Such regulations usually require either temporary or permanent flooring at each level where work is in progress. Such flooring is to extend over the entire working areas except for various necessary openings which shall have guardrails to protect workers. The regulations set out clearly the construction of all temporary flooring, and conformity with these regulations should not be considered a hardship, since a good working floor not only hastens work, but prevents loss of time resulting from needless accidents.

14.17   STAIRS AND RAMPS

The purpose of installing stairs and ramps during construction is not so much to speed up the work by improved access to different levels, but to reduce accidents to workers moving from one level to another.

Statutory regulations indicate where stairs are required and how long they must be maintained in a safe condition. When permanent stairs are installed, temporary wood treads are usually required. The regulations describe how temporary stairs are to be constructed and the form of guard-rails and toe boards to be provided.

14.18   DEMOLITION

The National Building Code (1995) in Part 8 sets out safety requirements for demolition.

Demolition work is as hazardous as any other form of construction work. In fact it is sometimes more dangerous than most. Special precautions are set out governing the actual work to not only protect the worker engaged in demolition, but the general public also. Such precautions are lengthy, but if complied with, it is likely that accidents arising out of this form of construction will be greatly minimized. Usually included among the regulatory demolition precautions are; the removal of glass before any other demolition; the manner in which demolition is to be performed; the manner in which debris is to be removed from the site; the use of swinging weights; the control of dust arising out of demolition; the prohibition of burning debris on the property; the proper stacking of the material removed; prohibiting the use of hoists for the vertical transportation of workers. The mechanical methods of demolition are treated at some length.

It is not unusual for such regulations to deal with the sequence of demolition, the lowering of structural members, the removal of masonry and concrete walls and the control necessary in respect of lowering removed materials.

Anyone, on becoming engaged in demolition work, would be well advised to review the statutory regulations of the place governing such work.

14.19   REGULATIONS OF WORKERS' COMPENSATION BOARDS

The various provincial Worker's Compensation Boards have published regulations related to construction accidents which must be complied with on the site of a work. These relate to the posting of the Board's Regulations and notices pertaining to injury and first aid; the provision of first aid services, first aid kits and casualty reports.

14.20   SUMMATION

Too many construction projects show not only a lack of regard for safety regulations, but also a lack of planning for such details as safe storage of materials, disposal of waste materials, resulting in untidy "housekeeping" which usually leads to a lack of safety performance.   Although about 20 per cent of construction accidents are caused by unsafe practices, the onus is upon Contractor, Owner and Worker alike to ensure that safety regulations are complied with to ensure safety during the performance of all work

About 80 per cent of all construction accidents are attributable to the acts of commission and omission by workers themselves, which indicates a lack of safety training education, and enforcement of safety regulations by the construction industry generally.   It should be a mandatory requirement that the learning of safety requirements be a part of learning any construction trade.

Accidents are for fools

- fools who are so careless as to neglect to wear the appropriate safety clothing,
- fools who are so careless to use unsafe ladders, work on scaffolds and staging where there are no guard rails,
- fools who use unsound planking to work on unsound scaffolding or staging,
- fools who will work in un-shored trenches when there is no need for a person to die in a trench, or other excavation for that matter,
- fools who remove guardrails and assume that it is some other workers responsibility to replace them,
- fools who break out light bulbs in temporary lighting as a prank leaving stairwells dark and dangerous.

Regulations regarding safety have been legislated in an attempt to protect man from himself and it is the responsibility of every one who is associated with the construction industry, no matter how remotely, to ensure the legislation in this regard is implemented fully.

TYPICAL QUESTIONS

1.   What part of the section National Building Code is related to construction safety?
2.   What special construction safety requirements are usually set out in statutory regulations in the interest of the public?
3.   List five (5) "housekeeping" items that contribute to safety.
4.   What is the purpose of regulating the handling and storage of construction materials?
5.   What are some of the sanitation requirements?
6.   What are some of the fire protection regulations?
7.   What are the regulations concerning electrical services?
8.   What are the dangers to be overcome in respect of scaffolding?
9.   What has been usually found in respect of scaffold accidents?
10. What do the regulations cover in respect of ladders?
15. Is inspection of hoists required?
16. What is the purpose of temporary, flooring?
17. What are some of the precautions to be taken in demolition work?

REFERENCES

The National Building Code (1995)

15

THE BUSINESS OF SUBCONTRACTING
by Evan B. Stregger, PQS(F), AScT, C.Arb, GSC

15.1 INTRODUCTION

Any discussion concerning construction by contract must take into consideration that all contractors are engaged in a highly competitive business. They are competing in a system which is controlled to a great extent by the checks and balances of their contracts, the conditions governing them, the composition of the specifications, the intent of the drawings, the testing of materials, the inspection of their work and the manner by which they are paid.

Construction has grown more complex over the years. As a result, there has been considerable growth in the number of specialized trades engaged in such works. As a general rule, these specialized trades, who are referred to as sub-contractors, work for a General Contractor and are responsible directly to the General Contractor and no one else.

Once a General Contractor has signed a contract, he assumes the responsibility for the entire work as set out in the Tender Documents. However, it is not unusual to find a General Contractor sub-letting 85% or more of a contracted work to specialist sub-trades. Ordinarily, the contractor is not allowed to sub-let any portion of a Construction Contract without written permission of the Owner, the Architect or Engineer. Where such consent is given, the General Contractor still bears the responsibility for the performance of the Work for which he has contracted. It would, therefore, be well to examine both the responsibilities and rights of sub-contractors engaged in the construction of a Work under the supervision of a General Contractor.

In Chapters two to nine inclusive, the basic general obligations and rights of the parties to a Construction Contract are set out. The generalizations, so set out, were possible because the major requirements of such contracts are generally similar in character, even though by the Law of Contract everything must be governed by the expressed intentions of the parties to the contract. Because of the similarity of the characteristics of Construction Contracts, it is possible to deal with many issues common to Construction Contracts in a general way.

Such generalizations are neither possible nor useful in the case of sub-contractors. Sub-contracts will vary as to the nature and extent of the requirements of work, scheduling for co-ordination with the work of other trades, etc. Each sub-contract must be given individual consideration in respect of the entire Work. In sub-contracts, the terms and conditions will be governed to a great extent by the nature and scope of the work being performed by the General Contractor and the various subcontractors.

The following article, General Condition "GC 3.8 SUBCONTRACTORS AND SUPPLIERS" is excerpted from the Canadian Standard Construction Document CCDC2 - 1994 clearly sets out contract conditions related to sub-contracts and supply contracts.

"3.8.1   The *Contractor* shall preserve and protect the rights of the parties under the *Contract* with respect to work to be performed under subcontract and shall:

.1   enter into contracts or written agreements with *Subcontractors* and *Suppliers* to require them to perform their work as provided in the *Contract Documents*;

.2   incorporate the terms and conditions of the *Contract Documents* into all contracts or written agreements with *Subcontractors* and *Suppliers;* and

.3   be fully responsible to the *Owner* for acts and omissions of *Subcontractors, Suppliers,* and of persons directly or indirectly employed by them as for acts and omissions of persons directly employed by the *Contractor.*"

The contractor therefore agrees that he will.

"3.8.2   The *Contractor* shall indicate in writing, at the request of the *Owner*, those *Subcontractors* or *Suppliers* whose bids have been received by the *Contractor* which the *Contractor* would be prepared to accept for the performance of a portion of the *Work*.   Should the *Owner* not object before signing the *Contract*, the *Contractor* shall employ those agrees to employ those *Subcontractors* or *Suppliers* so identified by the *Contractor* in writing for the performance of that portion of the *Work* to which their bid applies.

3.8.3   The *Owner* may, for reasonable cause, at any time before the *Owner* has signed the *Contract*, object to the use of a proposed *Subcontractor* or *Supplier* and require the Contractor to employ one of the other subcontract bidders.

3.8.4   If the *Owner* requires the *Contractor* to change a proposed *Subcontractor* or *Supplier*, the *Contract Price* and *Contract Time* shall be adjusted by the differences occasioned by such required change.

3.8.5   The *Contractor* shall not be required to employ as a *Subcontractor* or *Supplier*, a person or firm to whom the *Contractor* may reasonably object.

3.8.6   The Owner through the Consultant may, provide to a Subcontractor or Supplier information as to the percentage of the Subcontractor's or Supplier's work which has been certified for payment."

It should be noted there is no contractual relationship by a subcontractor and the Owner.

15.2   THE OWNER AND SUBCONTRACTOR

It is not unusual to find in either the Supplemental General Conditions of a Construction Contract, or in Division 1 of the Specifications, the following:-

> For convenience of reference and to facilitate the letting of contracts, these specifications are separated into titled divisions and sections. The separation into division and sections within the specifications shall not require the Architect to determine what part of the work shall be done by any subtrade, or to decide any limits of contract between the contractor and his subtrades.

From this it should be noted that the Consultant does not establish subcontracts, nor should he attempt to delineate trade responsibilities. These rest with the Contractor solely.

Although the Owner does not have a contractual relationship with subcontractors nominated by a General Contractor, he has a moral obligation. To prevent "shopping" after the acceptance of a tender, a tender form should contain an article with respect to selection of sub-contractors by a General Contractor, such as:

> I/We submit herewith a list of subcontractors whom we propose to employ for the performance of the work indicated. I/We have investigated the following subcontractors without the express approval of the Architect having been previously obtained in writing.

When a Contractor has entered into a subcontract, the subcontractor cannot bring an action against the Owner as there is no contract between the Owner and the Subcontractor. Because of the lack of contractual relationships with Owners, Subcontractors would be well advised to accept direction from the General Contractor only, thus requiring the Owner's Agent to act properly in respect of the administration of a Construction Contract.

15.3   THE CONTRACTOR AND SUB-CONTRACTOR

Since the Tender Documents usually consist of the Instructions to Bidders; the Tender Form or Proposal; the Contract Agreement; the General Conditions of the Contract; the Specifications and Addends; all Drawings pertaining to the Work; any Supplemental General Conditions; and the General Requirements of Division 1 of the Specifications, it is imperative that sub-contractors read these documents when bidding for a subcontract.

Contractor subletting portions of the work for which they have contracted, may word their contracts with subcontractors as they wish, including injustices which might be just within the Law. Unjust contract terms and conditions only give rise to serious contention and added costs, the latter being borne by the Owner ultimately. Good faith and confidence have no place in the preparation of a contact, the terms of which should be based upon justice and equity. Rarely does an Owner, or a Consultant on behalf of an Owner, approve a Contract Agreement between a Contractor and a Subcontractor of his to ensure that justice and equity is served and to do so may create to liability in tort.

GC 3.8.1 CCDC2 implies that the Contractor agrees to bind every Subcontractor by the terms of the contract documents, so far as applicable to his work.

Since the General Contractor is responsible for any division of the work, it is not unusual that potential subcontractors are given only those parts of the Contract Documents which the General Contractor considers applicable to that subcontractor.

As the terms and conditions of the contract between the Contractor and the Owner generally dictate the terms and conditions of a subcontract and the Contract Documents form the basis of the contractual relationship between the Contractor and subcontractor, they will be the source of information concerning both responsibilities and rights of a subcontractor.

Therefore, as a means of safeguarding rights, ascertaining both obligations and the basis of contractual relations with Contractors, no subcontractor should fail to read ALL of the Contract Documents before submitting a tender for his portion of the intended Work.

A just and equitable subcontract would require:-

1. The subcontractor to AGREE:

   a) To supply the labour and materials to do the portion of the work set out in the Agreement.

   b) To promptly prepare and submit necessary shop or setting drawings.

   c) To commence his portion of the work by the time and date set out in the Agreement.

   d) To complete his portion of the work described in the Agreement by a specified date.

   e) To be bound to the Contractor by the terms of the Contract Documents.

   f) To submit to the Contractor application for payment in such time as to enable the Contractor to apply for his payment according to the terms of the

Contract Documents. However, unless by contract, payment of the sub-contractor's claims is not dependant upon payment by the Owner to the General Contractor.

g)   To make claims for "extras" when justifiable, apply for extensions of time if necessary claim for damages arising out of delays caused by others, all to the Contractor, according to the terms of the General Conditions of the Contract for like claims between the contractor and the Owner.

h)   To be liable to the Contractor for additional expenses for which he has been responsible.

i)   To maintain adequate insurance according to the Agreement entered into with the Contractor.

j)   To provide such sureties as may be called for.

k)   To employ labour under conditions satisfactory to the Contractor.

l)   To not assign nor sublet any part of the subcontract without express approval of the Contractor.

2   <u>The Contractor to AGREE:</u>

a)   To be bound to the subcontractor by all the obligations the Owner assume to the Contractor according to the Contract Documents.

b)   To pay the subcontractor to such extent as may be provided by the Contract Documents or the Subcontract.

c)   To pay the sub-contractor on demand for his work and materials as far as they have been executed and fixed in place. Also, to pay for those materials on the site of the work not yet incorporated into the work, less an agreed-upon retained percentage. Payment to be made at the time the certificate should have been issued, even though the Architect should fail to issue the certificate for any cause not the fault of the subcontractor.

d)   To pay the subcontractor his just share of any fire insurance money received by him according to the General Conditions of the Contract.

e)   To make no demand for liquidated damages or other penalty for delay except as may be stipulated in the subcontract.

f)   To give the subcontractor the opportunity to be present at, and submit evidence on his behalf, in any arbitration proceeding involving his rights.

g)   To name as arbitrator in an arbitration proceeding the person nominated by the subcontractor, if the sole cause of the dispute is related to the work or materials, furnished by the subcontractor, or the rights or obligations of the subcontractor are in dispute.

3   The Contractor and Subcontractor should jointly AGREE:

a)   That in the matter of arbitration, their rights, obligations and all procedures, should be according to the General Conditions of the Contract.

b)   That nothing in the agreement between them shall create any obligation on the part of the Owner to pay any sums to any subcontractor.

15.4   PROGRESS PAYMENTS

It is essential that the subcontractor is paid regularly for the work that has been completed. In any agreement between the Owner and the Contractor, the conditions governing that agreement should be, but are not required to be, applicable in like terms to the agreement between the Contractor and Subcontractor, (insofar as they may be applicable to the particular Subcontract). The Contractor should therefore be required to pay the Subcontractor on the same basis as the Owner pays the Contractor.

Any holdback specified to be withheld is to protect the Contractor against all unpaid accounts of the Subcontractor. Similarly, the Owner retains holdback from the amount owing the Contractor to ensure protection against all liens of which he may have had notice.

A lien provides the right for a person to charge against the property for work done to the property. See Chapter 17 for full discussions on liens.

15.5   SEPARATE CONTRACTS

The General Conditions of a Construction Contract forbid either party to the Agreement to assign or sublet any part of the Contract without the consent of the other. This however, does not preclude the Owner's right to let separate contracts on the same project. The terms of General Conditions require the Contractor to connect to and co-ordinate his work with that of other GC 3.2 CONSTRUCTION BY OWNER OR OTHER CONTRACTORS of the Canadian Standard Construction Document CCDC 2 - 1994, states:

"3.2.1   The *Owner* reserves the right to award separate contracts in connection with othe rparts of the *Project* to other contractors and to perform the work with own forces.

3.2.2   When separate contracts are awarded for other parts of the *Project*, or when work is performed by the *Owner's* own forces, the *Owner* shall:

.1   provide for the co-ordination of the activities and work of other contractors and the Owner's own forces with the *Work* of the *Contract*;

.2   assume overall responsibility for compliance with the applicable health and construciton safety legislation at the *Place of the Work*;

.3   enter into separate contracts with other contractors under conditions of contract which are copatable with the condiitons of *Contract*;

.4   ensure that insurance coverage is provided to the requirements as are called for in GC 11 - INSURANCE and to co-ordinated such insurance with the insurance coverage of the *Contractor* as it affects the *Work*; and

.5   take all reasonable precautions to avoid labour disputes or other disputes on the *Project* arising from the work of other contractors or the *Owner's* own forces.."

15.6   PRETENDERING

Pretendering for a part of a project and subsequent assignment to a Contractor is another matter altogether. There are projects where it is known, well in advance, that certain items to be incorporated into the work may take many months to procure and unless these items are contracted for well in advance of the general contract, the completion of the total work may extend well beyond the required date for use and occupancy of the project.

An illustrative case is the matter of the supply and installation of steam generators for a central heating plant. The fabrication of these may take many months. It is, therefore, not unusual to negotiate with a manufacturer for these items well in advance of the architectural and structural planning. The specifications for steam generators will be usually incorporated in the mechanical specifications of the project. Also included in the specification will likely be the following notation:

15-B-2 (Pretendered Equipment)

    a.   The steam generator has been pretendered and the A.B.C. Company has been nominated as the supplier.

    b.   This Contractor shall obtain from A.B.C. Company, Valley City, Ontario, copies of the accepted proposal and shall include the supply and installation of the steam generator as part of the work of this Division.

The manufacturer will show in his proposal both the cost of the equipment and the extent of what he will actually provide, as related to the specification set out in Division 15. It will be the responsibility of the General Contractor to ensure the co-ordination between the manufacturer and the subcontractor in cases of this nature.

In cases of Pretendered Contracts, subsequently assigned to the General Contractor, matters to be considered are:-

1.   Obligations of the Owner. It is the Owner's responsibility to obtain tenders and quotations sufficiently in advance as to enable the General Contractor to carry out the work without interruption and economically. The owner must ensure that the nominated subcontractor is willing to enter into a subcontract with the General Contractor, consistent with the terms and conditions of the General Construction Contract. Further, the Owner must ensure that the nominated subcontractor will:

    a)   Provide the General Contractor with all requisite drawings and information within the contract period and in such reasonable time as not to delay the General Contractor's progress.

    b)   Make delivery according to dates agreed upon by the Owner and the nominated subcontractor. It is not necessary for the Owner to warrant delivery, provided the dates originally promised were satisfactory at the time of negotiation. The Owner is not likely to be held liable for delays caused by his nominated subcontractor as the General Contractor will have legal remedy against the nominated subcontractor in cases such as this.

2.   Nominated Subcontractor Defaults. Further problems might arise from death, liquidation (to cease doing business), bankruptcy or repudiation, resulting in the nominated subcontractor being no longer able, or willing to continue and complete the subcontracted work. In such a case, it has been frequently contended that the

Owner should nominate a new subcontractor, and that the general contract price be adjusted to accommodate the price of the tender of the new subcontractor.

3.   Rectification of Defects. In usual circumstances, as stipulated in the General Conditions, of a Construction Contract, a General Contractor agrees with an Owner that materials and workmanship, or both, shall be free from defects. He cannot, however, be held liable for the work of another, such as a nominated subcontractor, since he has no contractual obligation to the Owner in respect of the work of such a person. The contractual relationship between Owner and Nominated Subcontractor is separate from that Owner and General Contractor.

15.7   SUB-BIDS

It is essential that all sub-bids should be based upon all the contract documents, the plans and specifications related to, or interacting with, the sub-trade work.

It is, of course, essential that General Contractors receive subcontractors' bids sufficiently in advance of the time for filing their bids to the Owner in order to permit adequate analysis and selections for inclusion in the general bid.

It is unethical and unjust for General Contractors to disclose the amount of any sub-bid or quotation they may have received before the award of the contract, since such were obtained in confidence for the purpose of preparing the general bid. However, it continues to happen.

In order to ensure proper filing of sub-bids and to protect sub-bidders from unethical disclosure of their bids, Bid Depository Principles and Procedures were developed by the Canadian Construction Association. Such depositories are managed by either local construction associations or Builder's Exchanges across Canada. At first, these depositories were for the use of the electrical and mechanical sub-trades. As the use of these depositories proved their worth to the Construction Industry generally, the scope of trades using the depositories increased to include a number of sub-trades. The number of sub-trades eligible to use Bid Depositories varies with the local practice of the construction association or Builder's Exchange.

15.8   BID DEPOSITORY PRINCIPLES AND PROCEDURES

1.   Definition and Purpose

The Bid Depository is a system designed to improve tendering practices in the construction industry. It provides for the receipt of sealed tenders for sub-trade Contractors whereby the sanctity of bidding is protected and Contractors receiving subcontractors' tenders obtain firm quotations in writing and in adequate time to compile their bids completely and accurately. These procedures are thought to be the best interest of owners, architects, engineers and contractors.

2.   Management

Bid Depository is operated under the auspices of the local Builder's Exchange or Construction Association with the co- operation of associations of architects and engineers and under the supervision of a joint committee representing General and Trade Contractors.

3.   Scope and Eligibility

The facilities of the Bid Depository shall be available to all General and, in trades affected, Trade Contractors submitting tenders on projects for which the Bid Depository is being used, providing they adhere to these regulations and relevant provincial legislation and whether or not they are members of any association and regardless of their geographical location. No preference in any way shall be shown by the Bid Depository management to any local or other bidders in the operation of the depository.

4.   Printed Rules

Rules in printed form covering all phases of the operation shall be generally available and specifically for the information of bidders, architects, engineers and owners.

Note:
    Each Bid Depository is a localized unit, and the rules governing the operation of the depository are those which meet local needs, yet conforming with the intent of the Principles and Procedures being described.

5.   Tender Closing

The tender closing times used in Bid Depositories shall be so arranged as to give contractors sufficient time for the preparation and submission of their own tenders following receipt of tenders from Trade Contractors. In no case shall there be less than 24 hours between the two tender closing times.

6.   Envelopes and Fees

Bid Depositories should be financially self-supporting on the basis of the fees received for the service provided. All Trade Contractor tenders must be submitted in official envelopes purchased from the Bid Depository.

7. **Receipt of Tenders**

All white tender envelopes received by the Bid Depository shall be time-stamped. Those that are received after the appointed shall be retained unopened at the Bid Depository.

8. **Procedure for Trade Contractors**

a) Separate prices shall be provided for each complete trade section specifically requested in the tendering documents.

b) A lump sum bid may be quoted for two or more complete trade sections, but only if a separate price has been quoted on each trade section concerned, as determined by the specifications.

c) Trade Contractor's tenders shall be place in official envelopes as follows:-

-   a complete quotation, as described above, in a pink envelope addressed to each General Contractor by name (one tender per pink envelope).

-   a copy of each quotation to be retained by the Bid Depository (one copy per green envelope).

-   the above pink and green envelopes shall all be enclosed in a designated white envelope delivered to the Bid Depository, bearing the names of the Trade Contractor, and the project being bid, together with the total number of the green and pink envelopes enclosed. (Envelope procedure varies from place to place).

d) Written advice (including delivered telegrams) concerning amendments to the Trade Contractor's tenders may be submitted to the Bid Depository provided that each amendment and the white envelopes are received prior to the Bid Depository closing time. A copy of each amendment should be addressed to each General Contractor concerned and duplicates filed with the Bid Depository.

e) Tenders shall not be altered or amended in any way after the Bid Depository closing time.

f) Tenders may only be withdrawn up to ......hours prior to the tenders closing time for Prime Contractors and must be confirmed prior to the General Contractors' closing time. The responsibility of proof of time of effective withdrawal rests with bidder. It is the Trade Contractors' responsibility to notify the Bid Depository and All General Contractors affected of decisions to withdraw.

The time for withdrawal will be as decided by a Bid Depository. This withdrawal time may vary from three (3) hours before the tender closing time to a minimum of 48 hours when there are 96 or more hours between closing times for Trade and General Contractors. It may be stipulated by a Bid Depository that upon withdrawal no bid may be altered or resubmitted. Also the Bid Depository may allow withdrawals of bids by telephone provided such withdrawal has been confirmed to all parties by registered mail.

9.   Procedure for Contractors - Receiving Bids

The procedure to be followed by the General Contractors receiving tenders from a Bid Depository is as follows:-

a)   It is the General Contractors' responsibility to advise Trade Contractors that they are bidding and require prices submitted through the Depository.

b)   The General Contractor' shall advise the Bid Depository if they wish the tenders mailed to them, in which case the Bid Depository assumes no responsibility for delivery. Otherwise, it is assumed that the General Contractors will arrange to pick up their envelopes.

c)   A General Contractor need not accept an unsolicited tender and may return it unopened to the Bid Depository. He is bound to place a subcontract with one of the bidders who uses the Bid Depository, but not necessarily the lowest. A General Contractor intending to use his own forces or a subsidiary company for one or more of the complete trade sections shall deposit his bid in accordance with the Regulations of the Bid Depository even if he bids only to himself.

10.   Disposition of Envelopes

a)   Immediately after the Bid Depository closing time, the tender box shall be opened by an official of the Bid Depository and the white envelopes opened. The information shown on the Green envelopes shall be checked against the information shown on the pink envelopes and the pink envelopes made available to each addressee contractor. The green envelopes will be retained in the Bid Depository safe until the general contract has been awarded.

b)   At this stage, the Bid Depository shall select all of the green envelopes addressed to the successful General Contractor and tabulate them by trade sections. All other green envelopes shall be destroyed unopened. Only those

Trade Contractors whose tenders were accepted by the Bid Depository may then examine the tabulated list of prices for their trade(s). No one else is entitled to see the tenders except the members of a committee investigating a complaint.

11.   Compliance and Complaints

Failure by either General Contractor of Trade Contractor bidders to comply with these rules shall disqualify their tenders. Complaints concerning any irregularities shall be made formally, in writing, to the Bid Depository.

12.   Bonding

In those areas where the local Bid Depository has established a system whereby each Trade Contractor's tender must be accompanied by a form of surety, the local Bid Depository Regulations in this regard shall apply.

Some Bid Depository Regulations will require bonding, and others may not.

15.8   SUMMATION

The Owner through his Agent, the Consultant deals with the General Contractor directly. Subcontractors work under the direction and supervision of General Contractors and are directly responsible to them and no one else.

Since on most projects all subcontracts are let before work actually starts, subcontractors and their suppliers, should be given full information as to what will be required of them. The matter of who does what on union projects is often defined by union rules as to jurisdiction. When such matters are not clearly defined, subcontractors could become involved in jurisdictional disputes inadvertently. Such disputes disrupt the orderly progress of the work and all involved, however remotely, suffer, with subcontractors suffering more than others.

Where it is stated in any Section of any Division of the specifications that the Contract Documents form part of that Section or Division of the specifications, the onus is upon the subcontractor to ensure that he is aware of all requirements of these documents. Failure to read these documents could prove disastrous because of possible omissions at the time of bidding.

TYPICAL QUESTIONS

1. To whom is the subcontractor directly responsible, and why?
2. Does an Owner have any obligations toward a subcontractor, and if so what are they?
3. What is the purpose of dividing the specifications in respect of subcontracting?
4. What determines the contractual relationship between a General Contractor and a subcontractor?
5. Is the subcontractor bound to the Agreement between an Owner and a General Contractor?
6. Describe the subcontractor's rights to submit to arbitration. What must the General Contractor agree to?
7. What is a subcontractor's lien?
8. What is pretendering?
9. What are the Owner's obligations in respect of a nominated subcontractor?
10. What obligations has a General Contractor in respect of rectification of defects in the work of a nominated subcontractor?
11. What is the purpose of a Bid Depository?
12. What are the usual times for withdrawal of sub-bids?

REFERENCES
Immanuel Goldsmith - Canadian Building Contracts
Hudson's Building and Engineering Contracts
Stipulated Price Contract - Canadian Standard Construction Document CCDC 2 - 1994
Standard Canadian Bid Depository Principles and Procedures for Federal Government Projects

LABOUR LAW AND UNIONS
by Evan B. Stregger, PQS(F), AScT, C.Arb, GSC

"The trade unions are the legitimate out-growth of modern society and industrial conditions".

Samuel Gompers, 1898

16.1   INTRODUCTION

LABOUR LAW is a reference term used to include all rules of law governing the conditions by which employees work under the control of an employer. Any person who is employed be, and works under the control of, another, works in a relationship that is subject to legal regulation.

Whenever the relationship of employer and employee actually exists, the relationship is one within the sphere of labour law. It does not matter whether the work involves manual labour or otherwise. It is the subordination of the worker to the employer that is the test to be applied when labour law is considered.

It is not easy to differentiate exactly the division between a dependent worker and an independent worker, a contractor, or a professional. The professional may be a contractor or a professional may, at some time or another, be under the control of an employer. Although this chapter is mainly concerned with dependent workers, and how they are protected and assisted by Labour Laws, the employer cannot be overlooked entirely.

Labour Law can be divided into two categories:

1.   That law affecting the contractual relations between employer and employee and,

2.   That law expressly intended to protect the so-called weaker party, the worker, from injury, by imposing duties upon the employer which are enforceable by government authorities in quasi criminal proceedings and not by the worker as civil rights.

It is not possible to rule out any law expressly affecting employees and employers as such. There is, however, law relating to the civil rights of workers and for employers to organize in defence of their interests, such as membership in Unions or Associations.

Trade Unions are associations of employed persons, formed to collectively bargain about their conditions of employment, for the provision of benefits and legal defence, to promote

---

their members, interests and to collectively bring pressure upon governments by political action. Whereas, Employer Associations are formed to bargain with trade unions to protect their interests as employers.

There are a great number of statutes, both Federal and Provincial, which regulate the employment of a person or an individual, or persons as a union.

16.2   LABOUR LAW AND THE WORKER

There are laws regulating contracts of employment and laws for the express purpose of protecting workers, who have very definite obligations to their employers.

Any statutory law concerning the relationship between employer and employee is derived from that part of the Common Law related to "Master and Servant". This relationship is created by a contract generally referred to as a "contract of hiring and service" and, being a contract, carries with it certain legal obligations. Under such a contract, whether expressed or implied, the employer agrees to employ and pay, and the employee agrees to serve (work) for the pay offered, for a determinate time. The "contract of hiring and service", like any other contract, may be written, or be verbal, or be implied by the conduct of the parties to it.

Since the relationship between employer and employee is a contractual one, then the rights and obligations of each party to the contract must be considered.

16.3   THE OBLIGATIONS OF EMPLOYMENT

The obligations of each party to an employment contract are:

1.   Obligations of the Employer

   a)   The law imposes certain duties and obligations upon the employer, either by virtue of Common Law or by Statute Law, such as requiring the employer to supply sanitary facilities in the place of employment, to provide certain safety appliances on machinery, etc. The employer must ensure that employees have a safe place in which to work and must employ competent workers. He must issue rules, regulations and warnings where hazardous working conditions do exist.

   b)   An employer is required to pay an employee according to the minimum wage rates of the Province in which the employee is working. Each Province has enacted legislation establishing minimum wages, rates of pay, for workers in factories, shops, hotels, restaurants, etc. Employees cannot waive or forego any provision of such Acts. Also included in most of these Acts are provisions prohibiting employers from intimidation, or threatening to discharge employees for assisting in the enforcement of the Minimum Wage Acts. Most of these Acts make provision for an employee to recover the difference between the minimum wage and what was actually paid, should the employee have been paid less than the statutory minimum wage.

c)   In addition to being required to pay minimum wages according to Minimum Wage Acts, an employer is also required to pay fair minimum wages according to Industrial Standards Acts, where such are applicable. Such Industrial Standards Acts fix fair minimum wages as distinguished from minimum wages set by other statutes and apply, generally, to those particular industries described in the Acts.

d)   Finally, the employer must comply with legal requirements as to hours of work, holidays with pay, or pay in lieu of holidays as set out in the various statutes.

2.   Obligations of the Employee

a)   An employee is expected to use reasonable care and skill in the performance of work. If any employee is engaged because of a special skill the employee alleges to possess, he or she is expected to exercise that alleged skill.

b)   An employee is expected to be punctual as to the attendance at work, honest, courteous to the employer and obey instructions given to him.

c)   An employee must work daily, unless there is an express or implied agreements to the contrary.

d)   Flagrant violations of any of the above obligations may be grounds for the dismissal of an employee and, in certain circumstances, the employee could be liable for damages, such as a stoppage in pay for lateness.

It has been mentioned that an employer must protect employees by providing safe places in which to work, competent fellow-workers, and issue rules, regulations, and warnings in respect of hazardous conditions of employment. An employee is assumed to be aware of, and will take precautions against, risks inherent to employment. Employers can be held negligent with respect to their performance and, if negligent, cannot recover full damages for injuries they may have sustained by their own acts.

Employers are liable for the acts of their employees, so long as such acts are committed during the ordinary course of employment. Employers are however, responsible for acts committed by their employees, in pursuit of their own interests while employed, even though they may be permitted to do so by the terms of employment.

Employees are, of course, liable for the wrongful acts they commit, whether the employer is liable or not.

Since the relationship between employer and employee is a contractual one, the contract of hiring and service, either party can terminate the contract by:

1.   Mutual consent

2.   Completion of the work for which the employee was engaged, (the performance of the contract).

3.   Expiry of the term of employment.

4.   Death of either party.

5.   Bankruptcy of the employer.

6.   Dismissal of the employee.

7.   Leaving employment by the employee.

If an employee is wrongfully dismissed, he may sue his employer for damages arising out of a breach of contract. Wrongfully dismissed employees may sue their employers for damages arising out of a breach of employment contract. In fact, in the last decade or so, it has become commonplace and employers have been compelled to take great care in how and why they dismiss employees.

16.4   LABOUR LAW AND TRADE UNIONS

The first recorded legislation relative to labour was an ordinance issued by the Sheriff of Kent in England in 1349, whereby the wages of workmen and servants were then fixed at a specific level as a means to overcome excessive wage demands then being made.

During the next 500 years a great deal of labour legislation was enacted to prohibit the combines of workmen and to protect employers from demand by their employees for better wages and working conditions. The British Trade Union Act of 1871 made it lawful for workers to unite for the purpose of negotiating wages and working conditions with their employers. This Trade Union Act of 1871 still serves as a basis for much of the Labour legislation in force today.

Until comparatively recently in their history, Canadian trade unions were considered voluntary associations without legal status, unable to sue or be sued for damages in their own name as legal entities. They had no legal existence. The Canadian Trade Union Act of 1872 provided for the registration of trade unions. This Act also provides for the acquisition and holding of property as a trade union, and made trade unions legal entities for such purposes as initiating legal proceedings against persons who fraudulently obtained or misapplied union funds, or were, themselves, liable to prosecution for failure to register according to the Act.

The definition of a trade union in the Federal and Provincial statutes related to labour relations reflects the Common Law approach to a trade union as being a voluntary organization of physical persons having no legal entity or personality. Although there may be some differences in definitions, the common element is that a trade union is an organization of employees formed for the purpose of regulating relations between employers and employees.

The only entities know to Common Law are natural persons, corporations and partnerships. Trade Unions are none of these. During the past thirty years, however, there has been a gradual change regarding the legal entity of trade unions. Only by statutory provisions has it been possible to change the status of trade unions by giving them legal personality for all purposes, or for specific purposes as may be provided for in the legislation. At present most labour legislation has, in effect made trade unions legal entities, with the Provinces granting fully fledged entities for trade unions for any proceedings before the courts, including civil action for damages.

The Canadian Industrial Relations and Disputes Investigation Act of 1948, applies throughout Canada to employees and to employees in industries and enterprises under Canadian Government jurisdiction. Each Province has its own labour relations legislation, which, with few exceptions, applies to the employers and employees in the province and within provincial jurisdiction. The Canadian government has exclusive authority in respect of interprovincial and international road transport, pipelines extending beyond provincial boundaries, over stevedoring operations serving out-of-province shipping and over uranium mining and the processing of nuclear material.

16.5   COLLECTIVE BARGAINING

Collective bargaining is the procedure whereby employees, organized as a union, negotiate and come to an agreement with an employer regarding their terms of employment, both as to wages and working conditions.

The primary function of a union is to bargain for its members. The objectives of such bargaining may be for higher wages, hours or work, holidays with pay, retirement funds, or some other condition of work. In short, to win something for its members from the employer

Free collective bargaining implies that employees have the right to organize into unions and to have the employer bargain with them through their union representatives. It also implies that the employees have the right to refuse to work and the right to strike, without loss of permanent employment should a failure to agree occur.

Although at one time it was unlawful for employees to organize, to bargain and to strike, both Federal and Provincial statutes now permit all three. These statutes control the collective bargaining process, regulate the behaviour of employees, unions and employers in respect of organization, negotiation, to strike and to lock out. (The last being the closing of a factory or other place of business, including construction sites by employers in an effort to bring employees out on strike to come to an agreement of terms).

The various labour and industrial relations acts, while recognizing that employees must be free to join unions and unions must be free to organize employees, prohibit employers from taking action to discourage union organization, or to interfere with legitimate union activities during the course of bargaining.

The basic principle of "collective bargaining" means that a union speaks for all its members in the employ of an employer with whom it is bargaining. Non-union workers must bargain with their employers as individuals and no individual has the right to speak for another. In a shop, or firm, where there is no union, the employer can refuse, or consent to the demands each individual worker in turn. This is "individual bargaining".

Over the years, the legislation providing protection of workers for the purpose of negotiating better working conditions and wages, intended to redress the balance between weak unions and strong companies. In 1871 absolute power as to working conditions and wages rested with the employer. Today, by legitimate and other means this power has now shifted to the worker as represented by a union. Through apprenticeship clauses, hiring hall provisions, strike action, picketing and boycott, all won through the collective bargaining process, trade unionism have gained tremendous economic influence and power. It is held by many authorities that by means of collective bargaining trade unions have acquired greater economic power than that ever held by an employer. The reason causing this shift of imbalance from employer to employee is difficult to define, but would appear to be in the indirect result of gains arising out of collective bargaining.

Russel W. Cornell, FSWA, writing in the June 1976 issue of the Construction Specifier, remarked:

"Material and labour scarcities have been triggered by everything from legitimate strikes in contributing industries to deliberate holding down of union local memberships, in order to maintain a stronger bargaining position in the constant quest for higher wages. Whether real or rigged, the effect has been driving building costs constantly upward."

16.6   CERTIFICATION OF BARGAINING AGENTS

By 1950 the Industrial Relations and Disputes Investigation Act, R.S.C., had been amended to provide for the certification of a trade union as the bargaining agent of the employees in an appropriate bargaining unit. By this time, or soon after, most provincial labour legislation contained similar provisions. The federal and provincial statutes established Labour Relations Boards which were empowered to decide upon questions relating to employee representation by a union for the purpose of collective bargaining.

The basis for certifying a union as a bargaining agent is that the Labour Relations Board having jurisdiction must be satisfied that the majority of employees in a unit appropriate for collective bargaining are members of good standing in the union seeking certification. Also, the majority of the members of the unit must have by ballot, selected the union to be their bargaining agent.

By custom, two principles have been followed in determining how a unit will become recognized as a bargaining agent for the purpose of satisfying both federal and provincial acts:

1.   The Labour Relations Board having jurisdiction must satisfy itself that the requirements of the particular union constitution have been met in each case or, alternatively, that the applicant union is truly representing the bargaining unit and,

2   The Board must be satisfied that certain prescribed evidence as to membership is truly bonafide.

One of the most important functions of a Labour Relations Board is to determine whether the union applying for certification is the appropriate one for collective bargaining.

Any of the Boards, in determining whether an applicant union has sufficient membership support for certification, may include additional employees in a unit or exclude employees from it. In Ontario, the Board may, before certifying a union, conduct a vote of the employees of an employer for the purposes of ascertaining the wishes of the employees in respect of the applicant union as being the appropriate bargaining unit.

Most Labour Relations Acts specify that a unit means a group of employees and an appropriate group may be an employed unit, craft unit, technical unit, plant or other unit. In determining an appropriate unit as a bargaining agent consideration is given to the community of interest among workers as to location of work, hours of work, working conditions, pay, fringe benefits, vacations with pay, etc.

A unit or union certified as a bargaining agent has the exclusive authority to bargain collectively on behalf of the employees in the unit it represents and to bind them to an agreement, known as the "collective agreement", entered into between the employer and the unit or union on behalf of the unit which it represents. "Collective Bargaining, and Collective Agreement", as related to each other, may be defined as:

1. Collective Bargaining - until relatively recently, the negotiation between organized workers, as a unit or a union, and their employers for the purpose of reaching an agreement as to working conditions, pay, benefits, etc. Legislation established organizations of employers as accredited bargaining agents for units of employers. This legislation, which provides for collective bargaining by certified employers associations, was intended to provide a balance of negotiating power between labour and management and to lead to the return to genuine collective bargaining without compulsion by Labour Relations Boards.

2. Collective Agreement - is the agreement entered into by an employer, or an accredited employer's organization, and a certified bargaining agent for the employees of an employer, or of an accredited association. Such an agreement must be in writing.

16.7   THE COLLECTIVE AGREEMENT

A typical Collective Agreement usually contains terms and conditions related to:

1. The scope of the agreement.

2. Recognition of the Bargaining Agent.

3. Prohibition of discrimination against members of the unit or union.

4. The rights of the employer.

5. Security for the union by pay deductions by the employer from an employee's wages to be paid to the union directly.

6. Cessation or work such as strikes by the union and lockouts by the employer.

7. The procedures to settle and adjust employee grievances.

8. The discharge of a union member by an employer.

9. Matters related to seniority of employment, dealing with temporary promotions, job posting, rehiring, leave-of- absence, etc.

10. Hours of work.

11.   Wages.

12.   Vacations with pay.

13.   Safety and health.

14.   Notice boards to be provided by employer on premises for posting of union notices.

15.   Trades and trade classification.

16.   Apprenticeship.

17.   The authority of the Bargaining Agent to enter into the Agreement.

18.   Termination of the Agreement (its duration).

Of course, not all Collective Agreements are identical but, most include the above general terms and conditions. The Collective Agreement, once signed by the parties named, is a legal document and is enforceable. Reaching an agreement can be a prolonged and painful proceeding. The life of such a contract may be from one to three years depending upon the terms of the agreement.

Almost all Labour Relations Acts require every collective Agreement to provide for final settlement of disputes arising out of the agreement (during the life of it), without stoppage of work. This requirement is predicated upon the principle that private arbitration in the settlement of disputes and grievances is the most practical and acceptable method of settling questions relating to the interpretation, application and administration or violation of the agreement. Strikes and lock-outs are prohibited during the life of a Collective Agreement.

16.8   NEGOTIATING THE COLLECTIVE AGREEMENT

It is generally accepted that where a union is voluntarily recognized by an employer, or has been duly certified by a Labour Board, both the employer and the union have the duty to bargain in good faith and to make every effort to conclude a "collective" agreement. A refusal to bargain in good faith causes the party to be liable to prosecution in some provinces, as in Ontario and Quebec, or liable to rulings arising from proceedings of the Labour Boards of other provinces.

Most provincial statutes require that, where the parties fail to negotiate a "collective agreement", they must receive the services of a conciliation officer before strike or lock-out can be effected. The purpose of the conciliation officer is to aid the parties in negotiating a "collective agreement".

If, after a reasonable time in negotiation there is a failure to agree upon the terms of the "collective agreement", one or both of the parties may request the services of a conciliation officer. Such an officer is appointed by the Labour Relations Board having jurisdiction. Most Labour Relations Acts require that applications for conciliation services are to be made to the appropriate Labour Relations Board, which is obligated to review the applications made to it to determine whether the parties had, in fact, bargained and had failed to reach an agreement.

Conciliation is usually a two-stage procedure. First, a conciliator is appointed, who confers with the parties engaged in the bargaining process, and should he or she fail to achieve agreement by the parties the second stage is recommended, the appointment of a Conciliation Board. This consists of a nominee by each party and a chairman selected by the Minister of Labour having jurisdiction. This, conciliation is a form of arbitration.

The Conciliator, or the Conciliation Board, have a limited time in which to report their findings. "Collective Bargaining" can be prolonged. The normal conciliation process leaves the parties with either no recommendation, or with one which they are free to accept or reject. The prohibition of strikes and lock-outs is removed within a short period after the conciliation report has been filed with the Minister of Labour having jurisdiction.

Negotiating a Collective Agreement frequently involved confrontation by antagonists. The adversary confrontation approach can prolong negotiations which, not infrequently, can only be concluded following either a strike or lock-out, leaving much bitterness in their wake.

The adversary confrontation approach, in both the private and public sectors is serving Canada badly. The failure of this approach is evident in:

1.   More frequent and more strikes with increasingly required legislative intervention.

2.   A declining effectiveness of legislative intervention with a growing disrespect for the law by strikers.

3.   A growing disregard by strikers of the public interest and the exploitation of public discomfort as a bargaining weapon.

Against this background it is not surprising that both government and the private sector are seeking desperately for means to alleviate the growing aggressiveness in collective bargaining.

16.9   JURISDICTIONAL DISPUTES

The certification procedure, by defining the appropriate bargaining units and determining the exclusive agent for the employees in a unit, has been one effective way of dealing with questions of jurisdictional authority between unions by settling the question as to which union an employer should recognize as the representative of its employees. The jurisdictional dispute over the assignment of work, as to who should do what, has not been settled fully by the certification procedure.

Many a construction project has been closed down during its progress as a result of a dispute over work assignment, such as who should tape the drywall joints, the painter or the lather?

16.10   ENFORCEMENT OF LABOUR LAWS

Most Labour Relations Acts state that every person, trade union, or employers' association that does anything prohibited by the Act, or that refuses, or neglects, to comply with the provisions of the Act, is guilty of an offence and is liable, on summary conviction, to a fine or imprisonment or such other penalty as may be provided in the Act. Every person, trade union, or employers' association who refuses, or neglects, to comply with the lawful order of a Labour Relations Board is guilty of an offence and is liable, on summary conviction, to a fine for each day during which such refusal or neglect continues.

It should be noted that the Courts will uphold the findings of a Labour Relations Board.

16.11   INJUNCTIONS IN LABOUR DISPUTES

Labour relations legislation in Canada does not, as a general rule, consider injunctions as the best means of restraining prohibited activities arising out of labour disputes. Yet, injunctions have been secured with greater frequency in recent years. Such injunctions have been secured particularly to prevent either strikes or lock-outs.

An injunction is a court order restraining persons named in it from doing particular acts. The remedy of injunction originated with the Common Law of England and was adopted in Canada in 1867. The remedy has been amended or amplified by various provincial statutes and rules of the courts.

In labour disputes the Court may grant an injunction when it is convinced that the plaintiff may sustain injury, or property may be damaged if an injunction is not granted and that the injury or damage is of such a nature that it can be compensated by a monetary payment, but positively prohibits a behaviour described in the order. There are many forms of injunctions.

Injunctions are usually sought when strikes and picketing arise out of a labour dispute. The most common conducts for which injunctions are sought are intimidation, nuisance and trespass. A labour injunction may be applied against conspiracies to injure or commit unlawful acts, against inducing a breach of contract or interfering with contractual relations.

In recent years the courts have been active in restraining picketing, which is but one of the very few effective means that a union has to enforce a strike. In issuing injunctions against picketing the courts presume in advance that crimes would be committed or violence would erupt.

16.12   SUMMATION

Labour Law may be classified as that which affects the relationship between the employee and employer individually and the collective group of employees of an employer and the employers' association.

Labour Law establishes the legal basis for collective bargaining and compels employers to bargain collectively with their employees. To establish its legal rights a union must show that it was freely chosen by the majority of the workers it claims to represent. On this condition it is certified by the government having jurisdiction. The same laws forbid unfair labour practices such as discharging union leaders or interfering with the workers' choice of union. Labour must comply with certain standards governing union practices. A union cannot coerce prospective members.

TYPICAL QUESTIONS

1.   Define Labour Law.
2.   Into what branches may Labour Law be divided?
3.   What is a Trade Union?
4.   What is the form of contract of employment called?
5.   What are the obligations of an Employer?
6.   What are the obligations of an Employee?
7.   How must an employer protect an employee?
8.   To what extent is an employer liable for the acts of an employee?
9.   How may an employment contract be terminated?
10.   What is a Bargaining Unit?
11.   Who is a Bargaining Agent?
12.   Define - Certification of Bargaining Agents.
13.   Who certifies Bargaining Agents?
14.   What is meant by Collective Bargaining.
15.   Define Collective Agreement.
16.   What may some of the terms and conditions be in a Collective Agreement?
17.   How are disputes arising out of collective agreements settled?
18.   In what manner does conciliation resemble arbitration?
19.   What is meant by jurisdictional disputes
20.   What is an injunction?

REFERENCES

Construction Labour Relations - Goldenberg and Crispo (Published by the Canadian Construction Association)

Labour Relations and Trade Union Legislation - Department of Labour, Canada

Labour Unions, Collective Bargaining and Determination of Wages - Economics - R.G. Lipsey and P.O. Steiner,

Origin and Growth of the Canadian Labour Movement - Economics, Samuelson/Scott,

17

CONSTRUCTION, BUILDERS' AND MECHANICS' LIENS
by Evan B. Stregger, PQS(F), AScT, C.Arb., GSC

"A <u>Lien</u>, at Common Law, is the right to hold another's property as *security for debt. It is also the right to charge property in another's possession with the payment of a debt or performance of a duty. A <u>Lien</u>, is the right to retain (hold), <u>but not to take possession of</u>, the debtor's goods until paid."*

Fundamentals of Canadian Law
Chapman

17.1 INTRODUCTION

In common law, only those party to a contract acquire rights under that contract. Therefore subcontractors, suppliers and workmen who have provided valuable services to an owner to add value to the owner's property have no corresponding rights to compel the owner pay them if the contractor is either unwilling or unable. The subcontractors, suppliers and workmen acquire personal rights against the contractor or subcontractor they have contracted with but acquire no interest in the land which they have improved.

To correct this inequitable result that can result form common law Canadian provinces have adopted what was originally an American concept, the construction, builders' or mechanics' lien. While the legislation differs widely form province to province the basic premise is that certain specified persons who have performed work or supplied services or materials for the benefit of the owner of the land, whether under direct contract or under a subcontract, obtain some measure of security for payment by enabling them to register a lien against the owner's land.

The earliest appearance of this type of legislation is found in Roman Law, the purpose of which at the time was to provide the uneducated labourer with a means of protection, in a simple and expeditious manner, against nonpayment for work done or services provided.

"In its proper sense, <u>Lien</u> means the right of a person in possession to retain the property of another until certain claims have been satisfied. A <u>general lien</u> enables the property to be detained until the general account between the parties has been satisfied, a <u>particular lien</u> until the charges for the work done to the property in question have been met."

Hudson's Building and Engineering Contracts

In both cases, <u>the lien arises by operation of law, not by contract.</u> In these senses, no lien can arise out of the terms and conditions of a Construction Contract.

In any discussion concerning Construction, Builder's and Mechanics' Liens, the elements to be considered are - WHO can lien WHAT; for HOW MUCH, and HOW.

17.2   MECHANICS' AND WAGE-EARNERS' LIENS

"Under the provision of the Lien Acts of each Province every mechanic, machinist, miner, labourer, contractor or other person doing work upon or furnishing material to be used in the construction or repair of any building , or mine, or railway construction, etc., or supplying machinery of any kind in connection therewith for any owner, contractor, sub-contractor, has the right to place a lien upon such building, erection or mine and upon the land occupied thereby for a sum justly due for such labour, or material or machinery, unless he signs an express agreement to the contract."

Anger's Digest of Canadian Law

In general those who can lien in respect of a Construction Contract are the Contractor, Sub-Contractors, Wage-Earners, Suppliers, Vendors.   In some jurisdictions the design consultant have also been granted lien rights.   What they are able to lien is the Owner's interest in particular estates; dower land; leaseholds; lands under sale agreement; certain forms of municipal property (such as roads and streets before being dedicated), public property being generally exempt; public corporations; mining lands; mortgaged lands; money deposited in Courts of Law and fire insurance benefits.

It must be noted that a lien can be only claimed by those who do something in connection with the construction, alteration or renovation, etc., in respect of a building on a property just described, or who supplied material for such work.

Each individual would be well advised to determine their lien rights, depending upon the role played in any land development or building program and also depending upon the Province in which the work is to take place.

In the Province of Quebec there is no Mechanics' Lien Act. However, the Quebec Civil Code has provisions that are discussed later in this chapter.

In this chapter references will be made to the various Acts and the Acts listed in Table A below are the Acts being referenced. As these Acts are revised from time to time you are advised to ensure when dealing with the Lien Act of any Province or Territory you are referring to the Act currently in force. The Acts in force at the time of publication are:

Table A	
Province / Territory	Act Referenced
Ontario	Construction Lien Act R.S.O. 1990, C.30
Quebec	Quebec Civil code
Alberta	Builders' Lien Act, R.S.A. 1980, c.B12
British Columbia	Builders' Lien Act, S.B.C. 1997, c.45
Manitoba	Builders' Lien Act, R.S.M. 1987, c. B91
Newfoundland & Labrador	Mechanics' Lien Act, R.S.N., 1990, c. M-3
New Brunswick	Mechanics' Lien Act, R.S.N.B., 1973, c. M-6
North West Territories	Mechanics' Lien Act, R.S.N.W.T., 1988, c .M-7
Nova Scotia	Mechanics' Lien Act, R.S.N.S., 1989, c. 277
Prince Edward Island	Mechanics' Lien Act, R.S.P.E.I., 1988, c. M-4
Saskatchewan	Builders' Lien Act, S.S., 1984-85-86, c.71
Yukon Territories	Mechanics' Lien Act, R.S.Y., 1986, c. 112

How much may be the lien be for refers to the money due to the lien claimant and the amount for which the Owner is liable. The Owner's liability depends upon whether a lien claimant claims by registration of the lien; or by serving a written notice on the Owner or the person who engaged the claimant. In either of these cases, the person primarily liable must withhold, in addition to any holdback, all money owing the employer of the person who gave notice of lien. How to recover what is due refers to the procedure set out in the Acts, which state the time limit of a specified number of days in which to either register alien or given written notice.

17.3   THE NATURE OF A LIEN

The lien is of statutory origin under provincial jurisdiction, as mentioned previously. Such legislation makes provision that a lien attaches to the property for the agreed contract or subcontract price, or where no price has been agreed upon, the actual value of the services or materials supplied. However the lien claim is limited to any amount owing to the person having as superior contractual relationship with the owner.

These are two (2) classes of liens:

1. Liens for which a claim is not registered, and,

2. Liens for which a claim is registered.

Both classes of liens are binding upon the property for a number of days fixed by the provisions of the statutes. It should be remembered that the lien is granted by statutory provisions and exists independently of the registration of the claim.

Equally important to understanding the definition of alien is knowing what courses of action are open to a person who acquires a lien. These courses of action are:-

1.   Register the claim and make certain that the claim is registered within time period specified by the laws of the province or territory in which the work is located. Equally as important is to comply with the time period in which an action must be commenced to enforce payment. See Table B below for current time periods.

2.   Rather than register the claim, enforce the lien by way of suit in the Courts. In such a case, if a judgement is obtained and payment is not made, the claimant may garnishee such money in the hands of the Owner which may be still owing the Contractor.

Table B		
Province / Territory	Time period in which to file a lien after completion or abandonment	Time period in which to commence an action to enforce a lien.
Ontario	45 days	45 days after the last day in which to file a lien.
Quebec	30 days	6 months from date of registration
Alberta	45 days	180 days after date of registration
British Columbia	45 days	1 year from date of filing.
Manitoba	40 days	2 years from date of registration
Newfoundland & Labrador	30 days	30 days after filing
New Brunswick	60 days	90 days after filing
North West Territories	45 days	45 days after the last day in which to file a lien.
Nova Scotia	45 days	30 days from date of registration
Prince Edward Island	60 days	90 days from date of registration
Saskatchewan	40 days (also applies to early release)	2 years from date of registration
Yukon Territories	30 days	90 days after the last day in which to file a lien.
The above dates should not be relied upon for any action. It is recommended that legal counsel be consulted in reference to the above.		

Most statutes generally state that a creditor contractor or subcontractor may register a lien before, or during, the performance of the contract, or within a specified number of days following the completion of abandonment of the contract or subcontract, or refusal of the declaration of substantial completion. An interesting note concerning the completion of the work, in respect of the limited period in which to register a lien, is related to a "Change Order" affecting the value of the contract in the form of an "Extra". In a case where work has been performed as directed and the "Change Order" revising the value of the contract has not been issued before the completion of the work, the limited time for registering a lien commences with the date of issue of the "Change Order".

In cases of insolvency or bankruptcy, lien holders who have filed their liens within the prescribed statutory time limit will share on a pro rata basis in any sum recovered from the estate against which the lien has been filed, without any priority in respect of date of filing the lien.

The nature of a lien is such that it attaches itself to the property when work on it beings, or materials begin to be supplied to it, and the lien takes priority over any encumbrance on the property or assignment of it that was not recorded at that time.

It is a general rule that fixtures, such as furnaces, etc., installed as permanent parts of a building during the course of its construction, entitle the supplier to a lien against the person to whom the mortgage on the property is given, the mortgagee.

The nature of the project the lien be for is the estate or interest of an Owner in the land, as opposed to the Owner's car, income, etc. Two things to be always kept in mind in respect of liens are:

1.   The list of those having lien rights.

2.   The nature of the object the lien be for .

17.4   THE EXERCISE OF LIEN RIGHTS

Most statutes describe the manner by which a lien claimant should exercise his rights, such as:

1.   What should be entered on the claim form.

2.   The claim must be verified by an affidavit of the person claiming the lien, or his agent or his assignee (the person to whom the claim has been assigned).

3.   Register the claim and file copies of it in the appropriate Land Registry Office, this is often referred to a preserving the lien.

4.   The registration may be made any time fore the expiration of 45 days (in Ontario) after the end of work.

5.   A "preserved lien" will expire unless it is "perfected". This is accomplished by commencing an action to enforce the lien within the time period specified in the Act. (see Table B above)

6.   A lien will expire within if an action to enforce the lien has not been commenced within the time periods specified. (Table B)

17.5   COMBINING AND TRANSFERRING LIENS

A claim for lien may include claims against a number of properties registered in the same name, and any number of persons claiming liens upon an identical property may unite in a single lien against the property. However, each such lien must be verified separately by affidavits by each of the separate claimants. Any lienholder may assign his or her right in a lien. Such an assignment must, however, by in writing, If a lienholder dies, the right of lien passes to the heirs or personal representative, such as the executor or the estate.

17.6   THE PRIORITY OF LIENS

The various provincial Registration Acts establish the basic principle that as between registered documents the priority of registration must prevail. In other words, the first document registered takes precedent over all others that follow. Should the purchaser of a property upon which a building is being constructed register a title deed, his or her title will take priority over any liens registered subsequently.

In Mechanics' Lien Law, mortgages lie in either of two categories:

a.   Mortgages existing prior to the commencement of work on the property have priority over liens to the extent of the actual value of the property at the time work was actually started.

b.   Mortgages placed on the property subsequent to liens being registered are subject to the principle of priority of registration and the mortgagee's (the person to whom a mortgage is given) interest will follow the interests of the lien holders.

Liens of wage-earners for their wages have senior priority over all other liens. The Provincial Acts expressly declare that any effort by an owner, contractor or sub-contractor to defeat the priority of a wage-earner's lien for wages shall be null and void. This includes payments made by an owner to a contractor for the purpose of defeating a wage-earner's lien. The wage-earner shall have priority to the extent of 40 day's regular time working days' wages over all other liens of the same class.

Certain of the Federal and Provincial acts provide that taxes levied under the acts constitute a lien on the land of the owner. Some provinces have established such liens, referred to tax liens, as being privileged and taking precedence over other liens.

The various Provincial Workmen's Compensation Acts make an owner liable to pay any contribution under the Acts which his contractor is liable to make. Should the contractor fail in making his contributions, the owner becomes personally liable to the Workmen's Compensation Board. The Acts further state that when an assessment is not paid within 30 days after it becomes payable, the Boards may collect the assessment through the appropriate municipal tax collectors who are able to add the amount to any tax lien on the property.

If any property upon which a lien may be attached is wholly or partially destroyed by fire, the fire insurance paid is considered as taking the place of the property destroyed and the insurance payments are subject to lien attachment, similar to the money realized by the sale of the property to enforce a lien.

17.7   WAIVING LIEN RIGHTS

A waiver is a voluntary relinquishment of a right, privilege or advantage. To waive a lien right is to relinquish the right to a claim for lien. It has been shown that the statutes have given priority to the liens of those who earn less than a stipulated wage and who do not occupy supervisory positions. Such wage- earners cannot, by law, waive their lien rights.

A question often asked is, "Does a waiver cut off all lien rights?" In the case of Bill Boivin Plumbing and Heating Limited v. Flatt et al (l965) 2 O.R. 649, the Ontario Court of Appeal ruled that other lien claimants were not entitled to rely on a waiver of lien clause in the contract of one lien claimant as to prevent that lien claimant from sharing in the distribution of the holdback because the other lien claimants were not party to his contract and accordingly could not reply on its terms. In this case, some of the lien claimants has executed waivers of their lien rights, while others had not done so. Those who had not signed waivers of lien objected to the claims for lien by those who had waived. The Court ruled that all of lien claimants were entitled to share in the distribution of the hold-back, even though they had signed waivers of lien. Those who had not signed waivers argued that, since the section of the Act creating the right to lien states, "Unless he signs an express agreement to the contrary..." and if one who was entitled to a lien signed an express agreement to waive his lien rights, such rights never existed. In a case of similar circumstances the Alberta Court of Appeal disagreed with the Ontario ruling, saying that, if a claimant signed a waiver of his lien rights, the his lien "ceased to exist and, in fact, never became operative. Since such a party had no lien right he was not entitled to any benefits under the Act." The Albert Court ruled that it was the statute which deprived the claimant of his rights when he signed such an Agreement.

With the exception of wage-earners earning less than an amount stated in the Acts, lien claimants can contract themselves out of their lien rights. There is no great advantage to an Owner to seek lien waivers, for he or she still must retain holdback on behalf of wage-earners. There is an advantage to a Contractor to secure lien waivers from sub-contractors and material suppliers, for by so doing, there can be no attachment to the property and the Owner is able to pay him his progress payments. Immediately a lien is attached to the property, the Owner is prohibited, by law, from making any further payments to the Contractor until the lien has been discharged.

Since the Courts do not appear to be in accord as to whether a waiver cuts off all lien rights, it is suggested that a solicitor is consulted before waiving lien rights.

17.8 LIENS AND OWNER'S INTEREST

What is the Owner's interest against which a lien is filed? The estate or interest of the Owner must be an estate in reality, that which is real, an actual thing and not in a personality, that which constitutes the person, since the lien claimant's ultimate remedy is the sale of the statutory owner's interest to satisfy the liability created by the performance of the lien claimant.

The definition of "statutory owner" should not be confused with the legal or registered owner. The meaning of "statutory owner" is artificial. In most cases the statutory owner is also the legal or registered owner. There are, however, cases where this is not so. The statutory owner and, therefore, only the estate or interest of the tenant as statutory owner could be sold to satisfy lien claimants. A mortgagee, the person to whom a mortgage is granted, may be found to be the statutory owner, while the registration remains in the name of the mortgagor until the mortgage has been paid. In such a case only the statutory owner's interest could be sold to satisfy the lien claim.

Although it appears that the interest of the mortgagee may be liened, care must be exercised wherever mortgages are concerned. In considering the priority of mortgages, three criteria must be examined:

1. is the mortgage a building mortgage?
2. was the mortgage registered prior to the time when the first lien arose?
3. was the mortgage advanced prior to the time when the first lien arose?

There is also a priority affecting liens where a mortgage existed before work began and mortgages place don the property after work started. In the first instance the mortgage is known as the prior mortgage, which is not affected by lien claim. It would, therefore, be wise to check the Registry Office of Land Titles in order to ascertain who is a mortgagee and the extent of the mortgage on the property on which work is to be done, before undertaking any work which may be lienable, since the Acts provide that a mortgage has priority over liens if its existence has been registered before the first lien attaches itself to the property. It must be considered that prior existing mortgages may encumber a property to nearly its full value by prior to a lien arising   In this context settlement of a lien by disposal of the asset while discharging the lien would most likely not satisfy the lien claim.

A building mortgage is one granted to secure financing of the improvement. Liens have priority over the building mortgage to the extent of any deficiency in the holdback.

Where a lease is concerned, the lien also attaches not only to the lease, but to the ownership of thing leased also. If a contractor or supplier doing work or supplying material has notified the owner, who did not reply within ten days that he or she would not be responsible for the work or materials ordered by a tenant the contractor's supplier may attach a lien to the lease. It may be found that, after performing for a tenant the owner may try to cancel the lease to avoid a lien claim. The Acts, however, state the owner cannot cancel a lease except in cases of non-payment of rent. A remedy to avoid cancellation of a lease is to advise the owner that all rents owing will be paid, thereby keeping the lien valid. Such rental costs can be added to the lien claim.

A bona fide purchaser, not having knowledge of an unregistered lien has priority over such a lien. A purchaser of property is entitled to rely upon the protection of the Registry Act of the Province as against any liens of which he has not notice or knowledge. This fact of law points to the necessity of registering all lien claims promptly.

Under provisions of most acts public roads and streets are exempt from liens, because of the interest of the Crown, which cannot be liened. The most obvious reason for this exemption if, of course, that such works cannot be sold to realize a claim. Public Works such as roads, streets, sewers, etc., let to contract must contractually conform to the mandatory holdback requirement, which is a trust fund out of which lien-like claims may be discharged. Where the plan of a sub-division by an owner- developer includes the construction of roads and streets which have not been given over to pubic use by the owners, work on them does come within scope of lien attachment.

In respect of municipal, provincial and federal property, it appears the principle underlying the lienability of some and not others is whether the work was done for the public interest directly, or whether a structure could be sold or replaced, or was more of a private nature to the government concerned itself. The properties of public corporations, schools and universities and considered lienable.

17.9   WHAT FUNDS ARE AVAILABLE?

The details of the <u>quantum</u> of the lien, or "how much is there in the kitty" are of interest. This particular aspect of liens is not as distinct as the WHO, the WHAT and the HOW of liens, because problems concerning what funds are available are related, in varying degrees, to all three.

There are two things to be considered primarily in this regard:-

1.   The percentage of the contract price to be retained by the Owner, (which, varies according to the jurisdiction - see Table C below.)

2.   The limit of the Owner's liability.

<u>The percentage of the Contract Price to be Retained by Owners</u>

The various statutes require the owner of the property affected to retain, as the work proceeds, a certain percentage of the money owing a contractor for a stipulated period after the completion of the work as certified by the Architect, or its abandonment, out of which to pay the claims of workers and suppliers of materials whom the contractor failed to pay and for which liens are registered according to the Acts.

The Owner is not liable to pay a greater sum than this percentage to discharge any liens of which he has not received notice before making payment to the contractor. Such notice must be made in writing and the onus is on the writer to ensure that the Owner receives the notice within the period of retention of the holdback. Nor is the Owner liable after the stipulated time for any lien to be registered, or of which he has not received written notice; therefore, the Owner <u>must</u>, at the expiration of the withholding period, pay over to the contractor any balance owing.

Most statutes require that, before the contractor can claim final payment, he must furnish the Owner with a Statutory Declaration stating that all persons entitled to wages on the contract have been paid up fourteen days before the date of the Statutory Declaration. If payment is made by the Owner without such an affidavit from the contractor, or should he have an actual notice of unpaid wages, the payment is invalid and the Owner becomes liable.

Table C	
Province / Territory	Hold Back Percentage
Ontario	10 %
Quebec	not specified

Table C	
Alberta	15 %
British Columbia	10 %
Manitoba	7.5%
Newfoundland & Labrador	10 %
New Brunswick	20 % for contracts less than $15,000 15 % for contracts over $15,000
North West Territories	10 %
Nova Scotia	10 %
Prince Edward Island	20 % for contracts less than $15,000 15 % for contracts over $15,000
Saskatchewan	10 %
Yukon Territories	10 %

17.10   LIMIT OF THE OWNER'S LIABILITY

The Acts provide that the aggregate sum of liens of all classes should not be greater than the sum owing the contractor, including the holdback. The amount owing the contractor does not necessarily mean the contract price, but that which is owing the contractor at the time of the completion of the work and what he can legally claim at that time. In the case of liens other than those for wages, should a contractor default and by virtue of the terms and conditions of his contract forfeit what might be due him, it has been held that the liens of subcontractors and not merely wage liens may be enforced against the Owner.

The basis of <u>quantum</u> (how much) is that the Owner, contractor or subcontractor are not liable for more than the contract sum, or the amount actually owed to any one of these persons. At this point a question would appear to arise - "What is the sum payable under the contract, or the sum actually owed?"

It is a legal axiom related to contracts that you cannot be made to pay more than that for which you contracted. This principle holds true for a contract influenced by a Mechanics' Lien Act. It is held in Common Law, that when a purchaser pays for what he wants, at the price demanded, all the money is gone. What would happen if all the money had been paid out completely in respect of a construction contract? It could be that some worker who had not been paid would claim for his wages and, by virtue of Common Law, the Owner would have to pay. Such a case could involve a fairly complicated and costly lawsuit, probably beyond the means of the wage-earner to undertake. Such a case would not be fair to the Owner, for he would be in the precarious position of having to pay twice for identical work. On the other hand, non-payment of the worker's wage would not be fair. The Lien Acts takes fairness into consideration and has made it comparatively easy for the worker to be paid by requiring the Owner to withhold a percentage of the money owing the contractor for such a

Owner's precarious position also, by ensuring that the percentage withheld will be available to pay any wage claim. In this manner, the only person out of pocket will be the person who had to pay the wage in the first place.

If a worker feels that the holdback will not be enough to cover his own and other claims he can give written notice of intent to lien. The Owner is then obligated to retain all that is still owing on the contract. It must be noted that what has been paid out in good faith before the receipt of such a notice cannot be recovered. Holdback money is always subject to lien, except where a written notice has been given by a wage-earner to the Owner, in which case all the remaining sums still owing under the contract are retained until the wage lien has been discharged. If payments have been made in bad faith, the Owner could become liable for a greater amount than the contract sum.

A further protection to the contractor, sub-contractor, worker, supplier, etc., is that element of the Acts referred to as the <u>trust provision.</u> In most jurisdictions this <u>trust provision</u> of the Acts in no way provides for the establishment specific fund or account into which the holdback monies are deposited. The notable differences being British Columbia and Saskatchewan where the Act require the establishment of a trust account where the holdback fund retained. The British Columbia Act also places the Owner in default if the funds are not deposited and allows the Contractor to, on 10 days' notice, suspend the work until the default is corrected.

The trust provision applies to all sums received by a contractor, and sub-contractors on account of the contract price, which are also subject to the same retention requirements as imposed upon the Owner. Nowhere in the Acts does it say no one will be paid before the entire work is completed. The Acts do, however, stipulate that those who receive money for making payments, which is lienable, must not convert this money to their own use until all workers and all other persons have been paid for work done and materials supplied. It is this latter requirement which establishes the <u>trust provision</u> in the Acts.

It is mandatory for the person primarily liable under a contract to release the holdback under that contract by the time stipulated in the Act <u>after a Certificate of Completion or Substantial Performance has been issued by he Consultant or Payment Certifier</u> The method by which Substantial Performance is established also varies between jurisdictions as set out in Table D below.

Table D	
Province / Territory	**Substantial Completion is established when:**
Ontario	a) when the improvement to be made under that contract or a substantial part thereof is ready for use or is being used for the purposes intended; and b) when the improvement to be made under that contract is capable of completion , or where there is a known defect, correction, at a cost of not more than, (i) 3 percent of the first $500,000 of the contract price, (ii) 2 percent of the next $500,000 of the contract price, and (iii) 1 percent of the balance of the contract price.
Quebec	on completion of the work
Alberta	(1) Where a contractor is of the opinion that his contract is substantially performed he may issue and deliver to the Owner a certificate of substantial performance in respect of the contract.
British Columbia	(2) For the purposes of this Act, a head contract, contract or subcontract is substantially performed if the work to be done under that contract is capable of completion or correction, at a cost of not more than, (a) 3% of the first $500,000 of the contract price, (b) 2% of the next $500,000 of the contract price, and (c) 1% of the balance of the contract price.
Manitoba	a) the structure to be constructed under the contract or sub-contract or a substantial part thereof is ready for use or is being used for the purposes intended or, where the contract or sub-contract relates solely to improving land and the improved land or a substantial part thereof is ready for use or is being used for the purposes intended: and b) the work to be made under that contract is capable of completion the work to be done under that contract is capable of completion or correction, at a cost of not more than, (i) 3% of the first $250,000 of the contract price, (ii) 2% of the next $250,000 of the contract price, and (iii) 1% of the balance of the contract price.
Newfoundland & Labrador	12 (2) In the case of a contract that is under the supervision of an architect, engineer or other person upon whose certificate, in this section referred to as the "certificate" payments are to be made, where 30 days have elapsed after a certificate issued by that the architect, engineer or other person to the effect the subcontract has been completed to his or her satisfaction has been given to the person primarily liable upon that contract and to the person who became a subcontractor that by a subcontract made directly under that contract...."

Table D	
Province / Territory	Substantial Completion is established when:
New Brunswick	15 (4) Where (a) a contract is under the supervision of an architect, engineer or other person upon whose certificates payments are to be made, (b) the architect, engineer or other person referred to in paragraph (a) certifies to the owner and to a sub-contractor that the sub-contract has been completed to his satisfaction.
North West Territories	"completion of the contract"
Nova Scotia	13 (1) In this section a contract under which a lien can arise pursuant to Section 6 is deemed to be substantially performed (a) when the work or improvement is ready for use or is being used for the purpose intended; and (b) when the work to be done under the contract is capable of complete or correction a cost of not more than two and one-half percent of the contract price. Holdback reduced to 2% (3) Forty-five days after the contract is substantially performed the amount required to be retained pursuant to subsection (2) may be reduced to two and one-half per cent of the value of the work, service and materials actually done, placed or finished and this balance of two and one-half per cent may be retained by the person primarily liable upon the contract until all required work is performed completely.
Prince Edward Island	15 (4) Where (a) a contract is under the supervision of an architect, engineer or other person upon whose certificates payments are to be made, (b) the architect, engineer or other person referred to in paragraph (a) certifies to the owner and to a sub-contractor that the sub-contract has been completed to his satisfaction.

Table D	
Province / Territory	Substantial Completion is established when:
Saskatchewan	3. (1) For the purposes of this Act, a contract is substantially performed; (a) when the improvement o be made under that contract or subcontract or a substantial portion of the improvement is ready for use or is being used for the purposes intended; and (b) when the improvement to be made under the contract or subcontract is capable of completion , or where there is a known defect, correction, at a cost of not more than the aggregate of , (i) 3% of the first $500,000 of the contract price, (ii) 2% of the next $500,000 of the contract price, and (iii) 1% of the balance of the contract price.
Yukon Territories	completion of the construction

17.11   DISCHARGE OF LIENS

In many instance the Owner requires the title to be clear of liens to continue receiving financing on the project or to sell the property. In most jurisdictions it is provided in the Act that money equal to the lien amount may be paid into court and the court will discharge the lien. In some cases, the court may allow the posting of a "lien bond" in lieu of cash. Any money paid into court or a lien bond deposited with the courts according to the Act, takes the place of property and is subject to the claims of the lienholders in the same manner as if the money realized derived from the sale of the property

17.12   THE LAW OF CONSTRUCTION HYPOTHETICS IN QUEBEC

17.12.1 General

Under the law of Quebec the general rule of patrimoine is that the whole of a person's property is liable for the fulfilment of his obligations. Excepting property that has been declared exempt form seizure by the Civil Code. Another principle of Quebec law is that where a debtors assets are insufficient to satisfy all his debts his creditors will share equally on a pro-rata basis in the proceeds.

The Quebec equivalent of a construction lien arises out of the Civil Code article 2724(c) which give legal hypothec status to "claims of persons having taken part in the construction or renovation of an immovable". The Civil Code (C.C.) divides all property into two categories: movable and immovables; C.C. art. 899. Land and "works of a permanent nature located thereon and forming an integral part thereof" fall into the latter.

C.C. art.2668 expressly provides that property exempt form seizure cannot be hypothecated. Therefor as Crown property cannot be seized it cannot be hypothecated. Generally all property that is part of the public domain is exempt from seizure

17.12.2 Construction Hypothecs Equivalent to Mechanics' Liens

The term "mechanics' lien" is unknown in Quebec Law, but its equivalent is found in C.C. arts. 2724(2) and 2726. Article 2724 (2) provides that claims of persons having taken part in the construction of an immovable give rise to a legal hypothec. C.C. art. 2726, as amended by L.Q. 1992, c. 57, art 716(17) puts limits on this right as follows:

A legal hypothec in favour of the persons having taken part in the construction or renovation of an immovable may not charge any other immovable. It exists only in favour of the architect, engineer, supplier of materials, workman and contractor of sub-contractor in proportion to the work requested by the owner o of the immovable or to the materials or services supplied or prepared by them for the work. It is not necessary to publish a legal hypothec for it to exist.

Throughout the remainder of this section we refer to the legal hypothec created by C.C. Articles 2724(2) and 2726 is referred to as a construction hypothec.

These article contain two points which need to be remembered:

a)   they are concerned with a preference that only applies to the particular property to which the work and materials have been contributed, and not to the debtor's property as a whole, and

b)   the preference exists only to the extent of the additional value resulting from the work or materials.

17.12.3 Subsistence, Expiration and Extinguishment of the Construction Hypothec

The maintenance of a construction hypothec under Quebec civil law follows the same general rules set out in other Provincial Statues regarding liens. C.C. art. 2727 states that the construction hypothec "subsists" for a period of thirty days "after the work has been completed". Within that time a notice describing the charged immovable and the amount of the claim must be registered and served on the owner of the immovable, or the right is lost.

Similar to "perfection" C.C. 2727 also states that if the creditor has not either published an action against the owner of the immovable or registered a prior notice of the exercise of a hypothecary right within six months after the work is complete, the construction hypothec is extinguished.

Publication is made by registration in the land registry office of the division in which the immovable is situated.

17.12.4 Priority of Claims

In general rights are ranked according to date hour and minute of registration. The exception being that legal hypothecs in favour of persons having taken part in the construction or renovation of an immovable are ranked before any other published hypothec, for the increase in value added to the hypothec. Construction hypothecs always rank below prior claims and per C.C. art. 2651 they rank below:

1. legal costs and all expenses incurred in the common interest,

2. the claim of the vendor who has not been paid the price of a movable sold to a natural person who does not operate an enterprise

3. claims of the State for amounts due under fiscal law and

4. claims of municipalities and school boards for property taxes on taxable immovables.

The only advantage given is to the non-contractual workmen who, by virtue of C.C. 2728, do not have to give notice to the owner to claim a construction hypothec and as a group these creditors rank before any other published hypothec. However only to the extent of the increase in value added to the immovable.

Therefore if the amount owed to the claimants is no more than the value added to the immovable the workman no longer has a preferred claim for his entire wages. In these cases each claimant will suffer a proportionate reduction.

17.12.5 Notices to Owner Requirements

Notice requirements come into play on four occasions:

1. within 30 days after the work is completed a notice describing the charged immovable and the amount of claim must be served on the owner of the immovable.

2. all groups entitled to construction hypothecs, excepting workmen, must give a written declaration of the contract to the owner.

3. prior to the exercise of any hypothecary rights, notice must be served on the debtor and on any other person against which he intends to exercise his right. In construction hypothecs the "other person" would be the owner of the immovable.

4. for the holdback provisions to come into play notice of the contract must be given to the owner.

17.12.6 Extinction of Construction Hypothec

For a hypothec to exist the conditions of the Code must exist. There are several ways in which a construction hypothec can be extinguished. These are:

1. even if construction or renovation has been performed on an immovable, nu hypothetic rights arise if no value has been added to the immovable by the work.

2. failure to meet the time limitations for filing and serving the notice of charge and commencement of an action.

3. performance of the obligation

4. granting of a release by the creditor

5. loss or expropriation of the charged property

6. the passage of thirty years after the date of its registration or registration of a notice giving it effect or renewing it.

17.13 SUMMATION

It is most important to recall and understand the definition of:

a. A lien at Common Law

b. A Builder's or Mechanics' Lien

Equally important is knowing the courses of action in respect of liens, which are:

a.   By way of suit in court to recover what is owing.

b.   By registering the claim of lien.

By virtue of the various Lien Acts, all who contribute to the enhancement of a property have the ensured means of being paid for their services of whatever kind.

All who seek to recover what is owing them by lien action must be certain they comply with the statutory rules governing the attachment of liens and the subsequent action in respect of them. It is in this legal exercise that one may <u>sleep on his rights</u> and lose what he is justified in receiving. The Law will not help you, unless you help yourself. For this reason the manner in which one may exercise his lien rights must conform to the Acts.

The waiving of lien right could be a risky business. It would be advisable to seek legal advice before signing a waiver of lien.

The Owner's lienable interest is varied, and it is obvious this variety of Owner's interest well protects lien claims against a property.

As to how much money is available to discharge liens arising out of a construction contract, the retention of the percentage of money owing, the prohibition of prior payments, the prohibition of converting to personal use money received for payment to others, provide reasonable assurance there are sufficient funds available.

TYPICAL QUESTIONS

1. What is a lien?
2. What is the purpose of a Lien Act?
3. Who can lien in respect of a Construction Contract?
4. What is lienable?
5. What are the two classes of liens?
6. In respect of a Mechanics' Lien what two courses are open to a person who acquires a lien?
7. What are the time requirements for attaching a lien to a property?
8. What effect has a Change Order upon the time in which to register a lien?
9. Who is exempt as to priority in respect of liens?
10. Describe the manner by which a lien claimant should exercise rights.
11. What liens have senior priority?
12. Who is prohibited from waiving lien rights?
13. What is the Owner's interest against which a lien is filed?
14. What type of mortgage is unaffected by a lien attachment
15. Can a lease be attached by a lien?
16. Are public roads and streets lienable?
17. What is holdback and what is its purpose?
18. What is meant by quantum?
19. If a lien is registered what happens to the holdback?
20. What is meant by the trust provision?

REFERENCES

Anger's Digest of Canadian Law

Construction Builders' and Mechanics' Liens in Canada - Macklem Bristow

Hudson's Building and Engineering Contracts, 10th Edition

Canadian Building Contracts - Goldsmith

18

INSPECTION OF CONSTRUCTION CONTRACTS
by Claude Lawrenson, RSW, RHI

"The inspection of construction contracts can be divided into two correlated functions, the inspection of the Contractor's performance and independent inspection and testing for quality control. Each are essential to ensure that the intent of the Construction Contract Documents is being accomplished."

Anon

18.1   INTRODUCTION

The need for speed is becoming one of the most important elements in construction today. In fact, so much emphasis is being placed on speedy construction that skilled workmen are finding it difficult to avoid sacrificing quality workmanship. The link between the quality of finished work and the intent of the plans and specifications is control of the Contractor's performance.

Discussion of this subject separates into the following elements:

1.   The need for review of construction work.

2.   The scope of review.

3.   The Clerk of Works.

4.   The Contractor and the Clerk of Works.

Separate as these may appear, they are closely correlated and can be dealt within two sections, first Field Review and, secondly, Quality Control Inspection.

18.2   THE NEED FOR FIELD REVIEW OF CONSTRUCTION CONTRACTS

The review of a Contractor's performance is a major function of the Architect or Engineer. One of the basic obligations of an Architect or Engineer to his or her employer, or Client, is the certainty that actual construction complies with the design drawings and specifications comprising the Construction Contract.

The safety, suitability and economy of any structure depends upon the design skill and judgement of the Architect or Engineer <u>and upon the success with which the intent of the</u>

---

drawings and specifications has been executed. It is contended that this success can best be achieved through the constancy of qualified inspections of the actual work in progress.

Today, the multiplicity of materials performing identical functions available for construction and the growing need for the most advanced architectural and engineering principles and methods of construction have increased the need for closer integration and coordination of many design specialists. As a result, there is a continuing increase in responsibilities with respect to design. The more intricate the project, the greater need for consultation among specialists to produce much needed better drawings and specifications.

No longer are principals of the design office able to devote the considerable time necessary for the proper and complete field review of a construction contract in progress. This evolution is the result of the new construction practices which have grown out of the increasing complexities in the science of modern building. The situation now exists where it is necessary to maintain the closest contract possible between a design office and the project. This can only be achieved by providing contractors with the best of drawings and specifications. To produce such documents today, requires considerable research by architects, engineers and specification writers and extensive consultation and collaboration among design specialists. All this leaves designers little time for review of the actual work in progress.

It must be recognized that, as a general rule, the contractor is considered the expert in actual construction. For this reason, a contractor is given a relatively free hand in the methods he uses to construct a proposed Work. The terms and conditions of a contract, and the conditions governing the manner in which particular materials, equipment, etc., are to be incorporated into a Work. Any deviation from such specific instructions transfers liability in the event of failure. Frequently the structural stability of a Work is impaired by deviation from specific instructions, results in costly failures, sometimes with loss of life. It may be expected, from time to time, for reasons the contractor considers valid, attempts may be made to deviate from specified methods of construction or materials. Only by constant review of the Contractor's performance can such attempts be prevented. As mentioned previously, a Contractor's performance of the work is controlled by the checks and balances of the terms and conditions of the Construction Contract, including the requirements of the drawings and specifications. The actual review of the work and the testing of materials used.

Few contractors object to rigid specifications, provided they are as rigidly enforced as they are written. Of what use is it for specification writers to spend hours composing rigid specifications if the means for enforcing them either is lax or lacking? Far too frequently the Contractor's superintendent has not been forced by good field review to read the specifications and perform accordingly. It is the opinion of many in the Construction Industry, that firmer and more competent job supervisor is not only necessary, but is to their benefit.

Failure to review construction work in progress properly, or failures to enforce the intention of the plans and specifications comprising a construction contract are acts of negligence for which an Owner may hold their architect or engineer responsible.

In some cases, Architects or Engineers are not able to perform reviews of their Works, mainly because of the complexities mentioned previously. In such cases, Owners and their Architects or Engineers who wish to have their well designed projects well constructed, should be prepared to employ well-qualified inspectors to act on their behalf, of which there are too few available.

18.3   THE SCOPE OF FIELD REVIEW

The review of a Contractor's performance in respect of a Construction Contract consists of interpretation and enforcement of all terms and conditions of the Contract Documents, particularly the drawings and specifications, as related to materials, equipment, quality of workmanship, etc. The effectiveness of this inspection is influenced by several factors.

If inspection is to benefit the Owner, then under no circumstances should an inspector's authority, once it has been established, be subverted by the Owner, Architect or Engineer. Too much emphasis cannot be expressed in this regard, for many contractors are quick to suspect, or learn of, a subversion of authority and will exploit this weakness to their advantage to the detriment of the Owner.

Not infrequently, an Architect or Engineer, having the desire to achieve the ultimate in design, fails to gain fully his or her objective because of the lack of, or laxity in, review and failure to fix responsibility and delegate sufficient authority to the appointed reviewer.

Casual, indifferent and incompetent review invariably results in contention, arbitration and more often than desired, in litigation. These undesired results can be avoided to a great extent by constant, competent and authoritative review.

Finally, the Scope of Field Review varies with the desire of the Owner as to whether he or she wants the benefits of good review or is willing to accept the consequences of either inadequate or poor review. Far too frequently the scope of review is governed solely by the immediate costs, with little thought given to the possible results in the long run of casual or indifferent control.

18.4   THE CLERK OF WORKS

The position of the Clerk of Works in unique. He or she is not a member of the design term, yet, must ensure the design is accomplished. Nor is he or she the constructor, yet must see that the project is properly constructed. Like the Owner's Architect or Engineer, the Clerk of Works is an Agent of the Owner and, therefore, must exercise care, skill, judgement and diligence in the performance of his or her duties.

Because a Clerk of Work's functions may be manifold, the qualifications should be extensive. In some respects he or she must be a specialist. As so aptly stated by Mr. Russell W. Cornell, FSWA, in his editorial in the October 1962 issue of the Specification Associate, a Clerk of Works has: -

"the approach of a diplomat, the inquisitiveness of a private eye, the experience of an octogenarian, the knowledge of a scholar and the firmness of a county court judge - a collection of characteristics not ordinarily contained in any one person, and certainly not enough to meet the demand."

A qualified Clerk of Works must have basic knowledge and experience in respect of design and construction. He or she must know as much, or more, about the work than those whose performance is being inspected. Regardless of how complete the contract documents may be, they will not cover all situations which might arise during the progress of construction. For this reason alone, the more construction knowledge and experience a Clerk of Works has, the better he or she should perform his work.

Essential a qualified Clerk of Works should be:

1.   Able to understand the interpretation and applications of the Law in respect of Construction Contracts.

2.   Capable of checking the location and layout of a project in all its parts.

3.   Able to interpret and enforce authoritatively the application of the intent of the contract drawings and specifications.

4.   Able to measure and value variations to the original contract requirements, and determine the value of progress payments to the Contractor.

5.   Able to communicate intelligently with both the design authority and the contractor.

6.   <u>Courageous enough to accept and discharge responsibility.</u>

7.   Able to apply good judgement to all situations.

To achieve recognition, a Clerk of Works must be dedicated to his or her occupation, and:

1.   By study, continue to expend his or her personal knowledge of those elements that comprise his or her occupation, to more competently serve the Client.

2.   By competence, be able to substantiate personal opinions with an integrity that is above suspicion.

3.   Be able to accept and discharge satisfactorily all responsibility delegated to him or her.

4.   Be free from any bias that would prejudice his or her work.

5.   By reason of knowledge of construction and experience, appreciate the construction practices in use and be able to give authoritative direction concerning them when called upon to do so.

It should be a responsibility of the contractual authority to not only select qualified individuals as Clerk of Works but to also:

1.   Pay them adequately.

2.   Encourage them to increase their knowledge through intensive study.

3.   Train them to correct standards.

4.   Provide them with the proper equipment which to work, and

5.   Support them strongly when they are actively engaged on a project.

A Clerk of Works can only be as good as he or she wishes to become and to the extent he or she is encouraged and supported by the employer.

18.5   THE CONTRACTOR AND THE CLERK OF WORKS

A contractor's success, or failure, is not only dependent upon bidding skill, but also upon the efficiency of organization in the performance of a Construction Contract. To a great extent, the contractor's execution of a Work is influenced by the ability and the impartiality of the Clerk of Works.

Upon being awarded a contract, the contractor is confronted with the problem of establishing a sympathetic relationship with the Clerk of Works. Some contractors consider it necessary to "get along" with the Clerk of Works at all cuts short of fraud and collusion. As a result, the Clerk of Works is likely to be the recipient of a deference seldom enjoyed by anyone else on the project. Until the contractor has gained the confidence and respect of the Clerk of Works, he or she may be shrewd in early dealings with the Clerk of Works. However, it is most important for a Clerk of Works to remember that until he or she has gained the contractor's confidence and respect, he or she will be severely hindered in the performance of his or her duties.

If a Clerk of Works is to gain a contractor's confidence and respect, it appears he or she must:

1. Be firm, impartial and consistent regarding the contractor's compliance with the requirements of all the contract documents.

2. Be impartial in decision making and be governed by his or her competence and knowledge of the work being done. He or she must accept gracefully the fact that decisions may be questioned. However, when matters of contention cannot be resolved at the project level, he or she must be willing to refer such matters to higher authority and abide by their rulings. Such questioning and reference need not weaken his or her judgement, conviction nor his or her self-confidence.

3. Be courteous at all times to all persons. A courteous attitude will contribute to his or her personal success and will favourably influence the contractor's operation.

A Clerk of Work's reputation usually precedes him or her and is greatly dependent upon his or her harmonious relationship with contractors. Frequently, contractors have experienced costly difficulties which were attributable to inexcusable bad conduct, indecisive decisions and biassed judgements of the Clerk of Works. The Clerk of Works must always remember that his or her ability will be measured, to a great extent, by the quality of the work performed by the contractor. If a project has been well constructed, then they can justifiably accept some of the credit for good work.

All of the foregoing comments apply equally as well to any person, such as the Architect's field reviewer, who is required to monitor or supervise construction performance.

18.6   SUMMATION

Considering the complexity of modern construction and the emphasis upon fast completion of work, there is a need for more constant and better qualified control.

The quality of construction depends largely upon the review of the Contractor's performance of the requirements of a construction contract. If quality construction is to be obtained, then the Owner's representative, be it an Architect, Engineer or Clerk of Works, must be constantly in close contact with all phases of work in progress on a project.

The review or supervision of a construction contract, to be worthwhile, must be performed with integrity and the utmost impartiality by persons with adequate knowledge and experience in respect of all phases of the type of construction being reviewed.

The difference between a good construction job, and average, or poor one is the quality of control, which like any other commodity, is only as good as the price one is willing to pay.

18.7   QUALITY CONTROL INSPECTION

The rapid technological advances in the development of construction materials makes it imperative to seriously consider the subject of Quality Control, which is a specialized and technical form of inspection. This form of inspection may be defined as the means of provided systematic certification and establishment of desired standards of quality in materials or processes related to the materials of construction, such as structural and reinforcing steel; all types of concrete; compaction values of soils; asphalt paving, roofing materials and their application, etc.

Included in Quality Control is the matter of inspecting and testing both the manufacture and operational efficiency of such installed items as steam generators, heating, ventilating and air-conditioning systems, etc.

The Owner, Architect or Engineer; Contractor; Sub-Contractor; Material and Equipment Suppliers must determine and establish standards of quality in respect of construction materials. Such standards should be verified by visual check and the testing of them.

18.8   QUALITY CONTROL OF CONSTRUCTION MATERIALS

Quality Control of construction materials involves two functions:

1.   Inspections, which consist of observations of the processes and produces of manufacturers supplying construction materials to ensure that the specified quality is being supplied. It must be emphasized that inspection is most important in achieving quality control. Inspection, in this sense, means the examination of materials, both supplied and manufactured, including the testing of them to determine whether the materials' items conform to specified standards.

2.   Testing, which refers to the physical performance of experiments to determine quantitative measures of properties of materials of construction.

Inspection and testing are absolutely essential to establishing quality control of construction materials. They are the means by which it is scientifically determined whether materials conform to specified requirements.

18.9   THE INDEPENDENT TESTING COMPANY (ITC)

The phase of inspection in respect of quality control is divided between the Architect or Engineer and an Independent Testing Company (ITC) as to function.

An Owner pays their Architect or Engineer to review the contractor's performance to ensure the work is being done according to all terms and conditions of a construction contract, including the plans and specifications, particularly, to ensure the specified materials and equipment are being supplied and the intent of the design is being accomplished.

On the other hand, an ITC does not design. It may be asked to check upon the performance of something being built according to a design by someone else, nor does it specify, but may be called upon the check compliance with what has been specified. An ITC is an independent group of well qualified technical and scientific specialists.

18.10   WHO IS TO INSPECT WHAT?

It has been shown that the Owner pays their Architect or Engineer to inspect the work which they designed, to ensure that the design which, the Owner, has approved is accomplished. The degree of this inspection varies according to the will of the Owner.

There are differences of opinion as to what constitutes inspection. Inspection could mean a function of the supervision of construction, or it could mean, in a limited sense, the verification of the quality of construction materials or the efficiency or performance of equipment.

The function of review as related to the supervision of construction must remain with the Architect or Engineer. The function of inspection as related to the verification of construction materials or performance efficiency of equipment should be the responsibility of independent experts, and ITC.

The role of the Architect or Engineer, as related to the verification of quality and performance efficiency is limited to indicating when, how and to what extent such inspection is to be done by the ITC and assessing the extent to which the measured qualities and efficiency, as reported by the ITC, are acceptable in respect of what was specified.

18.11   PROVING AND TESTING

Many contractors have the mistaken belief that they may have recourse against an ITC, if the testing undertaken by it fails to discover defects. The contractor, by the terms and conditions of the construction contract, is required to furnish a complete project of specified materials and equipment, including the performance efficiency of the latter. Failure to do so is his or her responsibility, except where he or she may have been properly authorized to substitute alternatives. It is an important principle that the contractor proves, by testing, that the material he or she proposes to use, conforms to what has been specified. All such proving must be at the expense of the contractor.

Testing ordered by the Owner, on the other hand, is an additional and voluntary precaution to ensure that there is conformity to what has been specified.

To avoid conflicts arising out of the individual testing by, either the contractor or Owner, an ITC would do much to avoid possible contention.

18.12   SUMMATION - QUALITY CONTROL

By using quality control, it may be possible to increase allowable stresses, permitting reduction in dimensions of structural members, affecting economics in design.

Quality control ensures that materials incorporated into a Work are as specified.

With quality control the structural stability of a building is better ensured, provided the design is adequate.

TYPICAL QUESTIONS

1. Why is there need for field review of construction contracts?
2. What is the responsibility of the Architect or Engineer in respect of field reviews?
3. What is the scope of review?
4. How much review or inspection is demanded by an Owner?
5. What is the primary purpose of a Clerk of Works?
6. What are some of the suitable qualifications for a Clerk of Works?
7. What responsibility has the Owner, or his Architect or Engineering toward the Clerk of Works?
8. What should be the relationship between the Contractor and the Clerk of Works field reviewer?
9. What is meant by Quality Control?
10. What is an Independent Testing Company?
11. What two functions are involved in Quality Control?
12. What is the purpose of an ITC?
13. What is the relationship between an ITC and an Architect?

MEDIATION
by Clive E.J. Evans, FRICS, PQS(F), C.Arb.

I'd rather jaw, jaw, jaw, than war, war, war.

--Winston Churchill

19.1   INTRODUCTION

Mediation is currently probably the best known method of dispute resolution. The popular press often carry reports on the use of mediation in cases of labour disputes, hostage taking, public demonstrations, occupations of government offices, disputes in major sports e.g. the baseball strike in 1994 - 95, in fact many areas of political sensitivity. With the publication of CCDC 2-1994 a provision for the use of mediation in the resolution of disputes between the parties has brought mediation to the fore in the construction industry.

Mediation is often confused with negotiation as can be seen from the above examples appearing in the press. In fact mediation is negotiation through the assistance of a thirty party.

19.2   DEFINITION

Mediation can best be defined as the resolution of a dispute by the parties using the assistance of a third party as a facilitator.

A good example formed part of an article written by J.G. Coughlan, PQS, in the Construction Economist (the Journal of the Canadian Institute of Quantity Surveyors):

"A dispute has arisen in which a Contractor has made a claim based on ambiguous wording in the contract. Things have not been going well; the bankruptcy of a major sub-contractor, and arguably exceptionally inclement weather has delayed the work and put it in financial difficulty. If things had been going well it might not have made this claim, but in the circumstances it must claim every conceivable dollar to which it considers itself entitled.

The Owner has reluctantly approved previous claims which the Architect thought were not justified, because of the overriding importance of the completion date and the unacceptableness of delay, but now feels it is being ransomed and has to draw the line somewhere. Work is already behind and the Contractor is dragging its feet pending the requested Change Order. In caucus the Owner stressed to the mediator the importance of the completion date; commented that the amount of the claim was small compared to the

---

consequences of not completing in time, but that it could not keep surrendering to such circumstances. The Owner's comments also revealed uncertainty as to whether there was an element of self-defence in the Architect's position.

Agreement: The Contractor drops the claim. The Owner agrees to pay an agreed amount for double shifting for a period (not provided for in the contract), in return for a firm commitment on the completion date: with a penalty/bonus provision.

In this case, rather than dealing only with the specific item in dispute, both parties underlying concerns have been accommodated, and they now have a common interest. Because it is the parties themselves who make the agreement, it is essential that the decision makers from both sides be present."

19.3   THE PROCESS

Depending on the complexity of the dispute the mediation process can be quite simple. A written outline of each party's position will enable the mediator to become familiar with the disputes(s). Following the appointment of the mediator a conference of the parties with the mediator and advisors to the parties enables both sides to state their positions and the mediator to obtain a good outline of the dispute. This will be followed by the mediator meeting privately with each party in turn (caucusing) to further explore their particular positions, areas of strengths and weaknesses and possible concessions that could be offered. Further conferences with all parties present and caucusing as necessary, will likely provide the mediator with sufficient information to enable the parties to be swayed to an acceptable agreement.

To enable to process to work well it is necessary that all parties are well prepared when entering the first conference. It is important that both parties have the will to reach an agreement. It is equally important that the mediator is able to gain the respect and trust of the parties from the outset to provide confirmation that the process will work. Preparation of the parties will include having representation at the meeting by a person able to make decisions with authority and that where advice is being provided by professionals then that advice does not detract from the agenda of the party.

Agreement is by the parties and should be in writing and signed by the parties and the mediator. Where legal representation is present then the agreement should also be approved by them from a legal standpoint. The mediator cannot impose an agreement and should not offer one without the agreement of the parties.

It has been recorded by authorities in the USA that 90% of mediations in construction disputes are successful. But what if there remains and impasse? It is not necessarily the end of the road. It may be that some items can be agreed upon and that other items may be submitted to arbitration. All the evidence and discussion in mediation remains confidential and cannot be used to prejudice the parties position in arbitration or litigation.

19.4   CCDC 2 1994

Variations of mediation have taken place in construction disputes for many years where the consultant has acted as an intermediary between the Owner and Contractor. The process is now formalized and the appointment of a mediator has become a contract requirement.

GC 8.2 now requires parties to a contract to appoint a Project Mediator within 30 days after the contract is awarded or failing that within 15 days after either party gives notice in writing to the other party that a Project Mediator be appointed.

Where disputes under the contract are not resolved in the specified time through negotiation then the Project Mediator will be requested to assist the parties to reach agreement. The mediated negotiations should be conducted in accordance with the latest edition of the Rules of Mediation of CCDC 2 Construction Disputes. Where the dispute is not resolved within 10 working days after the Project Mediator was requested to assist or such further time as the parties may agree then the Project Mediator shall terminate mediated negotiations by giving written notice to the parties. The contract then provides for the dispute to proceed to arbitration. CCDC 40 refers to the process of mediation as it relates to CCDC 2.

19.5   ROLE OF THE MEDIATOR

The role of the mediator is similar in each case but he may function differently to suit the situation of a particular conflict. In every case the mediator's organizational and interpersonal skills and resourcefulness will be put to good use.

In the first instant it is the mediator's duty to bring the parties together in order to engage in face to face discussion. This will likely require dissolving barriers, reducing hostile attitudes and promoting communication.

Once the parties begin joining the process then the mediator becomes the conductor creating the facility by which discussions will proceed and continue to a successful agreement. It is important to note that the conductor is the facilitator or catalyst who advises, cajoles, persuades, suggests, translates and sometimes recommends ways to possibly solve a dispute. The mediator has no authority to impose a settlement.

From the outset the mediator sets a positive tone, sets behavioural guidelines, explains procedures, educates the parties to the process and at the same time controls the proceedings and communications between the parties. It is important that the parties trust is obtained to enable proper evaluation by the mediator of the issues and to enable suitable advice to be offered in dealing with the issues as the process evolves. On the contrary there will be occasions when the mediator should refuse to take part particularly in cases where the dispute is not suitable for mediation or the goals of the parties are other than reaching a settlement or are intent on seeking failure of the negotiations. The mediator must therefore decide whether the intentions of the parties are serious in resolving the dispute.

In training as a mediator it soon becomes obvious that good interpersonal skills are a great asset to a mediator. Whilst the talents of mediators vary in this area there are a number of other ways in which a mediator can work toward a successful conclusion, such as:

1.   obtaining a good understanding of a party's position, the strengths and weaknesses of the each point of argument and areas where concessions may be made.

2.   group issues and arrange sequential discussion particularly with inexperienced negotiators.

3.   defer settlement of certain issues including developing procedures to achieve this thus avoiding statement situations and hindering progress in agreement of other matters.

4.   opening channels of communication including translating and transmitting information.

5.   exploring alternate solutions offered by the parties or developed by the mediator.

6.   convey a party's rigid stand on an issue to the other to help avoid an impasse during later discussions.

7.   communicating areas of movement between the parties, showing progress in negotiation and evoking a similar response.

8.   reality testing of a party's position to determine the validity of the argument and to enable deflation of extreme positions.

9.   assessing the consequences of impasse against the values of remaining issues.

10.   finalizing and ratifying the agreement.

11.   monitoring the agreement may require the mediator to resolve complaints of non compliance or clarify any misunderstandings of the roles and obligations of each party. In fact the mediator could design an appropriate dispute resolution system to handle disagreements arising out of the agreement.

What do you do if an impasse is reached? The mediator has an obligation at this point to advise the parties that they are approaching an impasse and of the consequences of failing to reach an agreement to ensure that the parties realize the situation they are in. Have them calculate the time and cost they will face if they do not reach a settlement. Where agreement has been reached on certain issues the parties may be willing to settle. If all parties agree, including counsel then the mediator can offer an opinion as to how the matters may be settled but then he must leave the process. Other options are to proceed to arbitration as provided for in the CCDC 2 contract form or go to a mini trial.

19.6 SELECTION OF A MEDIATOR

How do you go about finding a mediator? Look up the yellow pages, ask your friends, call professional societies, approach the courts? It has been stated that the single most important factor in the success of the process is the mediator. In Canada we are able to call upon the Arbitration and Mediation Institute to offer suitable candidates. Provincial affiliates of the Institute can be approached in the Provinces where bodies have been established. The parties are still required to make a choice and therefore references should be called for a check of the qualifications, training and experience to determine the most suitable mediator. In his article in the Construction Economist J.G. Coughlan notes that in selection of a mediator broad experience in the field or industry is an advantage but the process also requires a perceptive and thoughtful listener; not domineering but with persuasive powers; and one who has the respect of the parties. They must feel comfortable and at ease with them; not intimidated.

19.7 BENEFITS OF MEDIATION

The basis of mediation is that it is the settlement of a dispute by the parties themselves. There is no imposition by another person or authority, no winner or loss of face and the parties will have retained a relationship which will in the long run likely be more valuable than the costs of a settlement. The process is relatively very quick and inexpensive and what is very important to many, it remains private. Compare this to litigation and out of court settlements.

19.8 FUTURE OF MEDIATION

As in all fields the success of the process or system will be judged by the users. To date mediation is reported to have a high rate of success. The early 1990's has seen a significant move toward mediation as an alternate way to resolved disputes (other than litigation). Whilst it may be perceived a good, quick and cheap system it is not suitable for all disputes.

Mediation has been used and publicized in many areas of dispute resolution as noted earlier and in some cases this has given the process a bad name. For mediation to prosper there must be adequate suitably trained and qualified mediators available who are willing to provide the service at acceptable costs to the parties.

The adoption by the construction industry of forced mediation is an interesting move and felt by many to be long overdue.

TYPICAL QUESTIONS

1.   Define Mediation.
2.   How does mediation differ from other forms of dispute resolution?
3.   What are some of the basic qualities needed to be a good mediator?
4.   How is a mediator appointed?
5.   List the steps you would take in running a mediation.
6.   What happens if you as a mediator cannot get the parties to a settlement?
7.   What are the benefits of mediation?

20

THE EXPERT WITNESS
by Evan B. Stregger, PQS(F), AScT, C.Arb., GSC

In Chapters 10 and 11 we discussed the benefit to the parties and the arbitrator of utilising an expert witness. The purpose of this chapter is to examine the role of the expert.

20.1   THE ROLE OF AN EXPERT

There is a common misconception that an expert witness is a "hired gun" brought in to make and argue a party's case before the courts or in arbitration. The role of the expert, in Canada, is to assist *the court or arbitration* in understanding technical issues that may not be addressed or adequately explained by the court through normal evidence.

20.2   WHEN TO ENGAGE THE EXPERT

As an expert, the Professional Quantity Surveyor (PQS) will examine the quantum of your claim or defence. In doing so the PQS may discard elements of your claim that are not directly attributable to the issue.

In construction disputes the issues usually revolve around quantity, cost, schedule or quality. In these matters the PQS can assist in quantifying the work, reviewing and vetting the actual costs, examining the schedule, and inspecting the quality of the work.

Engage the expert when or before engaging legal counsel or commencing an arbitration process. Because of the costs involved there is often a reluctance to engage the expert until the last possible moment. However, I have found that delaying is usually false economy. Several examples of this are:

▸ The general contractor who had a large overrun on concrete quantity which it had attributed to design changes and for which it was seeking compensation from the Owner. After spending considerable monies on legal fees, it retained the expert PQS to confirm the quantities, only to find that the reason for more than 90% of the overrun was due to errors in the original estimate, not design changes. The contractor had no claim.

▸ The lawyer being sued for $80,000 loss of profit by his client. After a settlement offer of $40,000 was turned down counsel engaged a PQS to review the alleged costs. The determination of the expert was that the loss was approximately $8,000. The courts awarded the Plaintiff the exact sum determined by the PQS.

> ▸ The client who, seeking to recover damages suffered due to a structural problem, submitted all of his costs to correct and repair the work. These costs included first class air fare, bar bills, and costs unrelated to the matter. The PQS reviewed the claim, identified the unrelated items which were subsequently removed from the claim, and the claim was adjusted accordingly.

In my experience, the earlier the PQS is engaged, the less likely it will be that you will have expended time and effort only to find that you have no claim, or that the claim has been over-stated or under-valued.

20.3　THE EXPERT REPORT

The courts have over the years set out guidelines for the expert to follow in order that his report may be admissible. These are in part:

> ▸ Assignment
>> What is it that the expert was engaged to give opinion on, who engaged him and when and that he was advised that his opinion was to be used in litigation or arbitration.

> ▸ The Expert
>> The name of the person who is giving the opinion and if there are more than one all must be signatory to the report. This does not preclude persons from assisting, but the work must be under the direction of the person giving the opinion and must be reviewed by him.

> ▸ Qualifications of the expert must be stated
>> The qualifications of the expert must be stated. This is usually done in summary form in the report with a more detailed curriculum vitae attached as an appendix to the report.

> ▸ Facts and Assumptions
>> Here it important that the facts and assumptions be given to the expert. The expert giving opinion must base it on a specific given fact or assumption. He cannot determine the fact as that is the role of court or arbitrator, and neither can he assume as that basis an opinion on an opinion. When writing an expert report it is always prudent to ensure that you have strictly based you opinion on the facts that were given to you.

> ▸ Documents Reviewed or Relied Upon
>> A specific listing of the documents used as the basis of his opinions should be included. To maintain continuity the expert should retain these documents or a copy of them for his file.

▶ Methodology

The methods used should be set down. For instance "all areas have been measured in accordance with the "*Measurement of Buildings by Area and Volume, by CIQS*". Using a published standard often helps the opinion, however having stated how the work has been done, the expert must ensure that they have followed the referenced standard.

Other examples may be:

Taxes are included.	Which taxes at what rates?
Overhead and Profit is included. .	What rate or percentage? How is it calculated.
Labour rates	Based on? Source?

▶ Summary of Opinion

If used, the summary can either proceed or follow the "Observations and Opinions"

▶ Observations and Opinions

This is the detailed section of the report where specific documents are reviewed, analysed and opinions given. The expert must be careful not to determine the facts as that is the court's or arbitrator's role.

Ideally the assignment should be to answer a series of questions. The expert in responding should cite the question, the documents reviewed, assumed facts, methodology (if applicable) and based on these, give his opinion. Do not give opinions on areas where you are not trained or have no expertise. Do not give opinions on issues for which you have not been asked. Ensure that all issues addressed are listed under the assignment.

20.4   THE EXPERT'S EVIDENCE

The expert's report is their evidence in chief. At trial or arbitration the expert's qualification will be reviewed and he will appear before the court or arbitration as an expert to give opinion on......... eg construction costing, scheduling, development analysis, etc.

If accepted as an expert by the court or arbitration panel, the expert can only address the opinions in his report he cannot give evidence on anything not in his report. His primary role in attending is for cross-examination. If in cross-examination new issues are raised, as is often done by opposing counsel, the expert is free to give opinions on those new areas as well.

20.5 WHO CAN BE AN EXPERT?

The simple answer is that anyone that is accepted as an expert by the court or arbitration panel can be an expert witness. However, to stream line the court and arbitration process, experts must bring something to the court or arbitration that either analyses very complex information or provides special expertise as required.

20.6 CHALLENGING THE EXPERT REPORT

There are many issues that may arise that will lead to an expert's report being challenged. Some of these are:

Issue	Problem	Resolution
- the report contains finding of facts	finding of facts is the role of the court or arbitration panel	facts should be given to the expert as an assumed fact.
- the report interprets the contract	interpreting the contract is the role of the court or arbitration panel	contract interpretation should be given to the expert as an assumed fact.
- the report is written as "we"	the expert will be asked to identify who else was involved in the writing of the opinion.	write the report in the first person - I did this...; In My opinion...; etc.
- the expert has no education or training the field of the opinion given.	the expert will not be accepted by the court or arbitration panel	agree to give opinions only in your areas of expertise.
- opinion was given on items not asked for.	the opinion on those items will likely be challenged under cross-examination and may not be accepted by the court or arbitration panel	adhere strictly to your assignment. If needed, the client can expand your assignment.
- Opinion asked for requires an assumption of fact, so the expert does so.	finding of fact is the role of the court or arbitration panel	have the client or their legal counsel provide you with the assumed fact.

20.7   ADDRESSING THE REPORT

You may have been engaged by the client ABC Co. Ltd. and your invoices may be addressed to them and paid directly by them, but your report is addressed to and delivered to their legal counsel. The purpose of this is to preserve privilege. If for some reason your opinion is not to the client's liking, the report in the hands of legal counsel is not available to the other party. If delivered to the client it becomes part of the client's files and is available for discovery. In this case, you could find yourself being called as an expert against the client who engaged you.

20.8   DRAFT REPORTS

In the course of forming an opinion, the expert may in fact look at more than one scenario and for various reasons some will be rejected or discarded by the time the final report is issued. There is no hard and fast rule regarding draft reports other than the courts have often accepted the office policy of the expert. If that policy is to retain all drafts then the expert could be asked to produce them for review. If the policy is not to retain any draft copies, then only the final report stands. The second policy is probably most efficient as it saves storage space and also avoids cross-examination on why you changed, altered or eliminated various opinions.

The exception to this would be to retain any draft that left your hands, as once the client has the report it is could be produced.

20.9   THE EXPERT'S FILE

The entire file of the expert, including electronic files, is producible at trial or arbitration and the expert should appear with the file available even if it is not asked for. For obvious reasons the expert should be very careful of what is put into writing. Equally, the expert must ensure that all correspondence etc. is included in the file. Normally, the files are asked for in hopes of discovering correspondence that will damage the report.

20.10   ATTENDANCE AT TRIAL OR ARBITRATION

Attendance at trial or arbitration, if asked for, is not optional. Normally subpoenas are not issued for civil litigation although they can be. In criminal matters subpoenas are always issued. The issuance of a subpoena protects your client in that they may be granted a continuance if the expert falls ill or for some other valid reason cannot appear.

Method of Measurement of Construction Works

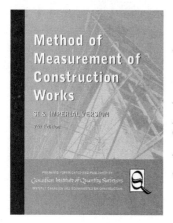

SI & Imperial Version

7th edition

2000

ISBN# 0-896606-28-8

Hard cover

(214 pages)

...is text provides a standard guide to the measurement of construction works. ...allow for easy cross reference to the project specifications and divisions of the ...ork, this Seventh Edition follows the most current edition of MasterFormat*, ...joint publication of Construction Specifications Canada and The Construction ...ecifications Institute (US).

...publishing the Fourth Edition in 1978, CIQS adapted the Method of ...easurement to conform with the requirements of the SI system of measurement. ...this Seventh Edition, recognizing that large segments of the construction ...dustry in North America have not converted to the SI system of measurement, ...QS has reintroduced the Imperial system into the publication.

...e Method of Measurement of Construction Works is an ideal reference for ...antity Surveyors, Architects, Engineers, Construction Estimators, Project ...anagers and other construction professionals, as well as an invaluable ...structional aid for colleges and universities.

Elemental Cost Analysis
Format • Method of Measurement • Pricing

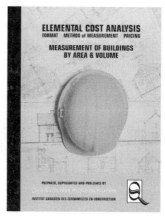

3rd edition

2000

ISBN# 0-896606-30-X

Hard cover

(94 pages)

A comprehensive method of cost analysis for use in cost planning and budget control. While originally based on the breakdown for cost planning which originated in the United Kingdom, this system is sufficiently different to make it uniquely Canadian. Through to 1971 this elemental cost analysis was tested and refined by consulting quantity surveyors and in 1971 the Canadian Institute of Quantity Surveyors established a sub-committee to review the breakdown. This third edition incorporates the advances made previously and adds illustrative sketches to assist the reader in correctly identifying the elements. The document has been reformatted for ease of reference.

This text now includes **Measurement of Buildings By Area & Volume**. The standardization of the rules of measurement of area and volume is critical to the use of cost data in "Elemental Cost Analysis".

Construction Budgeting

2nd edition

1998

ISBN# 0-896606-26-1

Hard cover

(205 pages)

...onstruction Budgeting" is a lucid and logical guide to building – profitably. ...e intricacies of construction economics are examined – before and beyond ...e drawing board stage – including estimating methods, statistical and ...athematical relationships of feasibility studies, yield analysis and life-cycle ...sting. Architects, engineers, contractors, developers, quantity surveyors, ...timators and allied building professionals will find the book an invaluable ...urce of practical and theoretical information on costing techniques and ...inciples; why and wherefores of construction economics which take into ...count the client's needs and objectives. Twelve chapters, with appendices, of ...lid guidelines and solutions to problems – routine and otherwise – are ...pported by detailed calculations, formulae, statistical data, sample ...ecklists and cost analysis forms.

Canadian Building Law

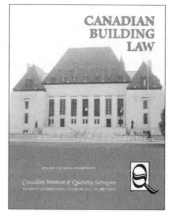

5th edition

2001

ISBN# 0-896606-34-2

Hard cover

(307 pages)

Persons involved in the construction industry – architects, engineers, specification writers, developers, owners, contractors – and students studying towards the Institute's examinations will benefit from the valuable information contained in this book.

Among the valuable information contained within;
• Nature of law in respect of contracts • Law of Contract • Labour Law & Unions • Forms of Contract • Tendering and contract execution • General Conditions of a construction contract • Construction Specifications • Sub-Contracting • Mechanic's and Builders's Liens • National Building Code; description and applications • Arbitration • Mediation • Expert Witness

This comprehensive look at the construction industry is presented in a practical and non-legal framework by six contributing authors.

For ordering information please contact the Canadian Institute of Quantity Surveyors at (905) 471-0882; E-mail: info@ciqs.org